LONGMAN STUDY GUIDES

GCSE/KEY STAGE 4

Higher level
Mathematics

**KENT
ARTS &
LIBRARIES**

Awarded for excellence

**Kent
County
Council**
ARTS & LIBRARIES

► LONGMAN STUDY GUIDES

SERIES EDITORS: **Geoff Black and Stuart Wall**

Titles available:

Biology
Business Studies
Chemistry
Computer Studies
Design and Technology
Economics
English
English Literature
French
Geography
German

Information Technology
Mathematics
Mathematics: Higher Level
Music
Physics
Psychology
Religious Studies
Science
Sociology
Spanish
World History

Addison Wesley Longman Ltd
Edinburgh Gate,
Harlow,
Essex CM20 2JE,
England and Associated Companies throughout the World.

First published 1988
Third edition 1997

British Library Cataloguing in Publication Data

A catalogue record for this book is available from the British Library

ISBN 0–582–30495–4

Set by 32 in 9.75/12pt Sabon

Produced by Longman Singapore Publishers Pte Ltd
Printed in Singapore

CONTENTS

► EDITORS' PREFACE

Longman Study Guides are written by experienced examiners and teachers, and aim to give you the best possible foundation for success in examinations and other modes of assessment. Examiners are well aware that the performance of many candidates falls well short of their true potential, and this series of books aims to remedy this by encouraging thorough study and a full understanding of the concepts involved. The Study Guides should be seen as course companions and study aids to be used throughout the year, not just for last minute revision.

Examiners are in no doubt that a structured approach in preparing for examinations and in presenting coursework can, together with hard work and diligent application, substantially improve performance.

The largely self-contained nature of each chapter gives the book a useful degree of flexibility. After starting with the opening general chapters on the background to the GCSE, and the syllabus coverage, all other chapters can be read selectively, in any order appropriate to the stage you have reached in your course.

We believe that this book, and the series as a whole, will help you establish a solid platform of basic knowledge and examination technique on which to build.

GEOFF BLACK AND STUART WALL

► ACKNOWLEDGEMENTS

I would like to thank the following people for their valuable contribution to the production of this book: Stuart Wall and Geoff Black for their efficient editing and encouragement; Terry Mullen for sharing his thoughts and insights during the preparation of the book; my pupils at Pope Pius X school for their constant inspiration and questioning that has helped to make this book relevant to GCSE students at large; my mother Mrs Elsie Speed for her dedication to the typewriter and to finding spelling mistakes; Gillian my wife, who has now learned to cope with my working into the early hours; and finally to my 'lads' James, John and Joseph, and my daughter Joy, who found an alternative sport to 'Dad baiting' for a while.

I am also indebted to the following examination boards for giving me permission to use some of their GCSE questions in this book:

EDEXCEL Foundation (London)
Midland Examining Group (MEG)
Northern Examinations and Assessment Board (NEAB)
Northern Ireland Council for Curriculum, Examinations and Assessment (NICCEA)
Oxford and Cambridge Schools Examination Board (OCSEB)
Welsh Joint Education Committee (WJEC)

The above groups do not accept any responsibility for the answers I have given to their questions. All suggestions and any mistakes in these answers are entirely my responsibility. I would be most grateful to any reader who informs me of any errors, should they occur.

BRIAN SPEED

INFORMATION ABOUT THIS BOOK

This book has been written as a study aid for use throughout your GCSE course in Higher level Mathematics. It is aimed specifically at the requirements of Higher level (or 'tier' Mathematics) for grades A*, A and B. Addison Wesley Longman also publish *Longman Study Guide Mathematics* (in the same series) which is a full range book for grades G–A* and so covers Foundation, Intermediate and Higher tiers for GCSE Mathematics. As this book *only* does Higher level it gives a lot more practice at A*, A and B.

The first chapter gives information on the National Curriculum assessment schemes for Higher level Mathematics offered by the various examination boards. The second chapter gives advice about preparing for and sitting the examination, and the skills that you will need to demonstrate. You should read these first two chapters carefully as they give invaluable advice which will be useful throughout your Higher level Mathematics course.

Chapters 3–11 then deal with the key topics areas that you will need to understand for your GCSE in Higher level Mathematics. Each chapter opens with a **Getting Started** page which is an introduction to the chapter and gives some useful definitions for you to learn. The Getting Started page also includes a **Topic Chart,** a table which, at a glance, shows the breakdown of the topics covered by the chapter and which topics are covered by the examination boards. The chart can also be used to check your study and revision progress over the two years. A Topic Chart looks like this:

London	MEG	NEAB	NICCEA	SEG	WJEC	IGCSE	TOPIC	STUDY	REVISION 1	REVISION 2
✓	✓	✓	✓	✓	✓	✓	Simple percentage			
✓	✓	✓	✓	✓	✓	✓	Increase and decrease			
✓	✓	✓	✓	✓	✓	✓	Backward percentage			
✓	✓	✓	✓	✓	✓	✓	Compound interest			
✓	✓	✓	✓	✓	✓	✓	Quantity as percentage			

Key to the initials	
London	EDEXCEL Foundation (formerly ULEAC)
MEG	Midland Examination Group
NEAB	Northern Examination and Assessment Board
NICCEA	Northern Ireland Council for the Curriculum, Examinations and Assessment
SEG	Southern Examining Group
WJEC	Welsh Joint Education Committee
IGCSE	International General Certificate of Secondary Education

Each topic listed is then explained in the **What you need to know** section – the core of the chapter. To help you with the theory of the Mathematics covered in the chapter there are numerous worked examples and exercises for you to try. The solutions to the exercises are found at the end of the section.

Further practice for what you have just learnt is then provided in the form of a series of examination questions followed by suggested answers. Try not to look at the answers until you have attempted to answer the questions yourself.

In each chapter there is also an examination question with a typical **student's answer,** some of the answers are excellent and some may have faults or weaknesses. These answers will help you to see what problems are identified by examiners and where you could improve your own examination answers.

At the end of each chapter there is a **summary box** which briefly identifies the key points about topics covered in the chapter. You should check that you know, and understand more fully, each of the key points listed.

Chapter

1

Higher level mathematics

GETTING STARTED

GCSE mathematics is at present unique in that it allows three levels of entry: Foundation, Intermediate and Higher. The Higher level (or tier) is intended *only* for those candidates who stand a reasonable chance of gaining a grade A*, A or B.

If the highest grade you expect to gain is a C, then you should enter for the Intermediate level, as there you will have the best chance to show what you can do. This book is written specifically for those entering the *Higher level* and aiming to obtain grade A*, A or B. This first chapter considers the different requirements and details from the various examination boards. (If you are entering for Intermediate or Foundation level then you should refer to the Longman/GCSE Key Stage 4 Study Guide *Mathematics*.)

As you work through this book you will be taken through *What you need to know* as regards each major topic area. You will find many *worked examples* and *exercises* (with solutions at the end of the chapter). You will also find many past *examination questions* (with answers) on that topic area, together with *student's answers* and *examiners' comments* on these answers.

INTRODUCING HIGHER LEVEL MATHEMATICS

▶ **Higher level of entry**

The target grades at this level are A*, A and B. Grade C can also be awarded, but if you do not achieve this standard then you will be unclassified.

As has already been noted, you should only be entered for this level if there is a *realistic chance* of your gaining a grade A*, A or B. If this is so and you have a bad day, then you should still end up with a grade C. If you are unclassified, then it will indicate that you were incorrectly entered. Unless a major change occurs in your learning or circumstances, then when you *next* take the exam you would be well advised to take the Intermediate level examination.

▶ **MA1 work (by coursework or examination)**

MA1 work is about understanding and applying mathematics to problem-solving. It is an important element within the GCSE in mathematics, with the maximum contribution being 20% of the total marks. Chapter 12 of this book will provide you with helpful advice on approaching MA1 work. Some syllabuses provide an end-of-course examination, others use coursework throughout the two-year course, but both methods are assessed to exactly the same criteria. You need to check with your syllabus (see below) and teacher to find out how your particular course is to be assessed.

SCHEMES OF ASSESSMENT

▶ **EDEXCEL Foundation (London)**

Syllabus A (1385)

Foundation tier	will sit Papers 1 and 2	both 1 hr 30 min
Intermediate tier	will sit Papers 3 and 4	both 2 hr
Higher tier	will sit Papers 5 and 6	both 2 hr

There is no choice of question on any paper and each paper is worth 40% of the final total. Coursework is worth 20% and is assessed over a two-year period by your own centre.

Syllabus B (1386)

The papers are set as for Syllabus A, but here the final 20% for MA1 is from a final task set and assessed by London.

▶ **Northern Examination and Assessment Board (NEAB)**

Syllabus A (1131)

Foundation tier	will sit Papers 1F and 2F	both 1 hr 30 min
Intermediate tier	will sit Papers 1I and 2I	both 2 hr
Higher tier	will sit Papers 1H and 2H	both 2 hr

There is no choice of question on any paper and each paper is worth 40% of the final total. Coursework (MA1) is worth 20% and is assessed over a two-year period by your own centre.

Syllabus B (1132)

The papers are set as for Syllabus A, but here the final 20% is an assessment of MA1 which is by a final paper, 3F, 3I or 3H. The length of these papers is:

3F	(Foundation)	1 hr 30 min
3I	(Intermediate)	2 hr
3H	(Higher)	2 hr

▶ **Midland Examining Group (MEG)**

Syllabus Mathematics (1662)

Foundation tier	will sit Papers 1 and 2	both 1 hr 30 min
Intermediate tier	will sit Papers 3 and 4	both 2 hr
Higher tier	will sit Papers 5 and 6	both 2 hr

There is no choice of question on any paper and each paper is worth 40% of the final total. Coursework (MA1) is worth 20% and is assessed over a two-year period by your own centre or by MEG.

Syllabus Mathematics – SMP 11–16

Foundation tier	will sit	Paper 1 (grades F, G)	1 hr 30 min
	and	Paper 2 (grades D, E, F, G)	1 hr 30 min
Intermediate tier	will sit	Paper 3 (grades C, D, E, F)	1 hr 45 min
	and	Paper 4 (grades B, C, D, E)	2 hr
Higher tier	will sit	Paper 5 (grades A, B, C, D)	2 hr
	and	Paper 6 (grades A*, A, B, C)	2 hr 30 min

There will be no choice of question on any paper and the total of the papers is worth 75% of the final assessment. The second paper in each tier is harder than the first.

Coursework tasks are worth 20% and are assessed over a two-year period. An orally-given non-calculator test is worth 5%, and is marked by MEG.

Syllabus Mathematics C (1666) – SMP Graduated Assessment

This is a modular approach. As well as terminal papers and coursework, there are three modular tests. These occur in March of the first year of the course, and in November and in April/May of the second year.

Foundation tier	will have	three module tests	1 hr each	(30%)
		coursework marked by the centre		(20%)
		one terminal paper	1 hr 45 min	(50%)
Intermediate tier	will have	three module tests	1 hr each	(30%)
		coursework marked by the centre		(20%)
		one terminal paper	2 hr	(50%)
Higher tier	will have	three module tests	1 hr each	(30%)
		coursework marked by the centre		(20%)
		one terminal paper	2 hr	(50%)

▶ Southern Examining Group (SEG)

Syllabus Mathematics (2500T)

Foundation tier	will sit Papers 11 and 12	both 1 hr 30 min
Intermediate tier	will sit Papers 13 and 14	both 2 hr
Higher tier	will sit Papers 15 and 16	both 2 hr

There will be no choice of question on any paper and the total of the papers is worth 75% of the final assessment.

Coursework tasks are worth 20% and are assessed over a two-year period and marked by your centre. An orally-given non-calculator test is worth 5%, and is marked by SEG.

Syllabus Mathematics (2500X)

This syllabus is exactly the same as syllabus 2500T except that the coursework is both set and marked by SEG.

▶ Welsh Joint Education Committee (WJEC)

Syllabus A

Foundation tier	will sit Papers Foundation 1 and 2	both 1 hr 30 min
Intermediate tier	will sit Papers Intermediate 1 and 2	both 2 hr
Higher tier	will sit Papers Higher 1 and 2	both 2 hr 15 min

Paper 1 will contain mainly number and algebra questions. Paper 2 will contain mainly shape, space and measures, and handling data questions.

There is no choice of question on any paper and each paper is worth 40% of the final total. Coursework (MA1) is worth 20% and is assessed over a two-year period by your own centre.

Syllabus B

The papers are set as for Syllabus A, but here the final 20% is an assessment of MA1 which is by a final Paper 3, the length of which is:

Foundation	1 h 30 min
Intermediate	2 hr
Higher	2 hr 15 min

▶ Northern Ireland Council for Curriculum, Examinations and Assessment (NICCEA)

There are three parts to the assessment at each level, Foundation, Intermediate and Higher.

(a) Written papers

At each level you will sit *two* written papers, each of which will consist of short-answer questions and long questions (most of which will be structured). There is no choice of questions. Each paper is worth 35% of the final assessment.

(b) Aural and computation

There is also an aural and computation test set for each level. This will test your mental arithmetic and how well you can understand a spoken instruction regarding information available on a separate document. This test is worth 10% of the assessment.

(c) Coursework

You will normally have to hand in three assignments. Your teacher will tell you what these assignments are. This coursework element is worth 20% of the assessment.

▶ International General Certificate of Secondary Education (IGCSE)

Syllabus 0580 (without coursework)

This syllabus has been designed to meet international needs while being based on the UK's national criteria as published by SCAA. There are only two levels available:

Core curriculum	grades C to G available
Extended curriculum	grades A to E available

The assessment is in two parts:

(a)   A written paper of short-answer questions
(b)   A written paper of structured questions

There is no choice of questions on either paper. The combinations of the two parts of the assessment are:

CORE:	(a) Paper 1	1 hr	(35%)
	(b) Paper 3	2 hr	(65%)
EXTENDED:	(a) Paper 2	1 hr 30 min	(35%)
	(b) Paper 4	2 hr 30 min	(65%)

Syllabus 0581 (with coursework)

This syllabus has been designed to meet international needs while being based on the UK's national criteria as published by SCAA. There are only two levels available:

Core curriculum   grades C to G available
Extended curriculum   grades A to E available

The assessment is in three parts:

(a)   A written paper of short-answer questions
(b)   A written paper of structured questions
(c)   Coursework

There is no choice of questions on any paper. The combinations of the different parts of the assessment are:

CORE:	(a) Paper 1	1 hr	(30%)
	(b) Paper 3	2 hr	(50%)
	(c) Coursework		(20%)
EXTENDED:	(a) Paper 2	1 hr 30 min	(30%)
	(b) Paper 4	2 hr 30 min	(50%)
	(c) Coursework		(20%)

▶ **Assumed knowledge**   Since this book is aiming at only the Higher level mathematics students, it will be assumed that you have a basic knowledge of mathematics already. Table 1.1 lists the syllabus for the *Foundation* level, which we assume you are familiar with. Tables 1.2 and 1.3 then list the content of the *Intermediate* and *Higher* level syllabuses. This is helpful since the Higher level syllabus contains all the items of the Intermediate syllabus, with many grade B/C questions coming from the content of the Intermediate syllabus.

Table 1.1 Assumed knowledge (Foundation tier syllabus)

Pattern in number	integers (whole numbers), odd, even, prime, multiples, factors, sequences, generalisations
Fractions	vulgar fractions, decimals, percentages, equivalent conversions between fractions, decimals and percentages
Directed number	in practical situations
Indices	index notation, square and cube, understanding standard form
Square roots	of perfect squares
Approximation, rounding off	estimations of calculations, significant figures and decimal places
General units	100 cm = 1 m, etc.
Time	12/24 hour clock and timetables
Finance	HP, interest, taxation, discounts, loans, wages and salaries, profit and loss, VAT
Use of tables and charts	tidetables, conversion tables, insurance tables, etc.
Reading scales	
Simple ratio	sharing, recipes, scale drawing
Rates	speed, foreign currency exchange rates
Formulae	use of and substitution

Table 1.1 (cont)

Coordinates	plotting points
Graphs	drawing graphs from given data
Interpretation	of given graphs
Angles	names of, and in triangles, parallels and polygons
Plane figures	triangles, quadrilaterals, circles, congruence
Symmetry	line, rotational
Solid figures	names of, nets, drawing solids
Perimeter	of circles and rectilinear shapes
Area	rectangle, triangle, circle
Volume	cuboid
Equipment	protractor, compasses, ruler
Construction	of triangle, rectangle, circle
Drawing	accurate and scale drawings
Bearings	compass points and three figure bearings
Transformation geometry	tessellations, reflections, enlargements, rotations of 90°, 180°
Charts	construction and interpretation of bar charts, pictograms,
Frequency distribution	pie charts, tally charts, frequency polygons and scatter diagrams
Averages	mode, median and mean
Probability	equally likely situations
Data collection	questionnaires and sampling

▶ **Higher tier**   The Higher tier includes the Intermediate tier syllabus, which we list below. The Intermediate tier syllabus is where the majority of the grade B and C type questions will come from in your examination. We deal with these topics in the chapter indicated in Table 1.2.

Table 1.2 Chapters and topics relevant to Intermediate tier examinations

3	**Number**	prime factors, sequences, using standard form, the 4 rules of directed numbers
4	**Approximation**	appropriate rounding off, significant figures and decimal places
5	**Ratio**	proportion
6	**Algebra**	transposition, algebraic factors, simplification, quadratic expansion, brackets equations: linear, simultaneous and quadratic inequalities, positive and negative indices
7	**Graphs**	constructing tables and graphs from equations gradients, travel graphs solution of simultaneous equations by graph graphing simple inequalities
8	**Geometry**	angles in polygons plane figures, angles in a semi-circle, tangents similarity, axes and planes of symmetry drawing quadrilaterals, bisectors, constructing angles and perpendiculars, loci
9	**Mensuration**	area of parallelogram and trapezium length of arc and area of sector volume of a cylinder and prism Pythagoras and trigonometry
10	**Transformation geometry**	reflections in lines $y = x$ and $y = -x$ rotations about points other than (0, 0) translations and fractional enlargements
11	**Statistics and probability**	histograms with equal interval, grouped data cumulative frequency and quartiles lines of best fit and their use probability and combined events
12	**MA1 work**	using and applying mathematics

The Higher tier of all GCSE syllabuses is the same. It includes the topics listed in Table 1.3 as well as those in the Intermediate syllabus. This table indicates the chapters and topics found only in the Higher level syllabus. It is from this list that the majority of the grade A and A* questions will come.

Table 1.3 Chapters and topics relevant to Higher tier examinations

4	**Accuracy**	limits of accuracy
5	**Ratio**	ratios of similar shapes and volumes direct and inverse proportion
6	**Algebra**	solving any quadratic equations, algebraic fractions fractional indices
7	**Graphs**	area under a graph, gradient at any point on a curved graph changes in graphs after transformations
8	**Geometry**	angles in a circle tangents to a circle
9	**Mensuration**	area and volume of a sphere, pyramid and cone 3D solutions using trigonometry and Pythagoras sine rule, cosine rule area using sine rule
10	**Transformation geometry**	enlargements of negative scale factor vectors
11	**Statistics and probability**	unequal interval histograms probability of a more complicated nature sampling, standard deviation
12	**MA1 work**	using and applying mathematics

▶ **EXAMINATION BOARD ADDRESSES**

London   **EDEXCEL Foundation**
Stewart House, 32 Russell Square, London, WC1B 5DN
Tel: 0171 331 4000
Fax: 0171 631 3369

MEG   **Midland Examining Group**
1 Hills Road, Cambridge, CB1 2EU
Tel: 0122 361111
Fax: 01223 460278

NEAB   **Northern Examinations and Assessment Board**
Devas Street, Manchester, M15 6EX
Tel: 0161 953 1180
Fax: 0161 273 7572

NICCEA   **Northern Ireland Council for Curriculum, Examinations and Assessment**
29 Clarendon Rd, Belfast, BT1 3BG
Tel: 01232 261200
Fax: 01232 261234

SEG   **Southern Examining Group**
Stag Hill House, Guildford, GU2 5XJ
Tel: 01483 506506
Fax: 01483 300152

WJEC   **Welsh Joint Education Committee**
245 Western Road, Cardiff, CF5 2YX
Tel: 01222 561231
Fax: 01222 571234

IGCSE   **International General Certificate of Secondary Education**
University of Cambridge Local Examinations Syndicate
1 Hills Road, Cambridge, CB1 2EU
Tel: 01223 61111
Fax: 01223 460278

Chapter

2 Examination and assessment techniques

GETTING STARTED

It is encouraging to know that if you *have been correctly entered* for the Higher tier of mathematics then you can do *at least half* of the examination questions well. This should give you a lot of confidence before you go into the examination. Being confident is helpful, since being anxious often means that students make careless mistakes.

Work through the many *worked examples* you will find in each topic-based chapter. Try all the *exercises* before checking your work with the answers at the end of the chapter. Also try the many *examination questions* set on each topic before looking at the answers at the end of each chapter. Look carefully at the *examiner comments* to be found alongside each *student answer* at the end of each chapter. There is no better way to prepare for mathematics examinations than to *do* as much practice as you can.

WHAT YOU NEED TO KNOW

▶ Calculators

All GCSE examinations allow you to have your calculator available. The questions will be set on the assumption that you have a calculator suitable to your level. For example, you will be asked some *trigonometry questions* at this Higher level, so make sure that you have a *scientific* calculator. It is up to **YOU** to be responsible for your calculator and not the examination board, school or college. Do have the right one, and make certain that the batteries are not going to run out on you (perhaps take some spares). Do use a calculator that you are familiar with, and not a strange one borrowed at the last minute.

When using the calculator in the examination, do not forget to *write out* your method of solution, otherwise you will often lose marks. In marking a recent examination paper the answer to one question should have been £1.99. Some candidates gave the answer as £1.98 with *no* working out, so they got no marks at all, even though it is quite likely that they *knew* what they were doing, but had just made a small error, perhaps in rounding off. You will throw marks away if you fail to put down your *method of solution*. Make sure you are familiar with the standard form notation on your calculator and how to use this with large or very small numbers. This is covered in Chapter 5 of this book.

▶ Formulae list

Each examination board will supply a formulae list for each syllabus, and for each tier in that syllabus. You are advised to become familiar with this list, so that you know where to find the formulae when needed. It is also important that you practise using these formulae. If you have practised using the formulae *before* the exam, then this will give you confidence in using them in the examination itself. Figure 2.1 presents the formulae list for the Higher tier.

▶ Revision

There is, of course, no substitute for hard work *throughout* the course, and for regularly doing homework and classwork assignments. Revision is, however, important and should be started well before the examination, best of all *before* the Easter holiday leading to the examination. The best way to revise mathematics is to *do* it. You should try as many questions as you can beforehand; this is why there are a lot of questions at the end of each chapter. Do not be afraid of going through the same question more than once during your revision. This will be helpful practice in using the correct technique for answering that type of question, and it should help boost your confidence. Do not revise for too long at a single sitting. You are advised to revise in short periods of between 45 and 60 minutes then to have a break before doing any more. Of course, this will vary with individuals, but if you've started your revision early enough this is usually the best way rather than a final fling!

Fig. 2.1 Formulae sheet: Higher tier

Area of triangle $= \frac{1}{2} \times$ base $\times$ height

Area of parallelogram $=$ base $\times$ height

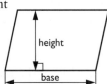

Area of trapezium $= \frac{1}{2}(a + b)h$

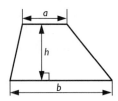

Volume of cuboid $=$ length $\times$ width $\times$ height

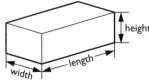

Volume of prism $=$ (area of cross-section) $\times$ length

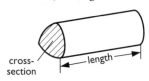

Volume of cylinder $= \pi r^2 h$
Curved surface of cylinder $= 2\pi rh$

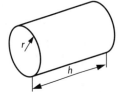

Volume of sphere $= \frac{4}{3}\pi r^3$
Surface area of sphere $= 4\pi r^2$

Volume of cone $= \frac{1}{3}\pi r^2 h$
Curved surface area of cone $= \pi rl$

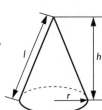

Pythagoras' theorem

$a^2 + b^2 = c^2$

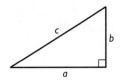

Circumference of circle $= \pi \times$ diameter
$= 2 \times \pi \times$ radius

Area of circle $= \pi \times$ (radius)^2

Trigonometry

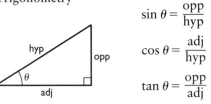

$$\sin \theta = \frac{\text{opp}}{\text{hyp}}$$

$$\cos \theta = \frac{\text{adj}}{\text{hyp}}$$

$$\tan \theta = \frac{\text{opp}}{\text{adj}}$$

In any triangle ABC

Sine rule $\dfrac{a}{\sin A} = \dfrac{b}{\sin B} = \dfrac{c}{\sin C}$

Cosine rule $a^2 = b^2 + c^2 - 2bc\cos A$

$$\cos A = \frac{b^2 + c^2 - a^2}{2bc}$$

Area of triangle $= \frac{1}{2}ab \sin C$

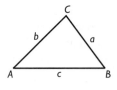

The quadratic equation

The solutions of $ax^2 + bx + c = 0$
where $a \neq 0$, are given by

$$x = \frac{-b \pm \sqrt{(b^2 - 4ac)}}{2a}$$

Standard deviation

Standard deviation for a set of numbers
$x_1, x_2, ..., x_n$, having a mean of $\bar{x}$, is given by

$$s = \sqrt{\frac{\Sigma (x - \bar{x})^2}{n}} \text{ or } s = \sqrt{\frac{\Sigma x^2}{n} - \left\{\frac{\Sigma x}{n}\right\}^2}$$

Use this book to remind you of the things you have been taught. Go through the *worked examples*; then try the *exercises* for yourself, *checking* the answer before going any further. Finally, try the *examination questions* at the end of each chapter, making sure that you put down all your working out, just as you will have to do in the examination itself.

▶ **Examination room strategy**

Remember, you can do *at least half* the questions, and there will always be some that cause problems. You must use your time properly, so do not waste it. The majority of GCSE examinations use 'question and answer books', which means that there is space for you to do your working and to give an answer on the examination paper itself. So it doesn't matter in what *order* you do the questions. Go through the paper and answer the questions *you can do* first, then go back and attempt the ones you've left out. If a question causes you particular problems and you cannot see what to do then leave it, go on to another, and come back to it later. In other words, 'do what you can do well' first. This will help you to 'put marks into the bank' and will help you gain confidence before you tackle the more difficult questions.

Most examination papers will tell you *how many marks* are available to a question: the more difficult a question is, the more marks that are generally given to it. So if you come across a question worth 5 marks and one worth 2 marks, you should expect the 2 mark question to be answered more easily than the 5 mark one. If you have managed to do the 5 mark question very easily, perhaps more easily than the 2 mark question, just check that you have in fact done the question that has been set and have not misread it.

If you are answering on an answer booklet do also use the *number of lines* left for your answer as a guide to the amount that you should write. If only one line is given for working, then you should not need to do a lot of working out. If, however, five lines have been given for working, then you should expect to need to complete a number of stages to get to the answer.

The number of marks per question will also give you some idea of how much *time* to spend on each question. Suppose an examination paper lasts $2\frac{1}{2}$ hours (150 minutes) and there are 100 marks, then each mark has an average time of $1\frac{1}{2}$ minutes, and hence a 5 mark question should not take more than 8 minutes. Of course, you should perhaps allow 10 minutes at the start of the exam for reading through the paper or booklet carefully and for choosing your early questions, and perhaps 10 minutes for checking at the end. In this case you would be able to use the rule of thumb that you have just over one minute per mark. Working out the minutes per mark should not be taken too far, but it does give you some idea of how to use your time well in the examination.

Finally, do not forget to *check* your answers, especially the sense and accuracy. If you have calculated the cost of a car to be £6, you ought to suspect that your answer is wrong and check it. Year after year examiners mark papers where 'stupid' answers are given, such as a man being paid a salary of £45 a year. Do check your answers, it will gain you marks. Also, check that you have *rounded off* suitably. Many questions will say 'round your answer to 1 decimal place', etc., in which case you could obtain marks for rounding off. Other questions might simply say 'calculate the distance ...', and if your answer is something like 8.273419 km, you are quite likely to lose a mark since your answer is not given to a suitable degree of accuracy. You must round off sensibly or be prepared to lose marks.

You ought to be doing many of these checks whilst answering the question the first time, but do go through the routine as a check at the end. It may be boring, but if it gains you a number of marks that you would otherwise lose, and this makes the difference between grades, it will have been well worth doing.

▶ **Examination equipment**

You will be required to calculate, draw and construct. You must therefore have the right equipment for the job. Do not rely on the school providing it, since if you provide the equipment you are familiar with, you can be more confident that you can use it and rely on it. Make certain you have the following:

- ▶ calculator
- ▶ batteries for calculator
- ▶ ruler
- ▶ sharp pencils
- ▶ pen (and a spare pen)

- ▶ pencil sharpener
- ▶ rubber
- ▶ protractor
- ▶ pair of compasses
- ▶ set square

▶ **Examination questions**   There are different *types* of question that you could meet, e.g. multiple choice, short-answer, structured and combination.

Short-answer questions

This type of question is usually given 1 or 2 marks, and you may have only a line or two on which to answer the question. You must first assess what you have to do, then be sure to write down the *method* you are using as well as the answer, suitably rounded off.

Example 1
Find the value of x such that $90 < x < 180$ and $\sin x° < 0.4567$ (NEAB)

Here you need to notice that the answer you want is between 90 and 180, hence the calculator answer to 0.4567 [INV] [SIN] which gives 27.17 (rounded off), needs to be taken away from 180, hence $180 - 27.17 = 152.83$ should be written down. If you showed no method of solution here, and wrote an incorrectly rounded answer of 152.9° only, then you are likely to gain no marks at all.

Structured questions

These are the longer questions that will use one answer *as part of the next stage of the question*. This may occur perhaps two or three times in the one question. It is also vital that you show *all* your method of solution here, as one wrong answer early on will make all subsequent answers wrong. To gain your marks you must show exactly what you have done.

Example 2
Karl won £2 000 in a competition and put it into a building society account that paid him 5% interest every 6 months. How much will he have in the account after: (a) 6 months, (b) 1 year, (c) 2 years?   (NEAB)

You can see how you use the answer to (a) to find the answer to (b) and then this answer to find the final answer to (c), and that any mistakes made earlier will make a wrong answer appear later ... so it is vital that you show all your method of solution in each section of the question. If you did this question correctly, then you would find that your final answer to (c) was £2 431.0125, which should be rounded off to give £2 431 or £2 431.01.

Combination questions

A longer question is often a *combination* of short-answer and structured questions.

Example 3
A fruit cake is a cylinder of height 7 cm and radius 9 cm. It is to have its top and sides covered in marzipan.

(a)   (i)   The top covering is 0.7 cm thick. Calculate this volume of marzipan.
       (ii) A strip of marzipan 7.7 cm wide is to be wrapped around the side of the cake. Show that it must be about 57 cm long.
       (iii) This strip is 0.5 cm thick. Calculate the volume of marzipan needed for the whole cake.
(b)   A family baker makes 12 such cakes. He buys marzipan in 500 g packs. Each pack has a volume of 180 cm³. How many packs will he need to cover the 12 cakes?
                    (MEG)

You should set out the parts (a)(i) and (ii) as short-answer questions, with your method clearly stated. The final part (a)(iii) is done by combining the answer to (a)(i) with information in (ii) to find the total volume of marzipan. Then the final answer to (b) is calculated by multiplying the volume of the marzipan for one cake (396 cm³), found in part (a), by 12, then dividing by 180 to give 26.4. Hence the baker needs to buy 27 packs of marzipan.

These answers must be clearly written down, since it is possible for you to have made a mistake in one of the earlier parts and the examiner marking your paper needs to be able to see what *you* have done, rather than have to do your calculation *himself* as a means of checking what you really have done!

Summary

To summarise this section we can simply say that at all stages you should show the method of solution, unless you are certain that there is only 1 mark for the question and that no method is being looked for.

COURSEWORK OR TERMINAL EXAMINATION IN MA1

▶ **Using and applying mathematics**

As we have already seen, each examination syllabus has to assess 'using and applying mathematics' (MA1). This is done either by coursework or by a terminal examination. This form of assessment may be the one thing that is very different between the examination syllabuses. However, each examination board has to use the same criteria to assess this work.

Table 2.1 presents a breakdown of the skills and understanding you need to display to gain marks in this particular assessment. As you can see, up to 8 marks are awarded for each of three criteria or qualities of your work: (i) making decisions, (ii) communication, (iii) reasoning.

Table 2.1 Scores (marks) awarded in each of three criteria

Score	(i) Making decisions	(ii) Communication	(iii) Reasoning
1	Make a start on organising a method to find something relevant	Explain how you are going to solve the problem	Give a simple example to show understanding of the problem
2	Find a suitable method to solve the problem	Present your results in a clear, organised way	Try out ideas to find a pattern
3	Get sensible information	Use symbols, words and diagrams (charts)	Explain the pattern found
4	Simplify a problem by breaking it down into simpler steps	Explain clearly how your diagrams and charts are related to the problem	Test out the pattern, make a prediction
5	Now find your own questions within the situation	Explain improvements made to the solution or the method as the problem has been solved	Explain why the pattern arises and how it will solve the problem
6	Develop these questions by using a range of mathematical skills	Make good use of algebra in explaining the patterns or solution	Make comments on the solution, showing a full understanding of why the solution works
7	Show clear thinking about why your approach was used	Be accurate and give clear reasons as to why the solution is what it is	Give good reasons as to why a solution works in a problem where there are quite a few different features
8	Use an area of mathematics that has been unfamiliar to you	Use good high-level mathematics to show the reasons why your solution works	Give a good mathematical proof to a mathematical idea you had not met before

Whether by a coursework project or a terminal examination, you will gain a score for *each* of the columns shown in Table 2.1. Your scores will then be added together. The chart below gives you an idea of the total scores expected at each grade.

grade	A*	score	22–24
	A		19–21
	B		16–18
	C		13–15
	D		10–12
	E		7–9
	F		4–6
	G		1–3

Your school or college will be responsible for giving you tasks, which will either be used as coursework or used as practice for the terminal examination of MA1. However, it is up to you to be as prepared and well organised as you can possibly be. This is an important part of the assessment, worth up to 20% of the total marks.

Most of the tasks that 'use and apply mathematics' are discovery or investigational tasks (although there is plenty of scope for them to be statistical or otherwise).

You will find that you are assessed on three aspects of the work:

▶ How you planned and prepared for the task, and how much relevant information you were able to obtain and use.

▶ Your ability to communicate what you have done, giving good reasons for why you did what you did.

▶ The extent of your reasoning or logic, in other words whether you were able to show why and how your solution is what it is.

You will be using some of these MA1 techniques at various times throughout your course. Nevertheless, you must provide clear evidence at this stage of the assessment that you can:

▶ Plan the work
▶ Do the work
▶ Communicate the work

Chapter 12 will provide more advice and present actual examples of how you can gain high marks in the coursework or terminal examination involving MA1, 'using and applying mathematics'.

Percentage and interest

 GETTING STARTED

The application of mathematics is often examined with the use of *percentages*. In this chapter we focus on those aspects likely to be met in the examination.

Sensible *rounding off* at the appropriate time is always needed here and we show you when and how to do this so that you will not lose marks for incorrect rounding. You can find more on rounding off under 'Limits of accuracy' in Chapter 4.

▶ Useful definitions

Discount	A deduction from the usual price.
Principal (amount)	Usually means the amount of money you start with in a bank account, etc.
Simple interest	Interest is paid on an *unchanged* principal amount. There is then a single formula to work out the amount of interest your money will earn.
Compound interest	Interest is paid at regular intervals (usually each year or half year), so the principal amount *changes* from year to year.

▶ Topic chart

The following topic chart can be completed for each of the topics in 'Percentage and interest'. Tick the appropriate box when you have first studied that topic. You can also keep a record of when you have revised that topic for the first and second time, etc.

London	MEG	NEAB	NICCEA	SEG	WJEC	IGCSE	TOPIC	STUDY	REVISION 1	REVISION 2
✓	✓	✓	✓	✓	✓	✓	Simple percentage			
✓	✓	✓	✓	✓	✓	✓	Increase and decrease			
✓	✓	✓	✓	✓	✓	✓	Backward percentage			
✓	✓	✓	✓	✓	✓	✓	Compound interest			
✓	✓	✓	✓	✓	✓	✓	Quantity as percentage			

 WHAT YOU NEED TO KNOW

▶ Simple percentage

All of this chapter is devoted to percentage, and as we will be assuming the general use of a calculator, we will always use percentage in the *decimal* form. For example:

$$1\% = 0.01, \quad 15\% = 0.15, \quad 130\% = 1.30, \text{ etc.}$$

WORKED EXAMPLE 1

Find 15% of £2.50.

15% of £2.50 is found by £2.50 × 0.15 = £0.375; we round up to give £0.38.

Exercise 1
Which is the larger, 81% of £5.99 or 5% of £95.99?

▶ **Increase and decrease**

Increase

To *increase* any amount by $x\%$, use the simple routine:

change % to decimal
↓
add on 1
↓
multiply by amount

WORKED EXAMPLE 2

'This is the quickest way to find an increase or a decrease, so do try to master it'

Increase Gillian's wage of £126 by $6\frac{1}{2}\%$.

$6\frac{1}{2}\% = 0.065$, so the increased wage is £126 × 1.065 = £134.19.

Exercise 2
When Sheffield Wednesday gained promotion to the Premier League their average attendance of 25 756 was expected to increase by about 22%. What was their new expected average attendance?

Decrease

To *decrease* any amount by $x\%$, use a similar routine of:

change % to decimal
↓
subtract from 1
↓
multiply by amount

WORKED EXAMPLE 3

After the Red Plague, the 526 000 population of Gallilee fell by 32%. What was the population after the Red Plague?

$32\% = 0.32$, hence population is now 526 000 × (1 − 0.32)
= 526 000 × 0.68 = 357 680

Exercise 3
I bought a car for £900, then sold it one year later at a loss of 30%. What did I sell it for?

▶ **Backward percentage**

We are often told a given percentage of some amount and then need to work out the amount. For example, the 5% of voters who voted for M. Potter totalled 917. How many voters were there?

In this situation, we again have a simple routine which basically finds 1%, then multiplies by 100 to find the whole amount. So follow this routine:

divide given amount by %
↓
multiply by 100

WORKED EXAMPLE 4

The $3\frac{1}{2}$ acre woodland of the Duke de Richleaux represents only 8% of his total estate. What acreage is the estate of the duke?

Calculate 3.5 ÷ 8 × 100 to give 43.75 acres.

Exercise 4
When Alison Metcalf was transferred from Sheffield FC to Santos Ladies team she received £162 000, which represented 18% of the transfer fee. What was this transfer fee?

WORKED EXAMPLE 5

Mr Cofield had a pay increase of 5% to give him a new salary of £1 092 per month. What was his previous monthly salary?

The statement in effect tells us that £1 092 is 105% of the previous salary, hence this is 1 092 ÷ 105 × 100, which is £1 040.

▶ **Compound interest**

'This is like repeated simple interest year after year, adding the interest onto the balance each time'

Compound interest is the type of interest used by the commercial sector for calculating interest payments; it is a way of paying interest on your investment. Again, it is calculated by a simple routine as illustrated in the formula:

$$\text{Final amount} = P \times (1 + R)^n$$

where P is the principal amount started with, R is the interest rate quoted, and n is the number of times this interest is being applied.

WORKED EXAMPLE 6

£60 is invested in an account that pays 8% compound interest each year. How much will this investment be worth in 5 years' time?

Since the principal amount invested is £60, the rate is 8%, and the number of times the rate is applied will be 5:

$$\text{final amount} = £60 \times (1.08)^5 = £88.159685$$
$$= £88.16$$

Note here that it is essential that you do no rounding off *until* the final answer. You should, of course, have used the $\boxed{x^y}$ button on your calculator to work out the power quickly.

WORKED EXAMPLE 7

'This is compound interest, you need to recognise it when it is needed'

A newborn octopus is known to increase steadily in body weight at the rate of $5\frac{1}{2}\%$ a day over the first few months of its life. What will be the weight of a baby octopus after 4 weeks if when it was born it weighed 4 kg?

The principal amount is 4 kg, the rate of increase is $5\frac{1}{2}\%$ each day for 28 days. Hence:

$$\text{final weight} = 4 \times (1.055)^{28}$$
$$= 17.9 \, \text{kg}$$

Exercise 5
When John started work he was given a starting wage of £50 a week and told it would increase by 4% every 6 months. How much will his weekly wage be after 5 years?

▶ **Quantity as percentage**

This is usually asked for as a percentage profit or loss. It is a simple extension of changing a fraction to a percentage by multiplying the fraction by 100.

WORKED EXAMPLE 8

Divinder had paid £575 for an old bike, done it up and then sold it for £750. What was his profit as a percentage of his original cost?

His profit was £750 − £575 which is £175. This as a percentage of the original cost of £575 is found by calculating $175 \div 575 \times 100$ which is 30.4% (rounded off).

Exercise 6
When a metal bar is heated to 300°C it expands from 41 cm to 41.3 cm. What is the expansion as a percentage of the original length?

▶ **SOLUTIONS TO EXERCISES**

S1 81% of £5.99 = 0.81 × 5.99 = 4.8519
5% of £95.99 = 0.05 × 95.99 = 4.7995
Hence 81% of £5.99 is larger than 5% of £95.99

S2 25 756 × (1 + 0.22) = 25 756 × 1.22 = 31 422 (rounded off)

S3 £900 × (1 − 0.3) = £900 × 0.7 = £630

S4 £162 000 ÷ 18 × 100 = £900 000

S5 Principal amount is £50, rate is 4% applied 10 times. Hence:

final wage $= 50 \times (1.04)^{10} = £74.01$ (or £74)

S6 Expansion is 0.3 cm. As a percentage of the original this will be $0.3 \div 41 \times 100 = 0.73\%$.

▶ EXAMINATION QUESTIONS

▶ **Question 1**

Fig. 3.1

DISCOUNTPRINT
30% BIGGER COLOUR PRINTS
Check your bigger print size here

FILM SIZES	135	110/DISC	126
DISCOUNT PRINTS	6×4	$5\frac{1}{4} \times 4$	4×4
STANDARD	$5 \times 3\frac{1}{2}$	$4\frac{1}{2} \times 3\frac{1}{2}$	$3\frac{1}{2} \times 3\frac{1}{2}$

(a) Use the dimensions given in the table in Fig. 3.1 to see if the '30% bigger' claim is true for film size 135. Show all your working.

(b) Figure 3.2 shows the actual sizes for a standard and a discount print for size 135. Measure these prints and check the claim from your measurements.

Fig. 3.2

(c) Comment on the results in (a) and (b). (MEG)

▶ Question 2

Fig. 3.3

32ND ISSUE CERTIFICATES
52%

NO TAX, NO RISK
NO HASSLE
NO FEAR OF
FALLING INTEREST
RATES

The interest that you can earn from National Savings Certificates is TOTALLY free from Income Tax and Capital Gains Tax. You don't even have to declare it on your Income Tax return.

The 32nd Issue offers a guaranteed return of 52% after five years. This is equivalent to 8.75% a year over the five years.

You can invest from £25 to £5,000, in addition to any other Issues you already hold.

Each member of your family can invest up to the full amount in their own names.

For full details ask at your bank or post office.

We guarantee freedom from tax, with high performance and absolute safety. There is nothing to touch National Savings Certificates.

NATIONAL
SAVINGS

The advertisement in Fig. 3.3 contains the following statement.

The 32nd Issue offers a guaranteed return of 52% after five years.
This is equivalent to 8.75% a year over the five years.

(a)   Investigate the truth of this statement by completing Table 3.1 to show the year-by-year growth of an initial investment of £1 000 at 8.75% a year.

Table 3.1

	Amount at end of year
Year 1	
Year 2	
Year 3	
Year 4	
Year 5	

From this table, write down, correct to 1 decimal place, the total percentage increase over the five years.

(b)   Given that National Savings Certificates are bought in multiples of £25, find the minimum amount of money which would have to be invested initially in order to produce a total of at least £1 000 at the end of the five years.

(NEAB)

▶ **Question 3**   Sally put £250 into a savings account which paid interest at the rate of 8% per annum.

(a)   Find the amount in the account at the end of one year.
(b)   She leaves this amount of money in the account for another year. During this year the rate of interest is 9.75% per annum for the whole year. Find, to the nearest penny, the amount in the account at the end of the second year.   (London)

▶ **Question 4**   A trade union negotiates the following rise in wages on behalf of its members:

5% of weekly wage or £6 per week, whichever is the greater

One employee finds that, for him, there is no difference between a rise of 5% and a rise of £6 per week. Calculate this employee's weekly wage before the rise.   (NEAB)

▶ **Question 5**   Supergrowth Unit Trust claims that the value of its units is likely to grow by 21% compound interest per annum. Assuming that this claim is true, calculate the value, after 5 years, of an investment of £1 000 in Supergrowth Unit Trust.   (MEG)

▶ **Question 6**   Figure 3.4 shows a floppy disc for a microcomputer. The useful area is shaded. Find the percentage of the area of the disc that is useful.   (MEG)

Fig. 3.4

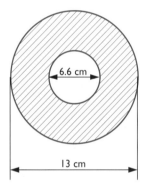

▶ **Question 7**   The information in Fig. 3.5 was given on two labels taken from a bottle of 'Blackvit', a blackcurrant drink. Calculate, from the information provided, the recommended daily intake of vitamin C.   (NEAB)

Fig. 3.5

BLACKVIT

25 ml of this product provide
173% of the recommended
daily intake of vitamin C

CONTENTS

Water
Glucose Syrup
Blackcurrant Juice
Colours
Vitamin C (52 mg per 100 ml)
Preservatives

▶ **Question 8**   Mr and Mrs Williams invest £1 000 in an investment account which pays 10.5% per annum interest.

(a)   How much interest do they get in a year?
(b)   They have to pay tax on this interest at the rate of 27p in the £1. How much tax do they pay? How much of the interest is left after paying tax?
(c)   What percentage is this 'after tax' interest of their £1 000 investment?   (WJEC)

▶ **Question 9**   A flower is placed in a vase. During the course of each day, it loses 5% of its water content. It will begin to droop after losing 25% of its original water content.

(a)   What percentage of its original water content will it lose in two days?
(b)   If the flower had drooped after x days, what is the minimum possible value of x?
(NEAB)

▶ **Question 10**   A man invests £200 in a savings account at an annual rate of interest of 7%. He makes no further deposits or withdrawals. Interest is added each year and then itself earns extra interest (i.e. compound interest).

(a)   How much will he have in his account at the end of the second year?
(b)   After how many complete years will he first have more than £300 in his account?
(MEG)

▶ **Question 11**   (a) Here $y = (1 + x)(1 - 0.6x)$ over the range $0 \leqslant x \leqslant 0.5$
(i) Complete Table 3.2.

Table 3.2

x	0	0.05	0.10	0.15	0.20	0.25	0.30	0.35	0.40	0.45	0.50
$1 + x$	1	1.05	1.10	1.15		1.25		1.35	1.40		1.50
$1 - 0.6x$	1	0.97	0.94	0.91		0.85		0.79	0.76		0.70
y	1	1.019	1.034	1.047		1.063		1.067	1.064		1.050

(ii) Draw the graph of y over the range $0 \leqslant x \leqslant 0.5$.
(b)   A theatre finds that when it raises its prices, the percentage increase in the price is directly proportional to the percentage decrease in the number of people attending the theatre. When the prices were increased by 10%, 6% fewer people came.
(i) What percentage reduction in the audience will there be for a 1% rise in prices?
(ii) What percentage change in the takings will there be for a 1% rise in prices?
(iii) Using your graph drawn in part (a), find what percentage rise in prices will give the greatest rise in takings.
(c)   The theatre takes £380 per night before the rise. What is the most it can take after the rise?
(WJEC)

EXAMINATION ANSWERS

A1   (a) Standard size area = $5 \times 3.5 = 17.5$
Discount size area = 24, an increase of 6.5
The percentage increase is $\frac{6.5}{17.5} \times 100 = 37\%$
Yes, the claim is true for the size 135.
(b) Standard size area = $12.9 \times 8.8 = 113.52$
Discount size area = $15 \times 10.2 = 153$, an increase of 39.48
The percentage increase is $\frac{39.48}{113.52} \times 100 = 34.8\%$
Yes, the claim is true for these measurements.
(c) The given sizes, which are probably rounded off imperial measurements, and the metric sizes, both give more than a 30% increase, which is what the advertisement is saying – at least 30% bigger.

A2   (a) The table can be built up by multiplying each previous figure by 1.0875 to give the figures:

'You ought to put down enough information to indicate what you are doing'

year 1 → 1 087.5
year 2 → 1 182.6562 (1 182.66)
year 3 → 1 286.1386 (1 286.14)
year 4 → 1 398.6757 (1 398.68)
year 5 → 1 521.0598 (1 521.06)

(The rounding off should only be done after all the calculations.)

The percentage increase is $\dfrac{1521.06 - 1\,000}{1\,000} \times 100 = 52.1\%$

Hence the statement is true.

(b) If £x is invested then after 5 years it will be worth

$$x \times (1.0875)^5 = 1.52106x$$

For this investment to be at least £1 000, then $1.52106x \geqslant 1\,000$, hence:

$$x \geqslant £1\,000 \div 1.52106$$
$$x \geqslant £657.44$$

Yet this value must be a multiple of 25, hence the value of x will be £675.

A3 (a) £250 $\times$ 1.08 = £270
   (b) £270 $\times$ 1.0975 = £296.325 = £296.33 (to nearest penny)

A4 If his wage before the rise is £x, then 5% is $0.05x$, which equals £6.
Hence $x = £6 \div 0.05 = £120$.

A5 Principal amount is £1 000, rate is 21%, applied 5 times, to give the final amount $1\,000 \times (1.21)^5 = £2\,593.74$.

A6 Inner circle $= \pi \times (3.3)^2$
Outer circle $= \pi \times (6.5)^2$
Useful area $= \pi \times (6.5^2 - 3.3^2)$
So the percentage of disc that is useful is given by:

$$\frac{\pi(6.5^2 - 3.3^2)}{\pi(6.5^2)} \times 100 = 74.2\%$$

A7 Bottle contains vitamin C at 52 mg per 100 ml, that is $(52 \div 4)$ mg per 25 ml, which is 13 mg.
Hence 173% of recommended dose = 13 mg, so

$$\text{recommended dose} = \frac{13}{173} \times 100 = 7.51 \text{ mg}$$

A8 (a) £1 000 $\times$ 0.105 = £105
   (b) 105 $\times$ 27p = 2 835p = £28.35 tax paid
      Interest left = £(105 − 28.35) = £76.65
   (c) $\dfrac{76.65}{1\,000} \times 100 = 7.665\%$

A9 (a) After the first day it has 0.95% of its original water content, then after 2 days it will have $(0.95)^2$% of its original water content, which is 0.9025, hence the plant has lost $(100 - 90.25)$% which is 9.75%.
   (b) If the flower has drooped after x days, then $(0.95)^x < 0.75$.
      By trial of $x = 1$, $x = 2$, etc. we find that $(0.95)^5 = 0.77378$
      and $(0.95)^6 = 0.73509$
      So the smallest integer value of x to satisfy the situation is 6.

A10 (a) $£(200) \times (1.07)^2 = £228.98$

'Do say so when your method is trial and improvement, it is quite acceptable as long as you indicate that this is what you have done and you've shown a logical approach'

(b) $200 \times (1.07)^x \geqslant 300$

$\rightarrow \quad (1.07)^x \geqslant 1.5$

By trial of $x = 1, 2, 3 \ldots$ we find that $1.07^5 = 1.40$

and $1.07^6 = 1.5007$

So after 6 complete years there will be more than £300 in the account.

A11 (a) (i) The final figures to put in the table will be $y = 1.056$, $y = 1.066$, $y = 1.0585$.

(ii) You should have a smooth quadratic curve like the top of a small hill.

(b) % increase in price $(P) \propto$ % decrease in audience (A).

Hence $P = KA$ (K being the constant of proportionality).

When $P = 10$, $A = 6$, hence:

$$10 = 6K \rightarrow K = \frac{5}{3}$$

(i) When $P = 1$, $A = 1 \div \frac{5}{3} = \frac{3}{5} = 0.6\%$

(ii) (Original takings) $\times 0.994 \times 1.01 =$ (Original takings) $\times 1.003\,94$.

So the change in takings will be 0.394% increase.

(iii) We can now see that the horizontal x-axis represents the percentage change in prices, while the vertical y-axis represents the percentage change in takings. The top of the hill on the graph will give us the maximum rise in takings. This is where the graph is at $x = 0.33$. So the percentage rise in prices is 33%.

(c) From the graph, when $x = 0.33$, $y = 1.067$, which represents the increase. So the most that the theatre could take would be £380 $\times$ 1.067, which is £405.46, which should be rounded off to give a final answer of £405.

Grade checklist	
For grade	**You should be able to do the following:**
B	Solve numerical problems.
A	Use a calculator to investigate compound interest problems.

EXAMINATION QUESTION WITH STUDENT ANSWER

Question

In January 1997, an engineering firm made 20% profit on its cost prices by selling machines for £3 200. The cost of manufacturing the machines was made up of wages, raw materials, electricity and maintenance in the ratios 16:6:2:1. During the year wages rose by 6%, the cost of raw materials rose by 15%, electricity charges rose by 12% and maintenance went up by 30%.

(a)   Find the manufacturer's cost price in January 1997.

(b)   Find the increase in the total cost of manufacturing during the year.

(c)   After these rises the firm decided to reduce its profit to 18% of the cost price. Find the new selling price.

(d)   Calculate the percentage profit at the end of the year if the selling price did not change from the beginning of the year.

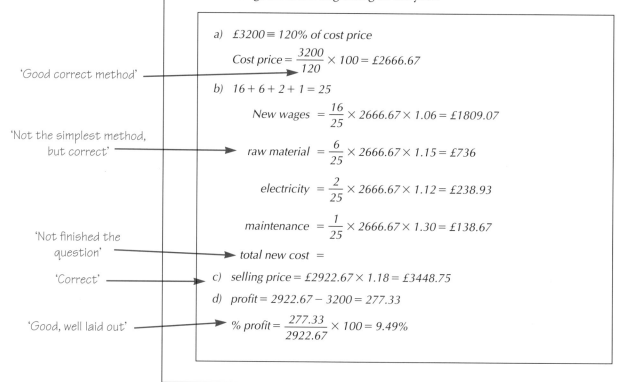

a)   £3200 ≡ 120% of cost price

$$Cost\ price = \frac{3200}{120} \times 100 = £2666.67$$

'Good correct method'

b) $16 + 6 + 2 + 1 = 25$

$$New\ wages = \frac{16}{25} \times 2666.67 \times 1.06 = £1809.07$$

'Not the simplest method, but correct'

$$raw\ material = \frac{6}{25} \times 2666.67 \times 1.15 = £736$$

$$electricity = \frac{2}{25} \times 2666.67 \times 1.12 = £238.93$$

$$maintenance = \frac{1}{25} \times 2666.67 \times 1.30 = £138.67$$

'Not finished the question'

$$total\ new\ cost =$$

'Correct'

c) $selling\ price = £2922.67 \times 1.18 = £3448.75$

d) $profit = 2922.67 - 3200 = 277.33$

'Good, well laid out'

$$\%\ profit = \frac{277.33}{2922.67} \times 100 = 9.49\%$$

'This good answer was somewhat spoilt by the simple error of not finishing the question in part (b). Otherwise, the answer has been very clearly presented showing what has been done.'

SUMMARY

▷   **Percentage of,** e.g. 8% of 45 kg = 8 × 0.45 = 3.6 kg

▷   **Percentage increase,** e.g. increase 72 by 8% ⇒ 72 × 1.08 = 77.76

▷   **Percentage decrease,** e.g. decrease 36 by 6% ⇒ 36 × 0.94 = 33.84

▷   **As a percentage,** e.g. 5 kg out of 8 kg is $\dfrac{5 \times 100}{8} = 62.5\%$

▷   **Compound interest**

   Total amount $= P \times (1 + R)^n$

   where P = amount started with, R = the percentage as a decimal, and n = the number of times the interest is applied

4 Number

GETTING STARTED

At the Higher level of GCSE you are expected to be able to *generalise* a number pattern and then to use this to make *predictions*. These patterns and iterations will occur in combination with quite a few other topics also, as you will see in the examination questions.

▶ Useful definitions

Generalisation	An algebraic rule to represent a pattern you have identified.
Iterative	A mathematical procedure in which repetition of the same process produces results getting closer and closer to some unknown value.
Limits of accuracy	The possible lowest and highest true values of a stated measurement *before* any rounding off has taken place.
Percentage error	$\dfrac{\text{error}}{\text{possible value}} \times 100$
Standard form	$A \times 10^n$ where $1 \leqslant A \leqslant 10$ and n is an integer.

▶ Topic chart

The following topic chart can be completed for each of the topics in 'Number'. Tick the appropriate box when you have first studied that topic. You can also keep a record of when you have revised that topic for the first and second time, etc.

London	MEG	NEAB	NICCEA	SEG	WJEC	IGCSE	TOPIC	STUDY	REVISION 1	REVISION 2
✓	✓	✓	✓	✓	✓	✓	Patterns in number			
✓	✓	✓	✓	✓	✓	✓	Searching for pattern			
✓	✓	✓	✓	✓	✓	✓	Generating a sequence			
✓	✓	✓	✓	✓	✓	✓	Generalising			
✓	✓	✓	✓	✓	✓	✓	Trial and improvement			
✓	✓	✓	✓	✓	✓	✓	Iteration			
✓	✓	✓	✓	✓	✓	✓	Limits of accuracy			
✓	✓	✓	✓	✓	✓	✓	Percentage error			
✓	✓	✓	✓	✓	✓	✓	Standard form			

WHAT YOU NEED TO KNOW

▶ Patterns in number

Both in coursework and in your final end-of-course examinations, you will be expected to investigate, work out and recognise a variety of number patterns. Some of these will be based on the following:

▶ Prime numbers: 2, 3, 5, 7, 11, 13, 17, 19, 23 ...
▶ Square numbers: 1, 4, 9, 16, 25, 36, 49, 64, 81 ...

These two sequences must be learned so that they might be readily recognised in unfamiliar places.

WORKED EXAMPLE 1

Find the next three numbers in the sequence, 4, 9, 25, 49, ...

First recognise that all the numbers are square numbers, and hence we can rewrite the series as:

$$2^2, 3^2, 5^2, 7^2$$

Now recognise that it is the prime numbers being squared, so the next three will be: 11^2, 13^2, 17^2, which is 121, 169, 289.

Exercise 1

Find the next three numbers in the sequence 1, 16, 36, 64, 81, ...

▶ **Searching for pattern**

The most common way is to look at the *differences*. This will in fact help you to find most of the patterns and then to continue them.

WORKED EXAMPLE 2

Find the next three numbers in the sequence 3, 7, 11, 15, 19, ...

Looking at the *differences* we see:

$$
\begin{array}{ccccc}
3\to & 7\to & 11\to & 15\to & 19\to \\
+4 & +4 & +4 & +4 &
\end{array}
$$

so the pattern can be continued by simply adding on 4 each time, to give 23, 27 and 31.

WORKED EXAMPLE 3

Find the next three numbers in the sequence 5, 6, 8, 11, 15, 20, ...

Looking at the *differences* we see:

$$
\begin{array}{cccccc}
5\to & 6\to & 8\to & 11\to & 15\to & 20\to \\
+1 & +2 & +3 & +4 & +5 &
\end{array}
$$

so the pattern can be continued by adding on 6 then 7 then 8 to give 26, 33 and 41.

Exercise 2

Find the next three numbers in each of the following sequences:

(a)   4, 6, 9, 14, 21, 32, ...
(b)   100, 95, 90, 85, ...
(c)   10, 11, 15, 24, 40, ...

It is vital that you look at the differences in a number sequence to help you find the pattern. However, sometimes you will need to consider the 'second differences' to continue the pattern.

WORKED EXAMPLE 4

Find the next three numbers in the sequence 2, 3, 7, 17, 36, ...

$$
\begin{array}{ccccccccc}
2 & \to & 3 & \to & 7 & \to & 17 & \to & 36 \\
 & +1 & \to & +4 & \to & +10 & \to & +19 & \\
 & & +3 & & +6 & & +9 & &
\end{array}
$$

It is now in the 'second differences' that we notice a pattern and can continue it to give:

$$
\begin{array}{ccccccc}
36 & \to & 67 & \to & 113 & \to & 177 \\
+19 & \to & +31 & \to & +46 & \to & +64 \\
+9 & +12 & & +15 & & +18 &
\end{array}
$$

hence the next three numbers are 67, 113 and 177.

'Sometimes you must look for second differences'

Exercise 3

Find the next three numbers in the sequence 1, 3, 6, 11, 20, 37, ...

This technique of looking for differences can, if required, be continued on to the 'third differences', or even further. When answering this type of question you should always illustrate *how* you found your pattern.

These patterns will very often be part of a longer investigation-type question where you would probably also be asked for the general term of the nth term, which we consider later in this chapter.

▶ Generating a sequence

At times you will be given a rule to follow so as to generate a number pattern.

WORKED EXAMPLE 5

U_n is the nth term in a sequence. If $U_n = \dfrac{n(n + 1)}{2}$ then generate the first five terms of this sequence and describe the type of number generated.

The first five terms are found by substituting into the formula $U_n = \dfrac{n(n + 1)}{2}$ the numbers $n = 1, 2, 3, 4, 5$ to give:

$$\frac{1 \times 2}{2}, \quad \frac{2 \times 3}{2}, \quad \frac{3 \times 4}{2}, \quad \frac{4 \times 5}{2}, \quad \frac{5 \times 6}{2}$$
$$= 1 \quad , \quad 3 \quad , \quad 6 \quad , \quad 10 \quad , \quad 15$$

This pattern is the 'triangle numbers' usually found by considering *triangular patterns* as in Fig. 4.1.

Fig. 4.1

Exercise 4

Generate the first few terms of the sequence given by $U_n = n(2n - 1)$.

Alternative notation

Generating a sequence can also be done by defining how the terms use the *one before* to build upon. For example, the nth term of a sequence could be given by the formula

$$U_n = 3 + 2U_{n - 1}$$

So where $U_1 = 5$, we would calculate the following terms as:

$$U_2 = 3 + 2 \times 5 = 13$$
$$U_3 = 3 + 2 \times 13 = 29$$
$$U_4 = 3 + 2 \times 29 = 61, \text{ etc.}$$

This process is more commonly used in *iterations* which we come across later in the chapter.

▶ Generalising

'Being able to do this will show that you are a grade B or better'

Generalising is where, from a given pattern of numbers, you try to state the pattern *algebraically*, as in the section above. This can be a long investigation by trial and error, but if you can learn some simple patterns to recognise, and some simple rules to follow, then you will find the generalisations more quickly.

Rules to follow

(a)   Look first to see if it is an obvious pattern or one that you've remembered.

(b)   Look at the *differences* to see what type of relationship you are looking for. If the *first* differences do not reveal anything, try the *second* or *third* differences, and so on.

(c)   Break the sequences up into *factors* to see what other links you can find.

We now look in more detail at these procedures.

(a) Common patterns

(i)   2, 4, 6, 8, 10 ....$2n$

(ii)   2, 4, 8, 16 ....2^n

(iii)   1, 4, 9, 16, 25 ....n^2

(iv)   1, 3, 6, 10, 15 ....$\dfrac{n(n + 1)}{2}$

Sequence (iv) is the triangle numbers, and are well worth recognising when you see them.

(b) Looking at differences

Same difference
If between each term you find the same difference, d, then where a is the first number in the sequence, the nth term will be given by

$$U_n = a + d(n-1)$$

WORKED EXAMPLE 6
Find the nth term in the sequence 4, 7, 10, 13, 16, ...

We notice that the difference is always 3, and the first term is 4, hence the nth term will be $4 + 3(n-1)$, which could be simplified to $3n + 1$.

Exercise 5
Find the nth term in the sequence 7, 12, 17, 22, ...

Multiple differences
If the differences give recognisable multiples of, say, m, then where the first term is a the nth term will be given by

$$U_n = a + m\,\frac{n(n-1)}{2}$$

WORKED EXAMPLE 7
Find the nth term in the sequence 1, 4, 10, 19, 31, ...

We notice that the differences are 3, 6, 9, 12, the multiples of 3, and that the first term is 1, hence the nth term will be given by

$$U_n = 1 + 3\,\frac{n(n-1)}{2}$$

Exercise 6
Find the nth term of the sequence 8, 15, 29, 50, 78, ...

Square differences
If the differences give the square numbers, i.e. 1, 4, 9, 16, 25, ..., then where the first term is a, the nth term will be given by

$$a + \frac{n}{6}\,(n+1)(2n+1)$$

WORKED EXAMPLE 8
Find the nth term in the sequence 6, 7, 11, 20, 36, ...

We notice that the differences are 1, 4, 9, 16, ..., and that the first term is 6, hence the nth term is given by

$$U_n = 6 + \frac{n}{6}\,(n+1)(2n+1)$$

Triangle differences
If the differences give the well known triangle numbers, i.e. 1, 3, 6, 10, 15, ..., and the first term is a, then the nth term will be given by

$$U_n = a + \frac{n}{6}\,(n+1)(n+2)$$

There are lots of different differences that can now link to one of the above types, and hence you can generalise the sequence. However, do look carefully at the differences as they may be a multiple or a factor of one of the above types.

WORKED EXAMPLE 9
Find the nth term in the sequence 8, 10, 16, 28, 48, ...

We notice that the differences are 2, 6, 12, 20, ..., which are not recognisable until you halve them to get 1, 3, 6, 10 ... (the triangle numbers). Hence the nth term will be given by

$$U_n = 8 + 2 \times \frac{n}{6}(n + 1)(n + 2)$$

$$U_n = 8 + \frac{n}{3}(n + 1)(n + 2)$$

Exercise 7
Find the *n*th term of the sequence 1, 9, 25, 49, ...

(c) Find factors

Sometimes we look at the differences and see nothing, we go to second differences and see nothing. If this is the case then we can look at *factors* of the sequence and see how they are being built up. For example, look at the triangle numbers:

'If you are stuck try the factors'

1, 3, 6, 10, 15, 21, ...

Looking at the differences gives us 2, 3, 4, 5, ..., but how does this help us to find U_n? Actually it can do, but that would be taking us into much higher mathematics. Suppose instead that we write down the *factors* of each term; we then have:

1	3	6	10	15	21
↓	↓	↓	↓	↓	↓
1×1	1×3	2×3	2×5	3×5	3×7

There seems nothing to see first of all; but then on closer inspection we see that if we *double the smaller of each factor* we get the interesting pattern:

1	3	6	10	15	21
↓	↓	↓	↓	↓	↓
1×1	1×3	2×3	2×5	3×5	3×7

Double the first term:

(1×2)	(2×3)	(4×3)	(4×5)	(6×5)	(6×7)
↓	↓	↓	↓	↓	↓
$\frac{1}{2}(1 \times 2)$	$\frac{1}{2}(2 \times 3)$	$\frac{1}{2}(3 \times 4)$	$\frac{1}{2}(4 \times 5)$	$\frac{1}{2}(5 \times 6)$	$\frac{1}{2}(6 \times 7)$
↓	↓	↓	↓	↓	↓
U_1	U_2	U_3	U_4	U_5	U_6

which gives us very neatly:

$$U_n \rightarrow \tfrac{1}{2}n(n + 1)$$

So, when looking for patterns:

(a) look for *familiar* patterns you've seen before;
(b) look at the *differences*;
(c) look at the *factors*.

Exercise 8
Find the *n*th term of the sequence 3, 8, 15, 24, ...

▶ **Trial and improvement method for solving equations**

This method does not imply random trial and error, but rather 'intelligent detective work' to find a good solution to a problem.
 For example, find the solution to $x^3 + x = 100$.

▶   The first thing to do is to try some whole numbers:

  try $x = 3$ $3^3 + 3 = 27 + 3 = 30$ too small
  try $x = 5$ $5^3 + 5 = 125 + 5 = 130$ too large

▶   I now know the solution is somewhere between 3 and 5, so try halfway between, which is 4:

  try $x = 4$ $4^3 + 4 = 68$ too small

▶ I now know the solution is somewhere between 4 and 5, so try halfway between 4 and 5 which is 4.5:

$$\text{try } x = 4.5 \qquad 4.5^3 + 4.5 = 95.625 \qquad \text{too small}$$

▶ The solution is between 4.5 and 5, but an intelligent look will suggest that it is nearer to 4.5 than 5. Since halfway between 4.5 and 5 goes to 2 decimal places, we choose a digit nearer to 4.5, say 4.7.

$$\text{try } x = 4.7 \qquad 4.7^3 + 4.7 = 108.523 \qquad \text{too large}$$

▶ We continue trying out values in this way, getting closer and closer to our solution all the time:

$$\text{try } x = 4.6 \qquad 4.6^3 + 4.6 = 101.936 \qquad \text{too large}$$

The solution is clearly between 4.5 and 4.6, so now we must move the search into 2 decimal places:

$$\text{try } x = 4.55 \qquad 98.746 \qquad \text{too small}$$
$$\text{try } x = 4.58 \qquad 100.652 \qquad \text{too large}$$
$$\text{try } x = 4.57 \qquad 100.014 \qquad \text{too large}$$

We can sensibly stop here, because the answer is *very* close to 100.
    Solution... $x = 4.57$

Note: we could have continued as long as we wanted, getting more and more accurate with each try.

WORKED EXAMPLE 10   Susan has to find, correct to 1 decimal place, the solution of the equation

$$x^2 + \frac{1}{x} = 8$$

By trying values of x and showing your working clearly, find a solution to Susan's equation.

$$\text{try } x = 3 \qquad\qquad 9 + 0.33 = 9.33 \qquad \text{too big}$$
$$\text{try } x = 2 \qquad\qquad 4 + 0.5 = 4.5 \qquad \text{too small}$$
$$\text{try } x = 2.5 \qquad\quad 6.25 + 0.4 = 6.65 \qquad \text{too small}$$
$$\text{try } x = 2.7 \qquad\quad 7.29 + 0.37 = 7.66 \qquad \text{too small}$$
$$\text{try } x = 2.8 \qquad\quad 7.84 + 0.357 = 8.197 \qquad \text{too big}$$

hence $x = 2.8$ is the solution to 1 decimal place.

Exercise 9
Find the solution to $x^3 + x = 50$ correct to 2 decimal places.

▶ **Iteration**   An *iteration* is when a *generating term*, U_n, is used to *keep generating terms* until a certain situation is satisfied.
    For example, a solution to the equation $x^2 - 2x - 3 = 0$ can be found by rewriting the equation in the form $x^2 = 3 + 2x$. Dividing by x gives:

$$x = \frac{3}{x} + 2$$

Suppose we assume a *starting solution* x_1 to this equation to be $x_1 = 2$. We now find the value that this starting solution makes the right-hand side of the equation. We find that

$$x_2 = \frac{3}{x_1} + 2 = \frac{3}{2} + 2 = 3.5$$

We then use this value of $x_2 = 3.5$ as a *better solution* in the equation. We now get

$$x_3 = \frac{3}{3.5} + 2 = 2.857 \text{ (the rest is in the calculator)}$$

By *continuing* this process we find:

'This is ideal to work through on a computer, have a go and just see how accurate it can be'

$$x_4 = 3.05$$
$$x_5 = 2.98$$
$$x_6 = 3.01$$
$$x_7 = 3.00$$
$$x_8 = 3.00$$

The process was continued until the value to 2 decimal places was the same twice. The actual calculator value was used each time in the iteration. Hence the solution here is $x = 3$, which can be shown to be correct.

WORKED EXAMPLE 11

Show that an iteration formula to solve the equation $x^3 - 5x + 1 = 0$ is

$$x_{n+1} = \frac{x_n^3 + 1}{5}$$

Starting with $x_1 = 0$, continue the iteration until you get a solution correct to 4 decimal places.

The equation $x^3 - 5x + 1 = 0$ can be rewritten to give

$$5x = x^3 + 1$$

hence

$$x = \frac{x^3 + 1}{5}$$

This can be solved using the iteration method where $x_{n+1} = \dfrac{x_n^3 + 1}{5}$

Working the iteration out to 4 decimal places (but keeping the accurate figure in the calculator):

$x_1 = 0$
$x_2 = (0 + 1)/5 = 0.2$
$x_3 = (0.2^3 + 1)/5 = 0.2016$
$x_4 = \qquad\qquad = 0.2016$

Hence a solution to the equation is $x = 0.2016$.

Exercise 10
Solve *to 3 decimal places* the equation $x^2 + 3x - 1 = 0$ by the iteration formula

$$U_{n+1} = \frac{1 - U_n^2}{3} \text{ (starting with } U_1 = 0)$$

and show it as a solution.

▶ **Limits of accuracy**

Whenever we round off or approximate we immediately bring a slight *error* into the figures. For example, if I said that my height is 173 cm, then I could be as small as 172.5 cm or as tall as 174.499 999 cm. This is because:

(a) the smallest figure that can *round up* to 173 cm is 172.5 cm;
(b) the largest figure that can *round down* to 173 cm is 173.499 999· cm

These lowest and highest values are called the *limits of the accuracy*.

Any stated measurement is rounded off to some *degree of accuracy*. This determines the possible true values *before* the rounding took place. In other words, the degree of accuracy used in the rounding process will determine the limits of the accuracy of the stated measurement.

Examples

▶ A length of 32.7 cm is rounded to 1 decimal place:
the smallest possible value is 32.65
the largest possible value is 32.749 999 9 …
i.e. $32.65 \leqslant \text{length} < 32.75$

'Find the limits of the accuracy when rounding-off has taken place'

▶ A weight of 5.34 kg is rounded to 2 decimal places:
it can have values $5.335 \leqslant \text{weight} < 5.345$

▶ A weight of 200 grams is rounded to 1 significant figure:
it can have values $150 \leqslant \text{weight} < 250$

▶ A length of 6.203 m is rounded to 3 decimal places:
it can have values $6.2025 \leqslant \text{length} < 6.2035$

Exercise 11
Write down the limits of accuracy for the values of the following measures:
(a) 8 cm;   (b) 6.3 m;   (c) 9.17 cm;   (d) 20 cm.

▶ **Percentage error**

The error made by the rounding off can be expressed as a *percentage error*.

$$\text{percentage error} = \frac{\text{error}}{\text{possible value}} \times 100$$

The greatest *absolute* errors occur at the limits of accuracy.

WORKED EXAMPLE 12

Calculate the greatest percentage error of a given height of 26 cm.

The possible values are $25.5 \leqslant \text{height} < 26.5$. The greatest errors, then, are at 25.5 and 26.5, both of which give an absolute error of 0.5 cm.

'The greatest percentage error is always at the lower limit of accuracy'

At 25.5 cm the percentage error is $\frac{0.5}{25.5} \times 100 = 1.96\%$

At 26.5 cm the percentage error is $\frac{0.5}{26.5} \times 100 = 1.89\%$

The greatest percentage error is 1.96%.

Exercise 12
Find the greatest percentage error of each of the following measures.

(a)   (i) 9 m   (ii) 14 kg
(b)   (i) 1.6 m   (ii) 0.5 kg
(c)   Tommy has 30 marbles. He weighs one marble at 75 g.
    (i)   What is the largest weight of his 30 marbles?
    (ii) What is the lowest weight of his 30 marbles?
    (iii) What is his greatest percentage error?
    (iv) What is his lowest percentage error?

Problems involving percentage errors and limits of accuracy

'Measuring areas and volumes leads to even greater rounding errors'

When we measure *areas* and *volumes* then the errors will be compounded upon each other to make still larger errors from the rounding process.

WORKED EXAMPLE 13

A rectangle has sides given as 5 cm and 8 cm. Calculate:

(a)   the greatest possible area that this rectangle could have.
(b)   the greatest percentage error in the calculated area.

(a)   The upper limit of each side is just under 5.5 cm and 8.5 cm respectively. Hence the greatest possible area is just under $5.5 \times 8.5 = 46.75$. So the greatest area is slightly less than 46.75 cm².
(b)   The greatest percentage error is at the *lower limit* of each side, giving an area of 4.5×7.5 which is 33.75 cm²
    The *given* lengths produce an area of $5 \times 8 = 40$ cm²
    Hence we have a possible error of $40 - 33.75 = 6.25$ cm²

    Greatest percentage error $= \frac{6.25}{33.75} \times 100 = 18.5\%$

Exercise 13
(a)   A rectangular plot of land has its sides measured to the nearest metre. The measurements recorded are 5 m and 3 m.
    (i)   Find the limits of accuracy for each measurement.
    (ii) What is the maximum possible area of the plot?
    (iii) What is the minimum possible value of the perimeter of the plot?
    (iv) What is the maximum percentage error of the area?

(b)   The volume of a cuboid is 154 000 cm^3. The area of the base is 618 cm^2. Both measurements are rounded to 3 significant figures. Find the limits of accuracy on the height of the cuboid.

▶ **Standard form**   *Standard form* is written as a number between 1 and 10 multiplied by ten raised to a power (index). This is a widely used method for displaying the multiplication of very large (and very small) numbers.

Here are some examples of standard form numbers:

$$9.134 \times 10^1 \quad 5.6 \times 10^3 \quad 3.45 \times 10^{16} \quad 7.035 \times 10^{27}$$

Write down ten more standard form numbers of your own. Notice how standard form numbers are made up of *two parts*:

▶   The *first part* being a number between 1 and 9.9999 … (less than 10).
▶   The *second part* being the number 10 raised to a power (or index).

In short, standard form is

$$A \times 10^n \quad \text{where } 1 \leqslant A < 10 \text{ and } n \text{ is an integer}$$

To change a number to standard form

Follow these rules:
(a)   Move the decimal point so that it lies between the first two digits. This gives the number A.
(b)   Count how many places you have moved the decimal point in order for it to be in that position. This gives n (the power).

Example
$$215\,000 \quad = 2.15 \times 100\,000 \quad = 2.15 \times 10^5$$
$$809 \quad\quad\; = 8.09 \times 100 \quad\quad\;\; = 8.09 \times 10^2$$
$$60\,000\,000 = 6.0 \times 10\,000\,000 = 6.0 \times 10^7 \text{ (we could have written } 6 \times 10^7)$$

Exercise 14
Find the square of each of the following numbers and give your answer in standard form:
(a) 3715; (b) 650; (c) 299; (d) 5 million; (e) $6\frac{1}{2}$ million

To change a standard form number back to a 'normal' number

Here we reverse the process we previously followed. For example,

$$9.6 \times 10^4 = 96\,000$$

Notice how we move the decimal point one place over the 6, and then a further three more places. So we put three zeros after 96.

Examples
$$7.31 \times 10^5 = 731\,000$$
$$1.9 \times 10^6 = 1\,900\,000$$
$$4.345 \times 10^2 = 434.5$$
$$6.07 \times 10^1 = 60.7$$
$$4.156 \times 10^3 = 4\,156$$

Exercise 15
First convert the following standard form numbers back to normal, then find their *square roots*: (a) 2.56×10^4; (b) 6.4×10^3; (c) 2.25×10^6.

Standard form for numbers less than 1

How can we write 0.000 53 in standard form?

To answer this question we start by doing exactly what we did before, i.e. following our two rules. However, the four places of decimal we have moved are in the *opposite direction* to that when the numbers are greater than 1. So this time we put in a negative sign in the power. This gives us 5.3×10^{-4}.

Examples
$$0.932 \qquad = 9.32 \times 10^{-1}$$
$$0.045\,1 \qquad = 4.51 \times 10^{-2}$$
$$0.000\,000\,71 = 7.1 \times 10^{-7}$$

Meaning of a negative power (index)

It is worth remembering that if we divide by a number, it is the same as multiplying by the reciprocal of that number. For example:

Examples
$$12 \div 6 = 12 \times \tfrac{1}{6} = 2$$
$$18 \div 3 = 18 \times \tfrac{1}{3} = 6$$

In the same way, when we divide by 10 raised to some power, it is the same as multiplying by '1 over 10 raised to some power'. For example:

Examples
$$800 \div 10^2 = 800 \times \frac{1}{10^2} = 8$$

$$936 \div 10^3 = 936 \times \frac{1}{10^3} = 0.936$$

Now, we write $\dfrac{1}{10^2}$ as 10^{-2}, and $\dfrac{1}{10^3}$ as 10^{-3}, and so on.

$$\boxed{\text{In general, } 10^{-n} = \frac{1}{10^n}}$$

So, when we use a negative power in the standard form notation, it tells us that we are multiplying by 1 over 10 raised to that power.

Examples
$$6.4 \times 10^{-2} = 6.4 \times \frac{1}{10^2} = 0.064$$

$$9.7 \times 10^{-3} = 9.7 \times \frac{1}{10^3} = 0.0097$$

Rounding off using standard form

Generally when dealing with standard form numbers you would want to round off to 1, 2 or 3 significant figures. Remember, it is only the first part of the number that would be rounded off.

Example
Round off the following:

(a) 5.621×10^{17} to 1 significant figure
(b) 7.053×10^{-8} to 2 significant figures

(a) $5.621 \times 10^{17} \approx 6 \times 10^{17}$
(b) $7.053 \times 10^{-8} \approx 7.1 \times 10^{-8}$
(*Note*: we do *not* use 6.0 in (a) as this would be *two* significant figures.)

Exercise 16

(a) Convert the following fractions to decimal numbers. Then express each decimal in standard form correct to 3 significant figures.

  (i) $\frac{1}{121}$ (ii) $\frac{4}{125}$ (iii) $31\frac{5}{36}$

(b) Write the answers to the following in standard form, correct to 2 significant figures.

  (i) 215^2 (ii) $\sqrt{(3\,710)}$ (iii) $(0.000\,31)^3$ (iv) $\sqrt{\left(\dfrac{1}{\pi}\right)}$

Estimation, approximation and other uses of standard form

We can estimate the rough size of some awkward arithmetic problems by using our work on standard form, as in the following examples. Notice how we break down each number in the problem separately into standard form before solving.

WORKED EXAMPLE 14

Find an approximate value of $390\,000 \times 62\,100\,000$.

We first approximate $390\,000$ to $400\,000$ and $62\,100\,000$ to $60\,000\,000$, then change each number to standard form, giving:

  $4 \times 10^5 \times 6 \times 10^7$

We now rearrange to give:

  $4 \times 6 \times 10^5 \times 10^7$

'Recall that
$10^m \times 10^n = 10^{m+n}$*'*

That gives 24×10^{12} which gives:

  2.4×10^{13}

WORKED EXAMPLE 15

Find an approximate value for $731\,520\,000 \times 0.000\,815\,34$.

  $731\,520\,000 \approx 700\,000\,000$
  $0.000\,815\,34 \approx 0.000\,8$

We change each number to standard form, giving:

  $7 \times 10^8 \times 8 \times 10^{-4}$

We now rearrange to give

  $7 \times 8 \times 10^8 \times 10^{-4}$

That gives 56×10^4 which gives:

  5.6×10^5

WORKED EXAMPLE 16

Find a rough estimate to the following problem:

  $0.000\,000\,005\,82 \div 0.000\,016\,45$

We first approximate and change each number to standard form, giving

  $6 \times 10^{-9} \div 2 \times 10^{-5}$

We now rearrange to give

  $(6 \div 2) \times (10^{-9} \div 10^{-5})$

'Recall that
$10^m \div 10^n = 10^{m-n}$*'*

That gives 3×10^{-4} (since $-9 - (-5) = -4$) which is $0.000\,3$.

WORKED EXAMPLE 17

Find a rough estimate to the following problem:

  $$\frac{615\,800\,000 \times 0.005\,971}{0.081\,62}$$

We first find an approximation and change each number to standard form, giving:

  $$\frac{6 \times 10^8 \times 6 \times 10^{-3}}{8 \times 10^{-2}}$$

We now rearrange to give:

$$\frac{(6 \times 6)}{8} \times \frac{(10^8 \times 10^{-3})}{10^{-2}}$$

That gives $\frac{36}{8} \times 10^{(8-3--2)}$ which gives 4.5×10^7.

Exercise 17
Use the idea of standard form to find rough estimates to the following problems, leaving your answer in a suitable form.

(a) $91\,500 \times 710\,000$
(b) $156\,100 \times 0.008\,156$
(c) $0.000\,615 \times 0.007\,59$

(d) $\dfrac{(2\,410\,000 \times 0.003\,14)}{3600}$

(e) $\dfrac{(580\,000 \times 0.790\,01)}{0.013\,0}$

Exercise 18
Evaluate the answers to the following in standard form to three significant figures.

(a) $\dfrac{4.08 \times 10^4 \times 1.89 \times 10^5}{9.15 \times 10^{-6} \times 4.95 \times 10^{-3}}$

(b) $\dfrac{8.7 \times 10^5 + 2.61 \times 10^7}{9.2 \times 10^4 - 8.5 \times 10^2}$

Rational numbers

'Higher level only'

Rational numbers are all the numbers that *can* be expressed as a vulgar fraction of two integers. For example:

5 is a rational number, since 5 can be written as $\frac{5}{1}$
9.16 is a rational number since it can be written as $\frac{916}{100}$
$\sqrt{9}$ is a rational number since it is 3 or -3

It is worth remembering that all the *recurring decimals* you met earlier came from fractions. For example, $\frac{2}{11}$ is $0.18\dot{1}\dot{8}\cdot$, $\frac{5}{7}$ is $0.\dot{7}1428\dot{5}\cdot$, and in fact all recurring decimals can be shown to be *rational* numbers.

Irrational numbers

Irrational numbers are all numbers that *cannot* be expressed as a vulgar fraction of two integers. For example, $\sqrt{2}$ cannot be expressed as a vulgar fraction, π cannot be expressed exactly as a fraction ($\frac{22}{7}$ is only an approximation to it).

▶ ## SOLUTIONS TO EXERCISES

S1   The sequence can be rewritten as 1^2, 4^2, 6^2, 8^2, 9^2, these are the squares of the non-prime integers, hence the next three numbers are 10^2, 12^2 and 14^2 which are 100, 144 and 196.

S2   (a)   Differences are the prime numbers, hence the next three numbers are 45, 62 and 81.
(b)   Differences are -5 in each case, hence the next three numbers are 80, 75 and 70.
(c)   Differences are the square numbers, hence the next three numbers are 65, 101 and 150.

S3   Look at second differences, these are 1, 2, 4, 8, (16, 32, 64) used to build down to give the next three numbers as 70, 135 and 264.

S4 $U_1 = 1;$ $U_2 = 6;$ $U_3 = 15;$ $U_4 = 28$

S5 The difference is always 5, and the first term is 7, hence the nth term is given by $7 + 5(n - 1)$ which could be simplified to $5n + 2$.

S6 The differences are 7, 14, 21, 28 which are the multiples of 7. The first term is 8, hence the nth term is $8 + 7\,\dfrac{n(n - 1)}{2}$.

S7 These are $1^2, 3^2, 5^2, 7^2$, the odd numbers squared. Hence we need to link up

$$
\begin{aligned}
\text{1st term} &\rightarrow 1^2 \\
\text{2nd term} &\rightarrow 3^2 \\
\text{3rd term} &\rightarrow 5^2 \\
\text{4th term} &\rightarrow 7^2
\end{aligned}
$$

hence the nth term $\rightarrow (2n - 1)^2$

S8 The differences helped me to predict the next few terms, but not the nth term so readily. However, on looking at the factors I noticed:

U_1	U_2	U_3	U_4	U_n
↓	↓	↓	↓	↓
3	8	15	24	
1×3	2×4	3×5	4×6	$n \times (n + 2)$

hence $U_n = n(n + 2)$

S9 3.59

S10 The iteration to 3 decimal places is:

$$
\begin{aligned}
U_2 &= 0.333 \\
U_3 &= 0.296 \\
U_4 &= 0.304 \\
U_5 &= 0.302 \\
U_6 &= 0.303 \\
U_7 &= 0.303
\end{aligned}
$$

so the solution is $x = 0.303$. By substituting $x = 0.303$ into $x^2 + 3x + 1$ we get $0.000\,9$, showing it to be very close to zero.

S11 (a) $7.5 \leqslant$ measure < 8.5
(b) $6.25 \leqslant$ measure < 6.35
(c) $9.165 \leqslant$ measure < 9.175
(d) $15 \leqslant$ measure < 25

S12 (a)   (i) $\dfrac{0.5}{8.5} \times 100 = 5.9\%$ (ii) $\dfrac{0.5}{13.5} \times 100 = 3.7\%$

    (b)   (i) $\dfrac{0.05}{1.55} \times 100 = 3.2\%$ (ii) $\dfrac{0.05}{0.45} \times 100 = 11.1\%$

    (c)   (i) $30 \times 75.5\,\text{g} = 2\,265\,\text{g}$ (ii) $30 \times 74.5\,\text{g} = 2\,235\,\text{g}$

        (iii) $\dfrac{0.5}{74.5} \times 100 = 0.67\%$ (iv) 0%, he could be accurate!

S13 (a) (i) $4.5 \leqslant$ length $< 5.5, 2.5 \leqslant$ width < 3.5
    (ii) $5.5 \times 3.5 = 19.25 \, \text{m}^2$, so greatest $< 19.25 \, \text{m}^2$
    (iii) $(4.5 + 2.5) \times 2 = 14 \, \text{m}$

    (iv) $\dfrac{5 \times 3 - 4.5 \times 2.5}{4.5 \times 2.5} \times 100 = 33\%$

(b) least height $= \dfrac{\text{least volume}}{\text{greatest area}} = \dfrac{153\,500}{618.5} = 248.18$

greatest height $= \dfrac{\text{greatest volume}}{\text{least area}} = \dfrac{154\,500}{617.5} = 250.2$

hence the limits of accuracy are $248.18 \leqslant$ height < 250.2

S14 (a) 1.38×10^7; (b) 4.23×10^5; (c) 8.94×10^4; (d) 2.5×10^{13}; (e) 4.23×10^{13}

S15 (a) 160; (b) 80; (c) $1\,500$

S16 (a) (i) 8.26×10^{-3}; (ii) 3.20×10^{-2}: (iii) 3.11×10^1
    (b) (i) 4.6×10^4; (ii) 6.1×10^1; (iii) 3.0×10^{-11}; (iv) 5.6×10^{-1}

S17 (a) 6.4×10^{10}; (b) 1.2×10^3; (c) 4.8×10^{-6}; (d) 2; (e) 3.5×10^7

S18 (a) 1.70×10^{17}; (b) 2.96×10^2

▶ EXAMINATION QUESTIONS

▶ **Question 1**

Fig. 4.2

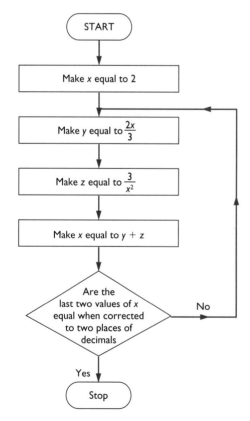

x	y	z
2	1.333	

'Try to make your comment on some mathematical insight you can notice'

(a) Work through the flow diagram writing down the value of x, y and z in a table, as shown in Fig. 4.2, recording only the first 3 decimal places of your answers.
(b) Cube the last value of x and comment on the result.
(c) Give the last value of x correct to 2 decimal places.   (MEG)

▶ **Question 2** A solution of the equation $x^3 + x = 12$ lies between 2 and 3.
Use the method of trial and improvement to find this solution of the equation

$$x^3 + x = 12$$

Give your answer to 1 decimal place.   (NEAB)

▶ **Question 3** Four rods are used to make a square, as shown in Fig. 4.3. Rods are then added to make a row of 2 squares, then 3 squares, and so on, as in Fig. 4.4.

Fig. 4.3    **Fig. 4.4**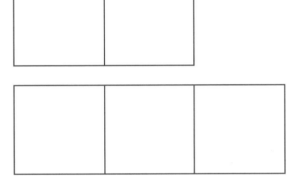

(a) How many rods are needed to make a row of
   (i) 5 squares
   (ii) 6 squares
   (iii) 15 squares?
(b) Find the formula which gives the number of rods, r, needed to make a row of s squares in the form: $r =$
(c) Use your formula to find how many squares could be made with 70 rods.
(d) Rearrange your formula in (b) into the form: $s =$
(e) What is the greatest number of squares you can make in a row with 120 rods? How many rods will you have left over?   (WJEC)

▶ **Question 4** Write down the missing TWO numbers in each of the sequences:

(a) 64, 32, 16, _, _, 2
(b) 1, 2, 6, _, _, 720   (London)

▶ **Question 5** In a sequence of fractions, the next term after $\dfrac{x}{y}$ is $\dfrac{x+y}{2x+y}$

The first term is $\dfrac{2}{3}$

(a) Write down the next four terms of the sequence $\dfrac{2}{3}, \dfrac{5}{7}, -, -, -, -$

(b) Find the *squares* of the values of these six terms to as many decimal places as your calculator will give. What do you notice about these squares of values?

(c) Find the term in the sequence which comes immediately before $\dfrac{2\,378}{3\,363}$

(d) One term in the sequence is $\dfrac{p}{q}$. Find, in terms of p and q, the term which comes immediately before $\dfrac{p}{q}$.   (MEG)

▶ **Question 6** Five of the numbers below are rational and five are irrational.

    (i) $\pi\sqrt{5}$ (vi) $2^0 + 2^{-1} + 2^{-2}$
   (ii) $\sqrt{2} + 1$ (vii) $(\sqrt{3})^4$
  (iii) $(\sqrt{2})^3$ (viii) $\sqrt{3} - 1.732050808$
  (iv) $16^{-1/2}$ (ix) $\sqrt{3}.\sqrt{12}$
   (v) $\frac{\sqrt{3}}{\sqrt{2}}$ (x) 0.3

  (a) Write down the five **rational** numbers.
  (b) Give an example of two different **irrational** numbers, a and b, where $\frac{a}{b}$ is a **rational** number.
                                                (London)

▶ **Question 7** A sequence is given by

$$x_{n+1} = \frac{12}{x_n + 4}$$

   (i) The first term, x_1, of the sequence is 3. Find the next three terms.
  (ii) What do you think is the value of x_n as n becomes very large?   (SEG)

▶ **Question 8** (a) Here is a sequence of numbers: 2, 4, 8, 16, 32, 64.
        (i) Write down a formula for the nth number in this sequence.
            You can get from any number of this sequence to the next number by adding on as in Fig. 4.5.

Fig. 4.5

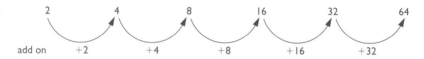

       (ii) The 'add on' numbers also form a sequence. What do you notice about this sequence?
      (iii) Use algebra to explain why this happens.
    (b) Now write down this sequence: 3, 9, 27, 81, 243, 729.
        (i) Write down the 'add on' numbers for this sequence.
       (ii) What is the connection between the 'add on' sequence and the original sequence?
      (iii) Use algebra to explain why this happens.
    (c) If instead of starting with 2 or 3, the original sequence starts: a, a^2, a^3, a^4, what is the connection between the 'add on' sequence and the original sequence?
    (d) Here is an 'add on' sequence: $+20, +100, +500, +2\,500$.
        (i) If the original sequence is of the type described in (c), write down the first five numbers of the original sequence.
       (ii) Write down the first five numbers of a different original sequence (not of the type described in (c)) which has the same 'add on' sequence.
      (iii) Write down a formula for the nth number in the sequence you have given in (ii).
                                                (OCSEB)

▶ **Question 9** (a) The symbol $n!$ (usually called 'factorial n') is used to stand for the result of multiplying together the first n whole numbers; so that, for example

$$10! = 1 \times 2 \times 3 \times 4 \times 5 \times 6 \times 7 \times 8 \times 9 \times 10$$

      My calculator gives the value of 10! to be 3 628 800. Explain how you could tell, without actually doing the multiplication, that the value of 10! ends in just two zeros.
    (b) The value of 100! is too large to be found on the calculator. Find, without using your calculator, how many zeros there are at the end of 100! Explain your reasoning clearly.
    (c) A book of tables states that 100! is approximately 9.33×10^{157}. Putting this together with (b), we know how many digits there are in 100!, that some are certainly zero and that some are certainly not zero. Making the assumption that each of the digits 0, 1, 2, ..., 9 occurs about the same number of times amongst the remaining digits, estimate how many zeros there are altogether in 100! when it is written out in full. Show your working.   (OCSEB)

▶ **Question 10**   Ranjit measures the dimensions of a rectangular field, correct to the nearest metre. He finds that the length is 105 m and the width is 63 m.

(a)   Between what bounds must the true length lie?
(b)   Calculate the upper and lower bounds for the area of the field.

▶ **Question 11**   The price of gold is £348.50 per ounce. The density of gold is 19.3 g/cm^3 (i.e. 1 cm^3 of gold weighs 19.3 g). There are 28.35 grams in one ounce. These figures can be treated as **exact** measurements.
     A solid gold bar, in the shape of a cuboid, has sides 4.15 cm, 2.04 cm and 5.96 cm. These measurements are made to the nearest 0.01 cm.

(a)   What is the range of prices for this bar of gold? Give your answers to the nearest £10.

The bar of gold was weighed on some scales which gave a value of 974 g to the nearest gram.

(b)   Estimate the range of prices for the gold bar using this value.
(c)   Explain why the weighing method appears to be better.

▶ **Question 12**   Given that the numbers 2.4, 4.3 and 0.8 are accurate to 1 decimal place, calculate upper and lower bounds for the calculation

$$\frac{2.4 + 4.3}{0.8}$$

▶ **Question 13**   (a)   A distance is measured as 100 m, correct to the nearest metre. What is the least value that the actual distance could be?
(b)   A student runs the distance in 14.3 seconds correct to 1 decimal place. What is the greatest time the athlete could have taken?
(c)   Calculate the least and greatest average speeds for the athlete in metres per second.

▶ **Question 14**   A light year is approximately 5 878 000 000 000 miles. Write this number in standard form.

▶ **Question 15**   (i)   Express 43.6×10^{-3} in standard index form.
(ii)   Calculate the value of $(1.3221 \times 10^{-2})(1.17 \times 10^{-4})$.

▶ **Question 16** $D = 1\,000 - 1.28 \times 16^2$. Use the formula to find the value of D.

▶ **Question 17**   The mass, M, of the Earth is 5.98×10^{24} kg.
                      The mass, m, of the Moon is 7.35×10^{22} kg.

(a)   Explain how it is possible to say which of these masses is greater, without doing any working.
(b)   Calculate the value of $\dfrac{M}{m}$. Give your answer in standard form.

▶ **Question 18**   Given that $m = 5 \times 10^{-2}$ and $n = 4 \times 10^3$, calculate, giving each answer in standard form:

(i) mn;   (ii) m^3;   (iii) $\dfrac{1}{m} + n$.

▶ **Question 19**   (a) When buying his groceries in a supermarket, George estimates the maximum amount he will have to pay by rounding up the price of each article to the nearest 10p (unless it is already a multiple of 10p). For example, an article costing £2.21 is rounded up to £2.30 and an article costing £1.58 is rounded up to £1.60.

On one particular occasion, he bought 12 articles and his estimate was £8.30.

What is the smallest possible total of the actual prices of the 12 articles? Show your working clearly.

(b)   Alyson uses a similar method but she rounds the price of each article to the nearest 10p (up or down as necessary with 5p always being rounded up). For example, an article costing £2.21 is rounded down to £2.20 and an article costing £1.58 is rounded up to £1.60.

She bought 12 articles whose total price was £12.56.

Calculate the greatest and least possible values of her estimate. Explain your method.

▶ **Question 20**   A **packet** of custard cream biscuits costs 33p and contains 24 biscuits. A **bargain box** of the same type of biscuits costs £3.29 and has a weight (excluding the box and packing) of 3.6 kg, correct to the nearest 0.1 kg. All the biscuits, whether from a packet or a box, have the same weight. Once opened, the contents of either a packet or a bargain box should be eaten within five days.

(a)   Ten of those biscuits were weighed on kitchen scales and found to be heavier than 120 g but lighter than 130 g.

Fig. 4.6

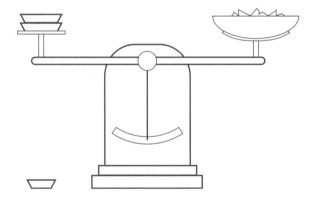

(i)   Estimate the weight of the biscuits in one packet.
(ii) Calculate the maximum possible number and the minimum possible number of biscuits in a bargain box.

(b)   The St Mithian Pensioners Club meets every weekday afternoon (Monday to Friday inclusive) for tea and chat. At these meetings every member present is given four custard cream biscuits with the tea. There are 28 members of the club.

(i)   How many packets of biscuits should the secretary buy on a Monday to be sure of providing four biscuits for every member who might be present on Monday?

The secretary assumes that over the whole week the average daily attendance will be 16 pensioners, and on Tuesday she buys sufficient biscuits for the rest of the week.

(ii) Calculate the total cost of biscuits for the week if she buys a bargain box on Tuesday.
(iii) Determine whether it would be cheaper to buy separate packets rather than a bargain box on the Tuesday.

(c)   The secretary now decides that she wants to buy sufficient biscuits for the whole week on Monday. Calculate the cheapest way of doing this.

▶ **EXAMINATION ANSWERS**

A1 (a) x y z

         2   1.333   0.75

         2.083   1.388   0.691

         2.080

    (b) Using the correct calculator value of x I get 9.000 065 8, and cubing 2.08 I get 8.998 9, both of which round off to 9. So it would appear that this iteration has found the cube root of 9 to 2 decimal places.

    (c) 2.08

A2 Your solution should indicate that you tried 2.5 … which gives 18.13 (too big) and then improve your range to get between 2.2 and 2.1. You should then try 2.15 which gives 12.08 (too big).

        Hence 2.1 is the solution to 1 decimal place.

A3 (a) Build up a table of results to give:

number of squares (s)	1	2	3	4	5	6
rods (r)	4	7	10	13	16	19

        The difference is 3 each time so the table can easily be continued, and with a difference of 3 each time and a start of 4 then the number of rods $r = 4 + 3(s - 1) = 4 + 3s - 3 = 1 + 3s$.

         Hence: (i) $r = 16$;   (ii) $r = 19$;   (iii) $r = 46$

    (b) The formula is $r = 1 + 3s$

    (c) When $r = 70$, solve the equation $70 = 1 + 3s$ to give $s = 23$

    (d) Rearrange to give $s = \dfrac{r - 1}{3}$

    (e) When $r = 120$, $s = \dfrac{119}{3} = 39.6$

        So there will be 39 squares with 2 rods left over.

A4 (a) 8,   4

    (b) The differences will not help here, but looking at the factors will, since:

$$1 \rightarrow 1$$
$$2 \rightarrow 1 \times 2$$
$$6 \rightarrow 1 \times 2 \times 3$$
$$?$$
$$?$$
$$720 \rightarrow 1 \times 2 \times 3 \times 4 \times 5 \times 6$$

        So the missing numbers are $(1 \times 2 \times 3 \times 4) = 24$ and $(1 \times 2 \times 3 \times 4 \times 5) = 120$.

A5 (a) $\dfrac{2}{3}$, $\dfrac{5}{7}$, $\dfrac{12}{17}$, $\dfrac{29}{41}$, $\dfrac{70}{99}$, $\dfrac{169}{239}$

    (b) 0.444 444 4

         0.510 204

         0.498 269 9

         0.500 297 4

         0.499 948 9

         0.500 008 7

        You should notice that these squares are getting closer to 0.5.

(c)   You will get a pair of simultaneous equations:

$$x + y = 2\,378$$
$$2x + y = 3\,363$$

which will solve to give $x = 985$, $y = 1\,393$. So the term is $\dfrac{985}{1\,393}$

(d)   Solve the pair of simultaneous equations:

$$x + y = p$$
$$2x + y = q$$

to give $x = q - p$ and $y = 2p - q$. So the term is $\dfrac{q - p}{2p - q}$

A6   (a) $16^{-1/2}$, $2^0 + 2^{-1} + 2^{-2}$, $(\sqrt{3})^4$, $\sqrt{3} . \sqrt{12}$, 0.3
(or iv, vi, vii, ix, x)

(b) $\dfrac{\sqrt{12}}{\sqrt{3}}$ or $\dfrac{\sqrt{3}}{\sqrt{12}}$

A7   (i) $x_2 = 1.714$; $x_3 = 2.100$; $x_4 = 1.967$
(ii)   You should have done a few more iterations just to convince yourself that the limit looks like being 2.

A8   (a)   (i) 2^n
(ii)   It is the same sequence as the original.
(iii)   Consider three consecutive terms of the original sequence, $2^x, 2^{x+1}, 2^{x+2}$. The add ons will be $2^{x+1} - 2^x$ and $2^{x+2} - 2^{x+1}$
which are $2^x(2 - 1)$ and $2^{x+1}(2 - 1)$
which are 2^x and 2^{x+1}
So we see the pattern as in Fig. 4.7.

Fig. 4.7

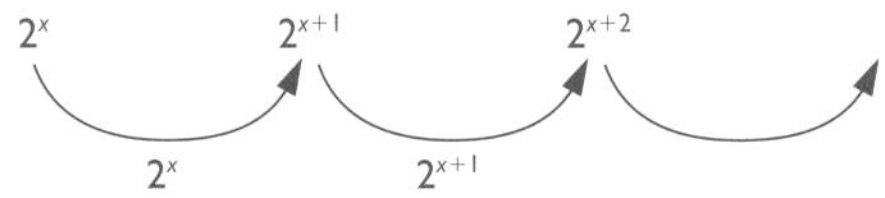

(b)   (i)   The add ons are 6, 18, 54, 162, 486.
(ii)   The add on sequence is exactly double the original.
(iii)   Consider three consecutive terms of the original sequence $3^x, 3^{x+1}, 3^{x+2}$. The add ons will be $3^{x+1} - 3^x$ and $3^{x+2} - 3^{x+1}$
which are $3^x(3 - 1)$ and $3^{x+1}(3 - 1)$
which are 2×3^x and $2 \times 3^{x+1}$
So we see the pattern as in Fig. 4.8.

Fig. 4.8

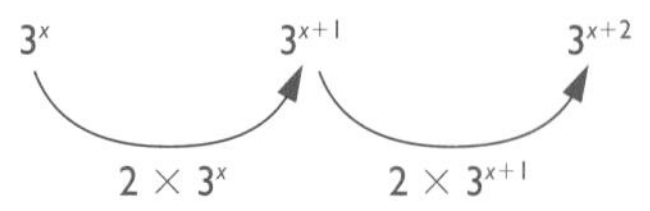

(c)   The add on sequence will be the original sequence multiplied by $(a - 1)$.
(d)   (i)   Then from (c): $a(a - 1) = 20$
hence $a^2 - a - 20 = 0$
which is the quadratic with solution $a = 5$ and $a = -4$. The only sensible solution is $a = 5$ which gives the sequence 5, 25, 125, 625, 3 125.
(ii)   1, 21, 121, 621, 3 121, ...
(iii)   The sequence 1, 21, 121, 621, 3 121, ..., U_n
Adding 4 on to each term will give 5, 25, 125, 625, 3 125, ..., $U_n + 4$
The nth term of this sequence is 5^n; hence $U_n + 4 = 5^n$, so the nth term will be $5^n - 4$.

A9 (a) Pairs of numbers that multiply to give a multiple of 10 can be found to be (2 × 5), and then 10 itself, each of which will give a zero on the end. None of the other numbers can multiply together to give any zeros. So just (2 × 5) and 10 contribute a zero, hence two zeros.

(b) Finding pairs that give multiples of 10, and the multiples of 10 give us:

(2 × 5), (4 × 15), (6 × 25), (8 × 35), (12 × 45) ... (24 × 95) [10 of them]
and × 10 × 20 × 30 × 40 × 50 × 60 × 70 × 80 × 90 × 100 [another 11 of them]

and each of the numbers 25, 50, 75 contains the factor 5 twice, hence with other even numbers not yet used, this will give three other zeros, this gives 24 zeros altogether. (Note you can only use any number once.)

(c) There will be 157 + 1 digits altogether, 24 of which are known to be zero, this leaves 134 digits. There is a $\frac{1}{10}$ probability of any other digits being a zero, hence I would expect to find one-tenth of 134, which is approximately 13 other zeros. So 13 + 24 = 37 zeros altogether.

A10 (a) 104.5 m ≤ length < 105.5

(b) Since 62.5 ≤ width < 63.5, the smallest value of the area will be given by 104.5 × 62.5 = 6 531.25 m² and the greatest by 105.5 × 63.5 = 6 699.25 hence 6 531.25 m² ≤ area < 6 699.25 m².

A11 (a) Least weight is (4.145 × 2.035 × 5.955) × 19.3 g = 969.455 82 g
(Keep accurate figures in calculator memory.)

Cost is $\frac{969.455\,82}{28.35} \times £348.50 = £11\,917.30$

Similarly the highest price is £12 024.91
Hence the range is £11 920 ≤ price < £12 020

(b) Least value is $\frac{973.5}{28.35} \times £348.50 = £11\,967.01$

Greatest value is $\frac{974.5}{28.35} \times £348.50 = £11\,979.30$

The range is £11 970 ≤ price ≤ £11 980.

(c) Part (a) price range is over £100 between lowest and upper. While (b) price range is only over £10, hence it is more reliable.

A12 Lowest = $\frac{\text{lowest numerator}}{\text{greatest denominator}} = \frac{2.35 + 4.25}{0.85} = 7.764\,7$

Highest = $\frac{2.45 + 4.35}{0.75} = 9.066\,7$

A13 (a) 99.5 m
(b) 14.35 seconds

(c) least = $\frac{99.5}{14.35} = 6.93$ m/s; greatest = $\frac{100.5}{14.25} = 7.05$ m/s

A14 5.878×10^{12}

A15 (i) 4.36×10^{-2}; (ii) 1.547×10^{-6}

A16 $D = 872$

A17   (a)   The Earth, since 10^{24} will make the number greater than 10^{22}.
        (b) 8.136×10^1

A18   (i) 2×10^2;   (ii) 1.25×10^{-4};   (iii) 4020

A19   (a)   He could overestimate by a maximum of 9p each time, making the least total $£8.30 - (12 \times 9p) = £7.22$.
        (b)   Greatest value is $£12.56 + (12 \times 4p) = £13.04$
              Least value is $£12.56 - (12 \times 5p) = £11.96$

A20   (a)   (i) $\dfrac{24 \times 125}{10}\,g = 300\,g$

              (ii) $\dfrac{3.55 \times 1\,000}{13} = 273$ minimum, $\dfrac{3.65 \times 1\,000}{12} = 304$

        (b)   (i) $\dfrac{28 \times 4}{24} = 4.67$, so buy 5 packets

              (ii) Total cost $= 5 \times 33p + £3.29 = £4.94$
              (iii) $16 \times 5 \times 4 = 320$ biscuits needed in the week
                    $320 - (24 \times 5) = 200$ biscuits needed after Monday
                    $200 \div 24 = 8.33$, so 9 packets needed at a cost of $£2.97$
                    Hence cheaper to buy packets
        (c) $320 \div 24 = 13.33$, so 14 packets would last the week ... $£4.62$
              $320 - 273 = 47$ extra to a bargain box $\left.\begin{array}{c} \\ \\ \end{array}\right\}$ $£3.95$
              $47 \div 24 = 1.958$ ... 2 packets extra needed
              The cheapest option is to buy 1 bargain box and 2 packets.

Grade checklist	
For grade	**You should be able to do the following:**
B	Search and explain number sequences.
	Calculate with numbers in standard form.
	Solve numerical problems, checking that the results are of the right size.
A	Generalise the number pattern.
	Understand upper and lower bounds of numbers expressed to a given degree of accuracy.
A*	Investigate number patterns to solve problems.
	Determine the possible effects of errors on calculations.

EXAMINATION QUESTIONS WITH STUDENT ANSWERS

Question 1

A black ball is placed on a table and is represented by T_1, as shown in the diagram.
It is then surrounded by white balls to form a triangular shape, T_2, as shown in the diagram.
Shape T_3 is formed by surrounding T_2 by black balls, and so on.

'Spelling incorrect, but as long as the word is recognisable then no marks will be lost'

(a)   What kinds of triangles are formed by the centres of the outside balls?

isosolese

T_1

'You have ended up in the right place, but have not specifically given the answer'

(b)   How many rows of balls will there be in

(i) shape T_7?   *1, 3, 5, 6, 7, 9, 11, 13*

(ii) shape T_n?

2n − 1

T_2

'Good generalisation, well done'

(c)   How many balls will there be in

(i) shape T_7?   *1, 9, 25, 49, 81, 121, 169*

(ii) shape T_n?

(2n − 1)²

T_3

'What a shame, you have made out a correct table but then not used it properly to find the answer'

(d)   What colour balls will be added

(i) to T_{17} to make T_{18}?

black

(ii) to T_{2n-1} to make T_{2n}?

white

Black	White
T_1	T_2
T_3	T_4
T_5	T_6
T_7	T_8
odd	even

'Although the answer is correct, there will be no marks because it does not agree with the part (i)'

(e)   How many balls will be added to T_{n-1} to make T_n?

1–	9–	25–	49–	81–	121–	169	T_{n-1}	T_n
	8	16	24	32	40	48		
	8	8	8	8	8		$(n-1)8$	
1x8	2x8	3x8	4x8	5x8	6x8	7x8	$=8(n-1)$	

'Very good, clearly showing how the final answer is found'

'A good answer showing high mathematical ability but a tendency to make careless errors which will be costly'

Question 2

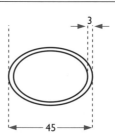

Each link of a chain has an outside length of 45 mm, and the metal is 3 mm thick.
Each measurement is given to the nearest mm.
The diagram below shows a chain which is made up of 4 links.

(a) Find the maximum length, in millimetres, of a chain which is made up of
  (i) 2 links
  (ii) 3 links
  (iii) 10 links
(b) Find an expression for the maximum length of a chain which is made up of n links.
(c) Use your answer to part (b) to find the smallest number of links required to make a chain at least 3 metres long.

'Good diagrams to help show the situation'

'A good generalisation'

'Clearly shown the method; good'

'Poor use of = sign'

'A clear, correct approach; well done'

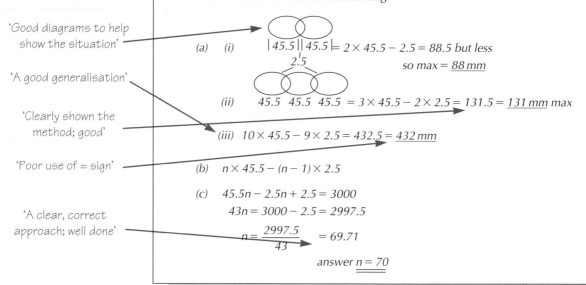

(a) (i) $|45.5||45.5| = 2 \times 45.5 - 2.5 = 88.5$ but less
2.5 so max $= \underline{88\,mm}$

(ii) $45.5\ \ 45.5\ \ 45.5 = 3 \times 45.5 - 2 \times 2.5 = 131.5 = \underline{131\,mm}\ max$

(iii) $10 \times 45.5 - 9 \times 2.5 = 432.5 = \underline{432\,mm}$

(b) $n \times 45.5 - (n-1) \times 2.5$

(c) $45.5n - 2.5n + 2.5 = 3000$
$43n = 3000 - 2.5 = 2997.5$
$n = \dfrac{2997.5}{43} = 69.71$

answer $n = \underline{\underline{70}}$

SUMMARY

▷ **Standard form**: A standard form number is written in the form:
$A \times 10^n$ where $1 \leqslant A < 10$ and n is an integer

▷ **Rational numbers**: are those numbers that can be written in the form of $\dfrac{a}{b}$ where both a and b are integers.

▷ **Irrational numbers**: numbers that are not rational. Common irrational numbers are π and $\sqrt{2}$.

▷ **As a percentage**, e.g. 5 kg out of 8 kg is $\dfrac{5 \times 100}{8} = 62.5\%$

▷ **Limits of accuracy**: any rounded off measurement will always be ambiguous between two limits, e.g.:
$6.35\,cm \leqslant 6.4\,cm < 6.45\,cm$

Ratio and variance

 GETTING STARTED

We consider here the ratios of similar shapes and the four different types of variance, all of which appear in the GCSE higher level mathematics syllabuses.

This section will incorporate quite a lot of algebra too.

▶ Useful definitions

Similar	Two shapes are similar if one is a mathematical enlargement of the other.
Enlargement	When all the respective dimensions of two shapes are in the same ratio.
Scale factor	The ratio which links two similar figures.
Variation	Where one or more variables are connected by an algebraic rule.
Direct variation	Where there is a simple *multiplying* relationship between the variables involved.
Inverse variation	Where there is a simple *dividing* relationship between the variables involved.
Partial variation	Where two or more variables are connected by some 'law of variation' in such a way that the independent variables can be *added* together.
Joint variation	Where three (or more) variables are connected with each other in combinations of direct and/or inverse proportion.
Proportional	Having a constant ratio.
Surd	An expression left in 'root' notation, e.g. $\sqrt{2}$, $\sqrt{15}$.

▶ Topic chart

The following topic chart can be completed for each of the topics in 'Ratio and variance'. Tick the appropriate box when you have first studied that topic. You can also keep a record of when you have revised that topic for the first and second time, etc.

London	MEG	NEAB	NICCEA	SEG	WJEC	IGCSE	TOPIC	STUDY	REVISION 1	REVISION 2
✓	✓	✓	✓	✓	✓	✓	Similar shapes			
✓	✓	✓	✓	✓	✓	✓	Variation			
✓	✓	✓	✓	✓	✓	✓	Direct variation			
✓	✓	✓	✓	✓	✓	✓	Inverse variation			
✓	✓	✓	✓	✓	✓	✓	Partial variation			
✓	✓	✓	✓	✓	✓	✓	Joint variation			

WHAT YOU NEED TO KNOW

▶ **Similar shapes**   Two shapes are said to be *similar* if all their corresponding angles are equal and the ratios of the corresponding lengths are also equal. An example is shown in Fig. 5.1.

Fig. 5.1

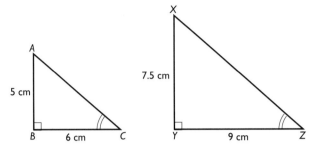

In the figure, all the corresponding angles are equal and the ratio of each pair of corresponding sides is 2:3, i.e.

$$\frac{5}{7.5} = \frac{6}{9} = \frac{2}{3}$$

So if the length AC is 7.8 cm, then the length XZ can be found by equating $\frac{XZ}{7.8} = \frac{3}{2}$ hence

$XZ = \dfrac{3 \times 7.8}{2} = 11.7$ cm. (Note how the ratio has been used.)

Ratios of similar shapes

Consider the two shapes shown in Fig. 5.2.

Fig. 5.2

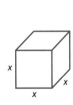 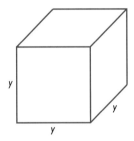

Both these shapes are *cubes*; hence each *corresponding angle* is the same, and each *corresponding side* is in the ratio $x : y$. We can now also see that by considering any *face*, the ratio of the areas is $x^2 : y^2$. The ratio of the *volumes* is $x^3 : y^3$.

We can summarise the situation by saying that for any similar solid that has lengths in the ratio $x : y$ then:

'These ratios are asked about every year; you must learn them'

ratio of **lengths** $x : y$ ratio of **areas** $x^2 : y^2$ ratio of **volumes** $x^3 : y^3$

WORKED EXAMPLE I   Two similar statues, one 8 cm tall, the other 15 cm, are on display. The smaller one has a base area of 4 cm² and a volume of 30 cm³. Find:

(a)   the base area of the larger statue,
(b)   the volume of the larger statue.

The length ratio $= \dfrac{15}{8}$

(a)   ratio of areas = (length ratio)² $= \left(\dfrac{15}{8}\right)^2$ so where *A* is the base area of the larger statue

'The larger value is the numerator because it is the area of the larger statue that we are looking for'

$$\frac{A}{4} = \left(\frac{15}{8}\right)^2$$

$$A = \left(\frac{15}{8}\right)^2 \times 4 = 14.0625 \qquad \text{Area} = 14 \text{ cm}^2$$

(b)   volume ratio = (length ratio)^3 = $\left(\dfrac{15}{8}\right)^3$

so where V is the volume of the larger statue

$$\frac{V}{30} = \left(\frac{15}{8}\right)^3$$

$$V = \left(\frac{15}{8}\right)^3 \times 30 = 197.75$$

Volume = 197.75 cm^3

WORKED EXAMPLE 2

A supermarket sold similar tins of beans.

    Small – which has a paper label of area 23 cm^2
    Medium – which has a paper label of area 45 cm^2
    Large – which has a paper label of area 75 cm^2

The medium sized tin is 7 cm tall with a weight of 350 g. Calculate:

'The sizes of the labels are in direct proportion to the sizes of the tins'

(a)   the height of the other two tins.
(b)   the weight of the other two tins.

(We have to be careful to get the ratios (fractions) the correct way up.)
(a)   Let h be the height of the small tin. Then, when area ratio = (length ratio)^2:

small tin   → $\dfrac{23}{45} = \left(\dfrac{h}{7}\right)^2 = \dfrac{h^2}{7^2}$
medium tin →

'Smaller number on top since it is the height of the smaller tin that we are finding'

i.e. $h^2 = \dfrac{23}{45} \times 49$

$$h = \sqrt{25.04}$$
$$h \approx 5$$

Let H be the height of the large tin. Then, where area ratio = (length ratio)^2:

$$\frac{75}{45} = \left(\frac{H}{7}\right)^2$$

'We put the larger number as the numerator because it is the height of the larger tin that we need to find'

i.e. $H^2 = \dfrac{75}{45} \times 49$

$$H = \sqrt{81.667}$$
$$H \approx 9$$

So the small height is 5 cm and the large height is 9 cm.
(b)   Let w be the weight of the small tin. Then the volume ratio = (length ratio)^3,
     i.e. weight ratio = (length ratio)^3:

'Weight is directly proportional to volume and so will behave in the same way'

small tin   → $\dfrac{w}{350} = \left(\dfrac{5}{7}\right)^3$
medium tin →

$$w = \left(\frac{5}{7}\right)^3 \times 350$$

$$w \approx 128$$

Let W be the weight of the large tin. Then weight ratio = (length ratio)^3:

large tin   → $\dfrac{W}{350} = \left(\dfrac{9}{7}\right)^3$
medium tin →

$$W = \left(\frac{9}{7}\right)^3 \times 350$$

$$W \approx 744$$

So the weights of the two tins are 128 g and 744 g.

Exercise 1

1. Find the volumes of the similar solids in Fig. 5.3. Give the answers correct to 3 significant figures.

Fig. 5.3a

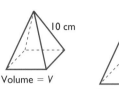

Volume = *V*

Volume = 900 cm³

Fig. 5.3b

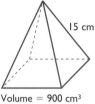

11 cm

5 cm

Volume = *V*

Volume = 40 cm³

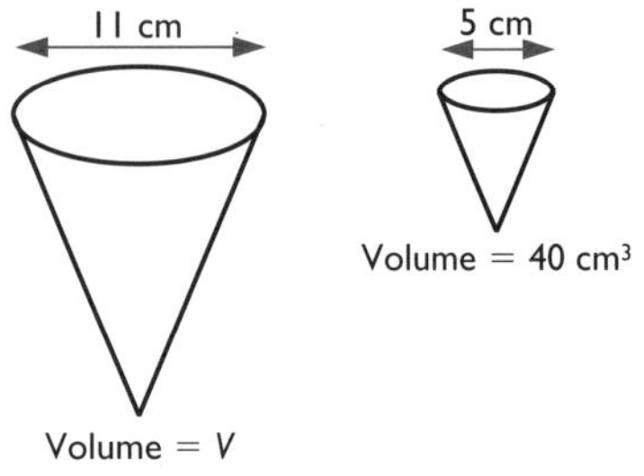

2. Find the volume *V* and the length *H* as indicated in Fig. 5.4. Give the answers correct to the nearest whole number.

Fig. 5.4

Height	5 cm	*H*
Surface area	22 cm²	32 cm²
Volume	14 cm³	*V*

▶ Variation

Variation is a term we use when one or more variables can be connected by some algebraic rule.

There are four types of variation – direct, inverse, partial and joint. We now look at each type in turn.

Direct variation

Look at these two examples.

▶   When you cycle at a steady speed, then the distance you travel increases as the time you are cycling increases.

▶   When you wish to exchange Singapore dollars for pounds sterling, then the more Singapore dollars you exchange, the more pounds you will receive.

Both of these are examples of direct variation.

'Direct variation involves a multiplying relationship'

Direct variation (or proportion) is when there is a simple *multiplying* relationship between the variables involved. So in a two-variable situation, as one variable increases so does the other.

The symbol we use for 'varies directly with' or 'is directly proportional to' is ∝. Hence the statement 'distance varies directly with time' can be written as:

distance ∝ time

This means that distance ÷ time is a fixed ratio; we call this ratio *K*.

We can therefore say that distance = *K* multiplied by time, or:

$$d = Kt$$

This *K* is called the *constant of proportionality* and the equation $d = Kt$ is known as the *law of proportionality* or the *law of variation*.

WORKED EXAMPLE 3

W is directly proportional to *N*, and *W* = 8 when *N* = 5. Find:

(a) the law of proportionality;
(b) *W* when *N* = 12.

$W \propto N$, so $W = KN$ where *K* is a constant. Since *W* = 8 when *N* = 5 then 8 = 5 *K*, i.e.

$$K = \frac{8}{5}$$

$$= 1.6$$

(a)   Hence the law of proportionality is $W = 1.6\,N$
(b)   When $N = 12$ then $W = 1.6 \times 12 = 19.2$

WORKED EXAMPLE 4   The weight of a metal sphere varies directly with the cube of the radius. If the weight of a metal sphere of radius 3 cm is 1.02 kg, find the weight of a metal sphere of radius 5 cm.

Let W be the weight and r the radius. $W \propto r^3$ so:

$W = Kr^3$ where K is a constant

Now, $W = 1.02$ when $r = 3$, hence:

$$1.02 = K \times 3^3$$

$$K = \frac{1.02}{27}$$

(Because it does not evaluate exactly, it is best left in the fraction form.) Hence:

$$W = \frac{1.02}{27} \times r^3$$

When $r = 5$ then $W = \dfrac{1.02}{27} \times 5^3$

$$= \frac{1.02 \times 125}{27}$$

$$W = 4.72\,\text{kg}$$

Exercise 2
If x varies directly with y and $x = 30$ when $y = 24$, find:

(a) x when $y = 10$;
(b) y when $x = 14$.

Inverse variation

'Inverse variation involves a dividing relationship'

Inverse variation (or proportion) is when there is a simple *dividing* relationship between the variables involved. So, in a two-variable situation, as one variable *increases* the other *decreases*, and decreases in such a way that the product of the two variables is constant.
     For example, as I drive home and decide to increase the *speed*, then the *time taken* for the journey decreases. So speed (S) and time taken (T) are inversely proportional and $S.T = K$ where K is some constant.
     For example, suppose you go on a journey of 240 km, travelling at an average speed of:

40 kph – the journey would take 6 hours
60 kph – the journey would take 4 hours
80 kph – the journey would take 3 hours
120 kph – the journey would take 2 hours

Notice how all these pairs multiply together to give a constant value (K) of 240.
     In general, if A varies inversely with B, then:

$$A \propto \frac{1}{B}$$

$$A = \frac{K}{B}$$

hence $AB = K$

WORKED EXAMPLE 5 T is inversely proportional to V and T is 18 when $V = 60$.
Find: (a) T when $V = 30$; (b) V when $T = 20$.

$T \propto \dfrac{1}{V}$ hence $T = \dfrac{K}{V}$ where K is a constant.

$T = 18$ when $V = 60$, hence $K = 18 \times 60 = 1\,080$, i.e.:

$$TV = 1\,080$$

(a) When $V = 30$, $T = \dfrac{1\,080}{30} = 36$

(b) When $T = 20$, $V = \dfrac{1\,080}{20} = 54$

WORKED EXAMPLE 6   The length of paper on a roll varies inversely with the thickness of the paper. A roll holds paper of length 90 m and the thickness of the paper is 0.8 mm. Calculate the length of the paper in a roll if its thickness is 1.2 mm.

Length $\propto \dfrac{1}{\text{thickness}}$ hence $L = \dfrac{K}{t}$ where L is the length, t the thickness and K is a constant.

Therefore $K = Lt$.
   Now, $t = 0.8$ when $L = 90$ hence $K = 0.8 \times 90 = 72$, i.e. $Lt = 72$, so when $t = 1.2$,

$$L = \frac{72}{1.2} = 60$$

Length is 60 m.

Exercise 3

(a) $A \propto \dfrac{1}{\sqrt{B}}$. If $A = 9$ when $B = 16$, find:

   (i) A when $B = 25$;
   (ii) B when $A = 30$.
(b) The number of small spheres which can be made from a given volume of metal varies inversely as the cube of the diameter of the spheres. When the diameter is 3 mm, the number of spheres is 240. How many spheres of diameter 2 mm can be made from the same volume of metal?

Partial variation

'The 'independent variables' in a formula are on the right-hand side of the equal sign'

Partial variation (or proportion) occurs when two or more variables are connected by some formula or 'law of variation' in such a way that the independent variables can be *added* together.
   In these cases there could well be two or more constants to be found (called *constants of variation* or *constants of proportionality*).

WORKED EXAMPLE 7 R is partly constant and partly varies as V^2. When $V = 40$, $R = 564$, and when $V = 60$, $R = 644$, find:

(a)   the law of variation;
(b) R when $V = 80$.

As R is partly constant and partly varies as V^2, then $R = C + KV^2$ where C and K are both constants.

'Remember, you can use the substitution or elimination method for solving simultaneous equations'

$V = 40$ when $R = 564$, so $564 = C + 1\,600\,K$
$V = 60$ when $R = 644$, so $644 = C + 3\,600\,K$

Solving the two equations simultaneously, we get

$$K = \frac{80}{2\,000} = \frac{1}{25}$$

$$C = 564 - \frac{1\,600}{25} = 500$$

(a)   The law of variation is $R = 500 + \dfrac{V^2}{25}$

(b)   When $V = 80$, $R = 500 + \dfrac{6\,400}{25} = 756$

WORKED EXAMPLE 8

The resistance to a car is partly proportional to its speed and partly proportional to the square of its speed. When the speed is 20 kph, the resistance is 80 N. When the speed is 30 kph, the resistance is 150 N. Find the resistance when the speed is 60 kph.

Let the resistance be R and the speed be V, then $R = CV + KV^2$ where C and K are constants.

When $V = 20$, $R = 80$, hence $80 = 20C + 400K$
When $V = 30$, $R = 150$, hence $150 = 30C + 900K$

Solving the equations simultaneously, we get $C = 2$, $K = \dfrac{1}{10}$, hence:

$$R = 2V + \dfrac{V^2}{10}$$

When $V = 60$, $R = 2 \times 60 + \dfrac{3\,600}{10}$

$$R = 480\,\text{N}$$

Exercise 4
(a) W varies partly as Z^2 and partly inversely as T. When $Z = 4$, $T = 6$ and $W = 19$, and when $Z = 5$, $T = 12$ and $W = 35$. Find:
   (i)   the law of variation;
   (ii) W when $Z = 6$ and $T = 10$.
(b)   The distance in which a car can stop after the brakes have been applied varies partly as the speed of the car at the time the brakes are first applied and partly as the square of the speed.
   When the speed is 20 kph, the stopping distance is 8 m
   When the speed is 40 kph, the stopping distance is 24 m
Find the stopping distance at 60 kph.

Joint variation

Joint variation occurs where three or more things vary with each other in combinations of direct and/or inverse proportion. There is just one 'constant of variation' in each case. For example:

$M \propto PT$, hence $M = K_1 PT$

$V \propto \dfrac{A}{B}$, hence $V = K_2 \dfrac{A}{B}$

$W \propto \dfrac{PT^2}{\sqrt{L}}$, hence $W = K_3 \dfrac{PT^2}{\sqrt{L}}$ where K_1, K_2, K_3 are constants

WORKED EXAMPLE 9

'Here, we are talking about proportionality, therefore we need not change all the thickness and radii to the same unit. Just make sure that all the units for thickness are the same (millimetres in this case)'

When gold medals of various radii and thickness are weighed, the masses will depend upon both the thickness and the square of the radius of the medal. A gold medal of thickness 2 mm and a radius of 2.5 cm has a mass of 45 g. What is the weight of a gold medal of thickness 3 mm and a radius of 3.5 cm?

If $M = $ mass, $R = $ radius and $T = $ thickness, then:

$$M \propto TR^2$$

Hence $M = KTR^2$ where K is a constant

Now, $M = 45$ when $T = 2$ and $R = 2.5$, so:

$$45 = K \times 2 \times 2.5^2$$

$$K = \frac{45}{2 \times 2.5^2} = 3.6$$

When $T = 3$ and $R = 3.5$, then $M = 3.6 \times 3 \times 3.5^2 = 132.3$ g.

WORKED EXAMPLE 10 T varies directly with P and inversely with the square of Q. If $T = 6$ when $P = 180$ and $Q = 0.03$, find:

(a)   the law of variation;
(b)   the value of P when $T = 3.5$ and $Q = 0.024$.

$$T \propto \frac{P}{Q^2} \text{ hence } T = K\frac{P}{Q^2}$$

$T = 6$ when $P = 180$ and $Q = 0.03$, so:

$$6 = K \times \frac{180}{0.03^2}$$

$$K = \frac{6 \times 0.03^2}{180} = 0.000\,03$$

(a) $T = \dfrac{0.000\,03\,P}{Q^2}$

(b)   When $T = 3.5$ and $Q = 0.024$, then

$$3.5 = \frac{0.000\,03 \times P}{(0.024)^2}$$

$$P = \frac{3.5 \times (0.024)^2}{0.000\,03}$$

$$= 67.2$$

Exercise 5
V varies directly as x and inversely as y^2. $V = 4$ when $x = 2$ and $y = 3$. Find:

(a)   the law of variation;
(b) V when $x = 4$ and $y = 6$.

▶ **SOLUTIONS TO EXERCISES**

S1   1.   (a)   Ratio of lengths is $10:15$ which simplifies to $2:3$. Hence the ratio of volumes $= 2^3 : 3^3 = 8 : 27$, so:

$$\frac{V}{900} = \frac{8}{27} \Rightarrow V = \frac{900 \times 8}{27} = 266.7$$

Rounding off gives 267 cm^3.

(b)   Ratio of lengths is $11 : 5$, ratio of volumes is $11^3 : 5^3$.

$$\frac{V}{40} = \frac{11^3}{5^3} = \frac{1\,331}{125} \Rightarrow V = 40 \times \frac{1\,331}{125} = 425.9$$

Rounding off gives 426 cm^3

2.   Area ratio is $22:32$ which simplifies to $11:16$, so length ratio is $\sqrt{11}:\sqrt{16}$, volume ratio is $(\sqrt{11})^3 : (\sqrt{16})^3$.

$$\text{missing height} = 5 \times \frac{\sqrt{16}}{\sqrt{11}} = 6 \text{ cm}$$

$$\text{missing volume} = 14 \times \frac{(\sqrt{16})^3}{(\sqrt{11})^3} = 25 \text{ cm}^3$$

S2 $x = Ky$; $30 = K \times 24 \Rightarrow K = \dfrac{30}{24}$

(a) $x = \dfrac{30}{24} \times 10 = 12.5$

(b) $y = 14 \div \dfrac{30}{24} = 14 \times \dfrac{24}{30} = 11.2$

S3   (a) $A = \dfrac{K}{\sqrt{B}} \Rightarrow 9 = \dfrac{K}{\sqrt{16}} \Rightarrow K = 9 \times 4 = 36$

(i) $A = \dfrac{36}{\sqrt{25}} = 7.2$ (ii) $\sqrt{B} = \dfrac{36}{30} = 1.2$ $B = 1.2^2 = 1.44$

(b) $n = \dfrac{K}{r^3} \Rightarrow 240 = \dfrac{K}{3^3} \Rightarrow K = 240 \times 27 = 6\,480$

$n = \dfrac{6\,480}{2^3} = \dfrac{6\,480}{8} = 810$ spheres

S4   (a)   (i) $W = CZ^2 + \dfrac{K}{T} \Rightarrow 16C + \dfrac{1}{6}K = 19$ (1)

$25C + \dfrac{1}{12}K = 35$ (2)

eliminate K by multiplying equation (2) through by 2 to give the solution

$C = 1.5$ $K = -30$

Law of variation is $W = \dfrac{3Z^2}{2} - \dfrac{30}{T}$

(b) $D = CS + KS^2 \Rightarrow 20C + 400K = 8$

$40C + 1\,600K = 24$

Eliminate C to give the solution $C = \dfrac{1}{5}$, $K = \dfrac{1}{100}$

Hence $D = \dfrac{S}{5} + \dfrac{S^2}{100}$, when $S = 60$, $D = 48$ m.

S5   (a) $V = K\dfrac{x}{y^2} \Rightarrow 4 = K\dfrac{2}{9} \Rightarrow K = \dfrac{4 \times 9}{2} = 18$

$V = \dfrac{18x}{y^2}$

(b) $V = \dfrac{18 \times 4}{36} = 2$

EXAMINATION QUESTIONS

▶ **Question 1**   The electrical resistance, R ohms, of a piece of wire of length 1 m is inversely proportional to the square of its diameter, d cm. This can be written as $R = K\left(\dfrac{1}{d^n}\right)$.

(a)   State the value of n.
(b)   A metre length of copper wire has resistance of 5 ohms. Find the resistance of a piece of copper wire of the same length which has three times the diameter of the first piece.   (MEG)

▶ **Question 2**   Figure 5.5 shows a measuring scoop used for measuring soap powder for a washing machine. It has a diameter of 8 cm and a height of 10 cm.

Fig. 5.5

'Ignore the handle, you then have a pair of similar cones'

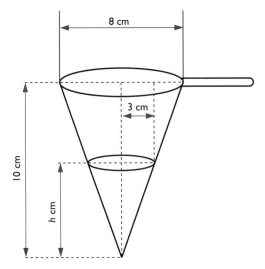

Calculate the height of the powder (*h* cm) in the scoop when the radius of the soap powder surface is 3 cm.   (NEAB)

▶ **Question 3**   The pressure needed to blow up the balloon in Fig. 5.6 varies as the cube of its radius. When the radius is 5 cm the pressure needed is 80 g/cm².

Fig. 5.6

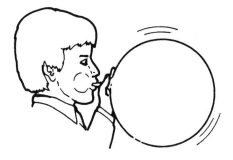

(a)   What pressure is required when the radius is 15 cm?
(b)   What is the radius of the balloon when the pressure needed is 640 g/cm²?   (WJEC)

▶ **Question 4**   Figure 5.7 shows two closed cylindrical cans, A and B. The radius of A is 4 cm and its height is 12 cm. The radius of B is 8 cm and its height is 6 cm.

Fig. 5.7

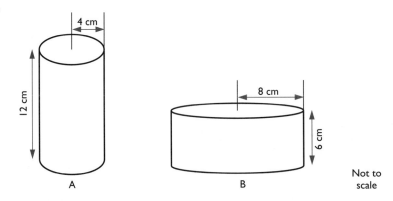

Not to scale

(a)   Find, in the form 1:*n*, the ratio
    (i)   volume of A : volume of B
    (ii)   total surface area of A : total surface area of B.
(b)   Two cylinders have the same volume. The first has radius *r* and height *h*. If the radius of the second is 2*r*, find its height in terms of *h*.   (MEG)

▶ **Question 5**   Figure 5.8, which is not drawn to scale, represents a symmetrical white sign fused on to a road with hot molten material. Angle *BAC* = 2 × angle *DAE*.

Fig. 5.8

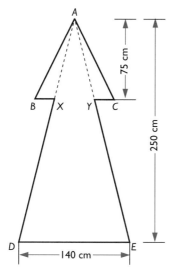

In the following calculations, work to 4 significant figures and give answers to 2 significant figures.

(a)   (i) Use similar triangles to calculate the length *XY*.
       (ii) Calculate the size of angle *DAE*.
       (iii) Calculate the length *BC*.
       (iv) Calculate the surface area of the sign.
(b)   Each sign is 3 mm in depth and the material for 30 such signs can be poured from a full cylindrical boiler, 40 cm in depth.
       (i) Calculate the volume of material used for each sign.
       (ii) Calculate the internal radius of the boiler.   (NEAB)

▶ **Question 6**   Information is provided in Fig. 5.9 about a sailboard. A scale model is to be made $\frac{1}{20}$ of the full size.

(a)   Calculate the length of the model in centimetres.

Fig. 5.9

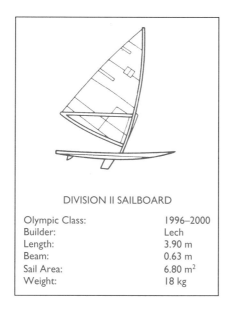

DIVISION II SAILBOARD

Olympic Class:	1996–2000
Builder:	Lech
Length:	3.90 m
Beam:	0.63 m
Sail Area:	6.80 m²
Weight:	18 kg

(b)   Calculate the sail area of the model in square centimetres.

▶ **Question 7**   In the triangle shown in Fig. 5.10, XY is parallel to BC.

Fig. 5.10

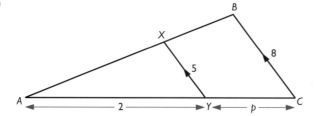

(a)   Explain why triangles AXY and ABC are similar.
(b)   Write down an equation involving p and solve it.

▶ **Question 8**   A right pyramid stands on a square base of side 20 cm (see Fig. 5.11). Its vertical height is 30 cm. It is cut through by a plane WXYZ, parallel to the base, and 15 cm above it.

(a)   Work out the length of XY.

(b)   Calculate $\dfrac{\text{volume of } OWXYZ}{\text{volume of } OABCD}$

Fig. 5.11

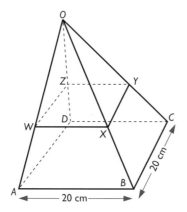

(c)   Find the size of the angle which OA makes with the base ABCD.

▶ **Question 9**   A small object P is tied to one end of a string and the other end of the string is attached to a fixed point. The object hangs at rest. When P is projected horizontally with a speed u metres per second, it is found to swing through a vertical height h centimetres before swinging back again. The table below shows the values of h (to the nearest whole number) for given values of u.

u (m/s)	1.4	1.7	2.2	2.4
h (cm)	10	14	24	25

(a)   Find which of the following statements best describes the variation between h and u:
       (i)   h varies as u^3;
       (ii) h varies as u^2;
       (iii) h varies as $\sqrt{u}$.
       Explain your reasoning.
(b)   Deduce an approximate value for h when u = 3.

▶ **Question 10**   The frequency of a radio wave is inversely proportional to its wavelength.
       Radio One broadcasts at a frequency of 1 053 kHz and a wavelength of 285 m.
       Radio Five broadcasts at a frequency of 909 kHz.
       Calculate the Radio Five wavelength. Write your answer to the nearest metre.

Question 11   A variable t is inversely proportional to the square of p and varies directly with the cube root of q.

  (a) Find the change in t when:
     (i) both p and q are doubled.
     (ii) q is doubled and p is halved.

  (b) State the connection between the changes of p and q that would leave t unaltered, and quote a particular instance when this will be true (not when both are unaltered!).

EXAMINATION ANSWERS

A1 (a) $n = 2$
   (b) Let the diameter of the first piece of wire be called d_1, then the diameter of the second piece of wire will be $3d_1$. So, for the first piece of wire we can state

$$5 = K\left(\frac{1}{d_1^2}\right) \Rightarrow K = 5\,d_1^2$$

Hence for the second piece of wire $R = K\left(\dfrac{1}{(3d_1)^2}\right) = 5\,d_1^2 \times \dfrac{1}{9d_1^2}$

$$R = \frac{5}{9}\ \text{ohms}$$

A2 Draw a simple sketch as in Fig. 5.12 to illustrate a pair of similar triangles. Then we can write:

Fig. 5.12

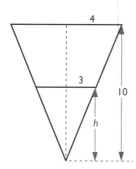

$$\frac{h}{3} = \frac{10}{4}$$

$$\Rightarrow h = \frac{30}{4} = 7.5\ \text{cm}$$

A3 From the question, $p \propto r^3$; hence $p = Kr^3$

When $r = 5$, $p = 80$, so $80 = K \times 125 \Rightarrow K = \dfrac{80}{125} = 0.64$

  (a) When $r = 15$, $p = 0.64 \times 15^3 = 2\,160\ \text{g/cm}^2$.
  (b) When $p = 640$, $640 = 0.64 \times r^3$
     Hence $r^3 = 640 \div 0.64 = 1\,000$
         $r = \sqrt[3]{1000} = 10$
         $r = 10\ \text{cm}$

A4 (a) (i) Volume of A $= \pi r^2 h = \pi \times 16 \times 12 = 192\pi$
          Volume of B $= \pi r^2 h = \pi \times 64 \times 6 = 384\pi$
          Hence volume A : volume B $= 192\pi : 384\pi$

$$= 1 \quad : \frac{384\pi}{192\pi}$$

$$= 1 \quad : \ 2$$

(ii) Total surface area of A $= 2 \times \pi r^2 + 2\pi rh = (2 \times \pi \times 16) + (2 \times \pi \times 4 \times 12)$
$$= 32\pi + 96\pi \qquad = 128\pi$$
Total surface area of B $= 2\pi r^2 + 2\pi rh \qquad = (2 \times \pi \times 64) + (2 \times \pi \times 8 \times 6)$
$$= 128\pi + 96\pi \qquad = 224\pi$$
Ratio of surface area of A : surface area of B $= 128\pi : 224\pi$

$$= 1 : \frac{224\pi}{128\pi}$$

$$= 1 : 1.75$$

(b) Volume $= \pi r^2 h$. So if another cylinder is of the same volume, yet radius $2r$, then, letting h be h_1,

$$\pi r^2 h = \pi (2r)^2 h_1$$
$$\Rightarrow \pi r^2 h = 4\pi r^2 h_1$$
$$\Rightarrow \frac{\pi r^2 h}{4\pi r^2} = h_1 \rightarrow h_1 = \frac{h}{4}.$$

A5 (a) (i) $\dfrac{XY}{140} = \dfrac{75}{250} \Rightarrow XY = \dfrac{75 \times 140}{250} = 42$ cm.

(ii) Sketch the triangle ADE as shown in Fig. 5.13 with P the foot of the perpendicular from A. Then:

$$\tan D\hat{A}P \;=\; \frac{75}{250} = 0.28$$

$$\Rightarrow D\hat{A}P \;=\; 15.64°$$
Hence $\qquad D\hat{A}E = 2 \times D\hat{A}P = 31°$ (to 2 significant figures)

(iii) In Fig. 5.14, since $B\hat{A}C = 2 \times D\hat{A}E$, then $B\hat{A}C = 62.57°$ (to 4 sig. figs). So when T is the foot of the perpendicular from A, then $C\hat{A}T = 31.28°$.

Fig. 5.13

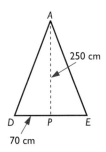

Fig. 5.14

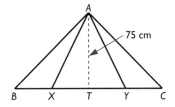

Hence $\dfrac{TC}{75} = \tan 31.28° \Rightarrow TC = 75 \tan 31.28° = 45.57$ cm.

Hence $BC = 2 \times TC = 91$ cm (to 2 sig. figs.)

(iv) Find area of the three triangles ABX, ACY (which are the same area) and ADE.

area of $ABX = \frac{1}{2}$ base $\times$ height $\quad = \frac{1}{2} \times (TC - TY) \times 75$
$$= \frac{1}{2} \times (24.57) \times 75 = 921.5 \text{ cm}^2 \text{ (4 sig. figs)}$$

hence $ABX + ACY = 921.5 \times 2 = 1\,843$ cm^2 (4 sig. figs)

area of $ADE = \frac{1}{2} \times 140 \times 250 = 17\,500$ cm^2

total area $= ABX + ACY + ADE = 19\,000$ cm^2 (2 sig. figs)

(b) (i) Volume for each sign will be (a) (iv) $\times$ 3 mm, which is $19\,343 \times 0.3 = 5\,802.9$ cm^3, which is $5\,800$ cm^3 (2 sig. figs).

(ii) Volume of cylinder up to height 40 cm will be given by $30 \times$ (b) (i) $= 174\,087$ cm^3 (as accurately as possible).
Volume of cylinder given by $\pi r^2 h$ then $\pi r^2 \times 40 = 174\,087$

$$\Rightarrow r^2 = \frac{174\,087}{40\pi} = 1\,385.34$$

$$\Rightarrow r = 37 \text{ cm (2 sig. figs)}$$

A6   (a) $3.90\,\text{m} \div 20 = 0.195\,\text{m} = 19.5\,\text{cm}$

(b)   length ratio $= 1:20$, hence area ratio $= 1:400$.

$$\text{sail area on model} = \frac{6.80 \times 100^2}{400} \text{ (to convert to cm}^2\text{)}$$

$$= 170\,\text{cm}^2$$

A7   (a)   Angle A is common, $\angle AXY = \angle ABC$ (corresponding angles)

$\angle AYX = \angle ACB$ (corresponding angles)

Hence all the angles correspond with each other.

(b) $\dfrac{2+p}{2} = \dfrac{8}{5} \Rightarrow 5(2+p) = 8 \times 2$

$$10 + 5p = 16$$

$$\Rightarrow \qquad 5p = \ 6$$

$$p = \ 1.2$$

A8   The ratio of the lengths is given by the heights $1:2$.

(a) $\dfrac{XY}{20} = \dfrac{1}{2} \Rightarrow XY = 10\,\text{cm}$

(b)   Ratio of volumes $= \left(\dfrac{1}{2}\right)^3 = \dfrac{1}{8}$

Fig. 5.15

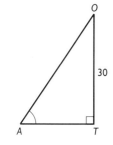

(c)   Trigonometry! Consider the right-angled triangle in Fig. 5.15. T is the centre of the square $ABCD$ where:

$$AC = \surd(20^2 + 20^2)$$
$$= \surd(800) = 28.2$$
$$AT = \tfrac{1}{2}AC = 14.14$$

Angle A given by

$$\tan^{-1} A = \frac{30}{14.14} \Rightarrow A = 64.8°$$

A9   (a)   If $h \propto u$ then $h = Ku$, then $\dfrac{h}{u} = K$ (a constant). Hence consider the tables of ratios as:

u	1.4	1.7	2.2	2.4	
h	10	14	24	25	
(i) $\dfrac{h}{u^3}$	3.6	2.8	2.2	1.8	not constant
(ii) $\dfrac{h}{u^2}$	5.1	4.8	4.9	4.3	could well be constant
(iii) $\dfrac{h}{\sqrt{u}}$	8.5	10.7	16.2	16.1	not constant

so (ii) best describes the variation, $h \propto u^2$

(b) $K = 4.8$ (the average of the results) hence $h = 4.8\,u^2$.

When $u = 3$, $h = 4.8 \times 3^2 = 43.2$. An approximate value of h will be 43

A10 $F \propto \dfrac{1}{W} \Rightarrow F = \dfrac{K}{W} \Rightarrow K = FW$

$$\Rightarrow K = 1\,053 \times 285$$

when $F = 909$

$$W = \frac{K}{F} = \frac{1\,053 \times 285}{909} = 330\,\text{m}$$

A11 (a) Since $t \propto \dfrac{\sqrt[3]{q}}{p_0^2}$ then $t = \dfrac{K\sqrt[3]{q}}{p^2}$

(i) If $t_0 = \dfrac{K\sqrt[3]{q_0}}{p^2}$ then, where p_0 and q_0 are both doubled:

$$t_1 = \frac{K\sqrt[3]{(2q_0)}}{(2p_0)^2} = \frac{K\sqrt[3]{2}\sqrt[3]{q_0}}{4p_0^2} = \frac{\sqrt[3]{2}}{4} \cdot \frac{K\sqrt[3]{q_0}}{p_0^2} = \frac{\sqrt[3]{2}}{4}\,t_0$$

$$t_1 = 0.315\,t_0$$

so t has been reduced by $(100 - 31.5)\%$, which is a reduction of 68.5%.

(ii) If $t_0 = \dfrac{K\sqrt[3]{q_0}}{p_0^2}$ then, where q_0 is doubled and p_0 is halved:

$$t_1 = \frac{K\sqrt[3]{(2q_0)}}{(\frac{1}{2}p_0)^2} = \frac{\sqrt[3]{2}}{\frac{1}{4}} \cdot \frac{K\sqrt[3]{q_0}}{p_0^2} = = 5.04\,t_0$$

so t has been increased by $(504 - 100)\%$, which is an increase of 404%.

(b) Let increase in $q = x\%$ and increase in $p = y\%$

then where $t_0 = \dfrac{K\sqrt[3]{q_0}}{p_0^2}$, $t_1 = \dfrac{K\sqrt[3]{\left\{\left(1 + \frac{x}{100}\right)q_0\right\}}}{\left(\left(1 + \frac{y}{100}\right)p_0\right)^2} = \dfrac{\sqrt[3]{\left(1 + \frac{x}{100}\right)}}{\left(1 + \frac{y}{100}\right)^2} \cdot \dfrac{K \cdot \sqrt[3]{q_0}}{p_0^2}$

when $t_0 = t_1$, then $\sqrt[3]{\left(1 + \dfrac{x}{100}\right)} = \left(1 + \dfrac{y}{100}\right)^2$

hence $\left(1 + \dfrac{x}{100}\right) = \left(1 + \dfrac{y}{100}\right)^6$

so there is no change when the increase in q is $x\%$ and of p is $y\%$

and $\left(1 + \dfrac{x}{100}\right) = \left(1 + \dfrac{y}{100}\right)^6$

So, for example, if the increase in q is 50%. then

$$1.50 = \left(1 + \frac{y}{100}\right)^6$$

$$1.0699 = 1 + \frac{y}{100} \Rightarrow y = 7\% \text{ increase}$$

i.e. when q is increased by 50% and p is increased by 7%, then t is unaltered.

Grade checklist

For grade	You should be able to do the following:
B	Understand direct and inverse proportion.
A	Express general laws in symbolic form. Understand the relationships between similar shapes.
A*	Understand joint and partial variation.

▶ EXAMINATION QUESTION WITH STUDENT ANSWER

Question

Jean and Bill use a set of scales to weigh some coins. They have four 50p coins whose total weight is 5 grams and two 20p coins whose total weight is 1 gram.

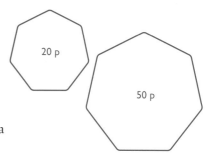

(a) (i) Make an estimate of the weight of a 50p coin and of a 20p coin.

> *5 ÷ 4 = 1.25*
>
> *1 ÷ 2 = 0.5*
>
> *The 50p will weigh 1.25*
>
> *the 20p will weigh 0.5*

'Correct working, but no units given on the final answer, this will lose marks'

(ii) Which estimate is likely to be the more accurate and why?

> *the 50p because you used more coins.*

'Correct answer, but answer is brief and more explanation is needed'

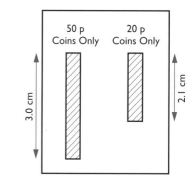

(b) A slot through which a 50p coin will just pass is 3.0 cm long. A 20p coin will just pass through a slot 2.1 cm long. The *faces* of the two coins have the same shape. Find the ratio of the areas of the faces of a 50p coin and a 20p coin in the form $n : 1$.

> *ratio of lengths is 3.0 : 2.1*
>
> *ratio of areas = 3.0 : 2.1²*
>
> *= 9 : 4.41*
>
> *= 2.04 : 1*

'Living dangerously here; fortunately the next line shows the student's intent to square each part of the ratio, but this should have been made clear here'

(c) The 50p coin is 2.5 mm thick. Assuming that both coins are made of the same metal, calculate an estimate of the thickness of a 20p coin.

> *We know that weight ∝ area × width, so weight = k area × width*
>
> *let area of 50p = 2.04 and area of 20p = 1 For 50p then 1.25 = K × 2.04 × 2.5,*
>
> *K = 0.245 For 20p then 0.5 = 0.245 × 1 × width*
>
> *width = 2.04 mm*

'A good sound method, but the final answer is too precise for an estimate. 2 mm would be the best answer'

SUMMARY

▷ **Variation**

Direct variation: there is a simple multiplying factor between two things, so that as one increases so does the other.

If x varies directly with y then $x = Ky$ where K is the constant of proportionality

Indirect variation: there is a dividing connection between two things, so that as one gets larger the other gets smaller.

If x varies indirectly with y then $x = K/y$ where K is the constant of proportionality

▷ **Similar shapes**: two shapes are similar if all their corresponding angles are equal and the ratios of the corresponding lengths are also equal.

Ratios of similar shapes: if two similar shapes have lengths in the ratio $x:y$, then the area ratio will be $x^2:y^2$ and the volume ratio will be $x^3:y^3$

6 Algebra

 GETTING STARTED

Algebra and how you use it is perhaps the key 'thing' that makes mathematicians a grade A or a grade C! Up to grade C, algebra is informal and is mainly concerned with simple situations. At the higher grades and beyond, algebra is an integral part of many situations, as you will already have seen.

You must understand and be able to cope confidently with algebra. This chapter is about how you should be manipulating your algebraic terms and expressions.

▶ Useful definitions

Coefficient	The whole number next to a variable, e.g. the coefficient of x^2 in $3x^2$ is the 3.
Constant	Not changing.
Expand	To multiply out brackets and simplify.
Factorise	Put into expressions containing brackets that multiply together to make the whole.
Generalise	Express in general terms, usually an algebraic formula.
Linear	An expression involving only single variables of power one, e.g. $x + y = 3$ or $2x = y + 7$.
Quadratic	An expression involving no power higher than a squared term, e.g. $5x^2 - 3x = 4$.
Simplify	To make easier, usually in algebra means to collect like terms or cancel.
Transposition	To change the subject of a formula or equation.
Variable	A letter which may stand for various numbers.

▶ Topic chart

The following topic chart can be completed for each of the topics in 'Algebra'. Tick the appropriate box when you have first studied that topic. You can also keep a record of when you have revised that topic for the first and second time, etc.

London	MEG	NEAB	NICCEA	SEG	WJEC	IGCSE	TOPIC	STUDY	REVISION I	REVISION 2
✓	✓	✓	✓	✓	✓	✓	Transposition			
✓	✓	✓	✓	✓	✓	✓	Linear equations			
✓	✓	✓	✓	✓	✓	✓	Factorisation			
✓	✓	✓	✓	✓	✓	✓	Quadratic equations			
✓	✓	✓	✓	✓	✓	✓	Simultaneous equations			
✓	✓	✓	✓	✓	✓	✓	Algebraic fractions			
✓	✓	✓	✓	✓	✓	✓	Fractional indices			

WHAT YOU NEED TO KNOW

 Transposition

'This is your basic rule to follow, learn it and use it'

All your manipulation of algebra lies in being able to understand the principle of:

If it's doing what it's doing to everything else on that side of the equation, then it can be moved to the other side and perform the opposite job.

Follow through the changes of subject of the formulae in the worked examples below and then try them yourself to make absolutely certain that you can confidently cope with this basic requirement of algebra.

WORKED EXAMPLE 1

Change $x = 5y - 7$ to make y the subject.

$$x + 7 = 5y$$

$$\Rightarrow \frac{x+7}{5} = y; \quad \text{hence } y = \frac{x+7}{5}$$

WORKED EXAMPLE 2

Change $p = \frac{t}{4} + 7$ to make t the subject.

$$p - 7 = \frac{t}{4}$$

$$\Rightarrow 4(p - 7) = t; \quad \text{hence } t = 4(p - 7)$$

WORKED EXAMPLE 3

Change $v = p(4t + 1)$ to make t the subject.

$$\frac{v}{p} = 4t + 1$$

$$\Rightarrow \frac{v}{p} - 1 = 4t$$

$$\Rightarrow \frac{v - p}{p} = 4t \quad \text{(easier to cope with if we simplify the left-hand side)}$$

$$\Rightarrow \frac{v - p}{4p} = t$$

WORKED EXAMPLE 4

Change $t = \frac{3w + 4}{5 - w}$ to make w the subject.

$$t(5 - w) = 3w + 4$$

$$5t - wt = 3w + 4 \Rightarrow 5t - 4 = 3w + wt$$

$$\Rightarrow 5t - 4 = w(3 + t)$$

$$\Rightarrow \frac{5t - 4}{3 + t} = w$$

Hence $w = \dfrac{5t - 4}{3 + t}$

WORKED EXAMPLE 5

Change $x = y^2 - 7$ to make y the subject.

$$x + 7 = y^2 \Rightarrow \sqrt{(x + 7)} = y$$

Hence $y = \sqrt{(x + 7)}$

▶ **Linear equations**

Linear equations are equations that involve single variables of power 1. They contain no expressions such as x^2, y^3, $\frac{1}{x}$, xy, etc.

You should be familiar with linear equations and how to solve them. You move numbers around *until* you have the unknown as the subject, then do any necessary calculations.

WORKED EXAMPLE 6   Solve the equation $8 = \dfrac{x+5}{5-x}$

Change first to $8(5-x) = x+5$
$$\Rightarrow 40 - 8x = x + 5$$
$$\Rightarrow 40 - 5 = x + 8x = 9x$$
$$\Rightarrow \frac{35}{9} = x$$
$$x = 3.9 \text{ (1 decimal place)}$$

Exercise 1

Solve the equation $\dfrac{x-3}{x+3} = 3$.

▶ **Factorisation**   *Quadratic equations* are those that involve no higher power than a 2, nor any less than a 1. For example, $3x^2 + 6x - 1 = 0$.

You will often need to factorise other quadratic expressions such as this:

$$2x^2 + 12x + 18$$

which is of the general form:

$$ax^2 + bx + c$$

where a, b and c are the integers $+2$, $+12$ and $+18$ respectively, and x is a variable.

There are a number of different methods that can be used to help you to factorise quadratic expressions:

Method 1

Follow through this worked example to see how the method works.

WORKED EXAMPLE 7   Factorise $12x^2 + x - 35$.

Factorise by trying to put this expression into two brackets (   )(   ). The -35 indicates that the signs are different, hence (+)(−). Now the first numbers in each bracket (the coefficients of x) must multiply together to give 12, whilst the end two numbers in each bracket (constants) must multiply together to give 35. This gives us quite a few possibilities; e.g. $(6x + 7)(2x - 5)$, but the combination of the *outer two* and the *inner two* products (multiplications) must give us $+1x$. In effect, we have the choices given by:

$$\begin{pmatrix} 12 \\ 1 \end{pmatrix} \times \begin{pmatrix} 35 \\ 1 \end{pmatrix}, \ \begin{pmatrix} 12 \\ 1 \end{pmatrix} \times \begin{pmatrix} 1 \\ 35 \end{pmatrix}, \ \begin{pmatrix} 12 \\ 1 \end{pmatrix} \times \begin{pmatrix} 5 \\ 7 \end{pmatrix}, \ \begin{pmatrix} 12 \\ 1 \end{pmatrix} \times \begin{pmatrix} 7 \\ 5 \end{pmatrix}, \ \begin{pmatrix} 6 \\ 2 \end{pmatrix} \times \begin{pmatrix} 35 \\ 1 \end{pmatrix}, \ \begin{pmatrix} 6 \\ 2 \end{pmatrix} \times \begin{pmatrix} 1 \\ 35 \end{pmatrix}$$

$$\begin{pmatrix} 6 \\ 2 \end{pmatrix} \times \begin{pmatrix} 5 \\ 7 \end{pmatrix}, \ \begin{pmatrix} 6 \\ 2 \end{pmatrix} \times \begin{pmatrix} 7 \\ 5 \end{pmatrix}, \ \begin{pmatrix} 3 \\ 4 \end{pmatrix} \times \begin{pmatrix} 35 \\ 1 \end{pmatrix}, \ \begin{pmatrix} 3 \\ 4 \end{pmatrix} \times \begin{pmatrix} 1 \\ 35 \end{pmatrix}, \ \begin{pmatrix} 3 \\ 4 \end{pmatrix} \times \begin{pmatrix} 5 \\ 7 \end{pmatrix}, \ \begin{pmatrix} 3 \\ 4 \end{pmatrix} \times \begin{pmatrix} 7 \\ 5 \end{pmatrix}$$

But here the *difference* in the diagonals must give us $+1$. This is done in the combination:

$$\begin{pmatrix} 3 \\ 4 \end{pmatrix} \times \begin{pmatrix} 5 \\ 7 \end{pmatrix}, \text{ i.e. } (3 \times 7) - (4 \times 5) = 21 - 20 = 1$$

So the factorisation is $(3x - 5)(4x + 7)$, the positive product is the larger of the two products since the coefficient of x is positive $(+1)$.

Exercise 2
Factorise: (a) $x^2 + 10x + 24$;   (b) $2m^2 - 5m - 3$;   (c) $8t^2 + 14t - 15$

Method 2

Although this method involves a certain amount of 'trial and error' we can follow a simple 'routine' to factorise the quadratic $ax^2 + bx + c$.

'A useful routine for factorising quadratic expressions'

Routine

1. Find the product ac.
2. Write down factor pairs of ac, remembering the signs.
3. Find the factor pair that adds up to b.
4. Rewrite the expression, with the middle term now expressed, using this factor pair.
5. Factorise by grouping.

We now use this routine with a number of quadratic expressions.

WORKED EXAMPLE 8

'We can ignore negatives since there are no negative signs in the expression'

Factorise $t^2 + 6t + 8$ ($a = +1, b = +6, c = +8$).

Product ac: $1 \times 8 = 8$
Factor pairs of ac: $1 \times 8, 2 \times 4, (-1 \times -8, -2 \times -4)$
Which of these factor pairs adds up to 6? Answer: (2, 4).

$$\begin{array}{ll} t^2 + 2t + 4t + 8 & \text{(rewriting)} \\ = t(t+2) + 4(t+2) & \text{(factorise} \\ = (t+4)(t+2) & \text{by grouping)} \end{array}$$

OR

t $\diagdown$ $+2$ ← factor
t $\diagup$ $+4$ ← factor
$\overline{2t \quad + \quad 4t = 6t}$
$t^2 + 6t + 8 \ = (t+2)(t+4)$

WORKED EXAMPLE 9

Factorise $x^2 - 9x + 20$ ($a = +1, b = -9, c = +20$).

Product ac: $1 \times 20 = 20$
Factor pairs of ac: $(1 \times 20, 2 \times 10, 4 \times 5, -1 \times -20, -2 \times -10, -4 \times -5)$
Which of these factor pairs adds up to -9? Answer: $(-4, -5)$.

$$\begin{array}{ll} x^2 - 4x - 5x + 20 & \text{(rewriting)} \\ = x(x-4) - 5(x-4) & \text{(factorise} \\ = (x-5)(x-4) & \text{by grouping)} \end{array}$$

OR

x $\diagdown$ -4 ← factor
x $\diagup$ -5 ← factor
$\overline{-4x \quad - \quad 5x = -9x}$
$x^2 - 9x + 20 \ = (x-4)(x-5)$

WORKED EXAMPLE 10

Factorise $x^2 - 5x - 24$ ($a = +1, b = -5, c = -24$).

Product ac: $1 \times -24 = -24$
Factor pairs of ac: $(-1 \times 24, -2 \times 12, -3 \times 8, -4 \times 6,$ and sign vice versa)
Which of these factor pairs adds up to -5? Answer: $(3, -8)$

$$\begin{array}{ll} x^2 + 3x - 8x - 24 & \text{(rewriting)} \\ = x(x+3) - 8(x+3) & \text{(factorise} \\ = (x-8)(x+3) & \text{by grouping)} \end{array}$$

OR

x $\diagdown$ $+3$ ← factor
x $\diagup$ -8 ← factor
$\overline{3x \quad - \quad 8x = -5x}$
$x^2 - 5x - 24 \ = (x+3)(x-8)$

WORKED EXAMPLE 11

Factorise $2x^2 + 11x + 12$ ($a = +2, b = +11, c = +12$).

Product ac: $2 \times 12 = 24$
Factor pairs of ac: $(1 \times 24, 2 \times 12, 3 \times 8, 4 \times 6)$
Which of these factor pairs adds up to $+11$? Answer: (3, 8)

$$\begin{array}{ll} 2x^2 + 3x + 8x + 12 & \text{(rewriting)} \\ = x(2x+3) + 4(2x+3) & \text{(factorise} \\ = (x+4)(2x+3) & \text{by grouping)} \end{array}$$

OR

x $\diagdown$ $+4$ ← factor
$2x$ $\diagup$ $+3$ ← factor
$\overline{8x \quad + \quad 3x = 11x}$
$2x^2 + 11x + 12 \ = (x+4)(2x+3)$

WORKED EXAMPLE 12

Factorise $8x^2 - 14x - 15$ ($a = +8, b = -14, c = -15$).

Product ac: $8 \times -15 = -120$
Too many factor pairs of -120, so only search until you find the sum of one factor pair is -14 (i.e. $1 \times -120, 2 \times -60, 3 \times -40, 4 \times -30, 5 \times -24, 6 \times -20 \ldots$). Stop, we have it: $(6, -20)$ will add up to -14.

$$\begin{array}{ll} 8x^2 + 6x - 20x - 15 & \text{(rewriting)} \\ = 2x(4x+3) - 5(4x+3) & \text{(factorise} \\ = (2x-5)(4x+3) & \text{by grouping)} \end{array}$$

OR

$2x$ $\diagdown$ -5 ← factor
$4x$ $\diagup$ $+3$ ← factor
$\overline{-20x \quad + \quad 6x = -14x}$
$8x^2 - 14x - 15 \ = (2x-5)(4x+3)$

WORKED EXAMPLE 13

Factorise $6x^2 - 17x + 5$ ($a = +6, b = -17, c = +5$).

Product ac: $6 \times 5 = 30$
Search the factor pairs of 30 until you find the sum of -17 (i.e. $-1 \times -30, -2 \times -15, \ldots$).
Stop since the factor pair adds up to -17.

$$6x^2 - 2x - 15x + 5 \quad \text{(rewriting)}$$
$$= 2x(3x - 1) - 5(3x - 1) \quad \text{(factorise}$$
$$= (2x - 5)(3x - 1) \quad \text{by grouping)}$$

OR

$$\begin{array}{ll} 2x & -5 \quad \leftarrow \text{factor} \\ 3x & -1 \quad \leftarrow \text{factor} \\ \hline -15x \quad - \quad 2x & = -17x \\ \hline 6x^2 - 17x + \; 5 & = (2x - 5)(3x - 1) \end{array}$$

This routine method is very useful for completing the factorisation. There are, of course, times when you can see the answer without going through all this process. Again, the aim is that you become so familiar with the process that you are able to do the easier ones in your head!

Exercise 3
Try the method you are most comfortable with to factorise:
(a) $4m^2 - 20m + 25$;   (b) $4x^2 - 4x - 15$;   (c) $18t^2 - 63t + 49$

▶ **Quadratic equations**

The hardest part of solving *quadratic equations* is to factorise them. Factorisation has been well covered earlier in this chapter. First, put the quadratic equation into the *general* form of:

$$ax^2 + bx + c = 0$$

We can then factorise, to give an equation in the form of:

'For the product of two numbers to be zero, either one or both the numbers must be zero'

$$(x + m)(x + n) = 0$$

Since both factors multiply to give zero, then one or both of the factors must be zero. This then usually leads us to two simple linear equations to solve.

WORKED EXAMPLE 14

Solve $(x + 3)(x - 2) = 0$.

Either $(x + 3) = 0$ or $(x - 2) = 0$
Hence $x = -3$ or $x = 2$

WORKED EXAMPLE 15

Solve $(2x + 3)(3x - 4) = 0$.

Either $(2x + 3) = 0$ or $(3x - 4) = 0$
Hence $2x = -3$ or $3x = 4$

$$x = \frac{-3}{2} \quad \text{or} \quad x = \frac{4}{3}$$

WORKED EXAMPLE 16

'First, put the equation into the general form before factorising'

Solve $4x^2 + 15x = -9$.

Rearrange to give $4x^2 + 15x + 9 = 0$
Factorise to give $(4x + 3)(x + 3) = 0$
Hence $4x + 3 = 0$ or $x + 3 = 0$

$$x = \frac{-3}{4} \quad \text{or} \quad x = -3$$

WORKED EXAMPLE 17

'Sometimes there is only one solution'

Solve $x^2 - 6x + 9 = 0$.

Factorise to give $(x - 3)(x - 3) = 0$
$$(x - 3)^2 = 0$$
Hence $x - 3 = 0$
$$x = 3$$

Exercise 4
Solve the equations:
(a) $18t^2 + 63t + 49 = 0$;   (b) $25x^2 + 16 = 40x$
(c) $4x^2 - 12x + 9 = 0$;   (d) $8y^2 - 6y = 9$

Solve by completing the square

You may have done that last exercise quite quickly, or you may have taken quite a time to solve it. The equations we have looked at so far have all factorised nicely to give a pair of brackets, and so a solution. Not all equations will factorise, so we now show you another way of finding a solution: it is called the method of *completing the square*. This follows through the simple procedure:

$$ax^2 + bx + c = 0$$

Divide throughout by a to give $x^2 + \dfrac{b}{a}x + \dfrac{c}{a} = 0$.

Move the constant term to the other side, to give $x^2 + \dfrac{b}{a}x = -\dfrac{c}{a}$.

On the left-hand side (LHS), drop the square term, add half the coefficient of x, place within brackets, and square:

$$\text{LHS} = \left(x + \frac{b}{2a}\right)^2$$

On the right-hand side (RHS), add $\left(\dfrac{b}{2a}\right)^2$

$$\text{RHS} = -\frac{c}{a} + \left(\frac{b}{2a}\right)^2$$

This gives $\left(x + \dfrac{b}{2a}\right)^2 = -\dfrac{c}{a} + \left(\dfrac{b}{2a}\right)^2$, which will have given you an equation like

'Don't give up yet, this really is a good method'

$$(x + d)^2 = e$$

$$\Rightarrow x + d = +\sqrt{e} \quad \text{and} \quad -\sqrt{e}$$

$$\Rightarrow x = +\sqrt{e} - d \quad \text{and} \quad -\sqrt{e} - d$$

It looks worse than it actually is. Follow through worked example 18, then try this method in Exercise 5; then try it again in Exercise 4.

WORKED EXAMPLE 18

'Halve the coefficient of x and follow the rule'

Solve the equation $3x^2 + 5x - 4 = 0$.

Divide throughout by 3 to give $x^2 + \frac{5}{3}x - \frac{4}{3} = 0$.

Move the constant term to the other side, to give $x^2 + \frac{5}{3}x = \frac{4}{3}$.

$$\left(x + \frac{5}{6}\right)^2 = \frac{4}{3} + \frac{25}{36} \qquad \text{(look where things have come from)}$$

Hence $\left(x + \dfrac{5}{6}\right)^2 = 2.0278$ (use your calculator memory)

$$\Rightarrow x + \frac{5}{6} = 1.424 \text{ and } -1.424$$

$$x = (1.424 - 0.833) \text{ and } (-1.424 - 0.833)$$

$$x = 0.59 \text{ and } -2.26$$

Exercise 5
Solve the equations: (a) $4x^2 + 12x + 5 = 0$; (b) $3d^2 - 5d - 4 = 0$.

Solve by the formula

There is a well known, loved and trusted *formula* which will also always work to solve equations of the type $ax^2 + bx + c = 0$. This formula is:

'The formula method will
always work'

$$x = \frac{-b \pm \sqrt{(b^2 - 4ac)}}{2a}$$

(It is the formal next stage to completing the square.)

WORKED EXAMPLE 19   Solve the equation $2x^2 + 5x - 3 = 0$.

Using $x = \dfrac{-b \pm \sqrt{(b^2 - 4ac)}}{2a}$, where $a = 2$, $b = 5$ and $c = -3$, then:

$$x = \frac{-5 \pm \sqrt{(25 + 24)}}{4} = \frac{-5 \pm \sqrt{49}}{4} = \frac{-5 \pm 7}{4}$$

$$x = \frac{-12}{4} \text{ and } \frac{2}{4}$$

$$x = -3 \text{ and } 0.5$$

Try this method on the exercises 2, 3, 4 and 5 if you wish to compare. All three methods are good and useful. You need to use the method that you are most confident with, or which best suits the situation at the time.

Solve by the difference of two squares

When we have an expression that is made up of two square expressions (or numbers) and subtracted, then they can *always* be factorised as:

$$A^2x^2 - B^2y^2 = (Ax + By)(Ax - By)$$

WORKED EXAMPLE 20   Factorise the equation $16x^2 - 9y^2$.

$$16x^2 - 9y^2 = (4x + 3y)(4x - 3y)$$

Exercise 6
Factorise the expressions: (a) $9t^2 - 4p^2$;   (b) $4x^4 - 9y^2$.

Problems solved by quadratic equations

There are quite a few situations that can most easily be solved by the use of quadratic equations. The difficult part, usually, is putting the problem into the 'general' quadratic form in the first place. So go through the following examples carefully.

WORKED EXAMPLE 21   Two numbers have a product of 117 and a sum of 22. What are the numbers?

Let one of the numbers be x, then the other must be $22 - x$, since they both add up to 22. Then:

$$x(22 - x) = 117$$
$$\Rightarrow \quad 22x - x^2 = 117$$
$$\Rightarrow \quad\quad\quad 0 = x^2 - 22x + 117$$

Factorising, we have:

$$0 = (x - 9)(x - 13)$$
$$\Rightarrow \quad x - 9 = 0 \quad \text{or} \quad x - 13 = 0$$
$$\Rightarrow \quad\quad x = 9 \quad \text{or} \quad\quad\quad x = 13$$

The two numbers are 9 and 13.

WORKED EXAMPLE 22   A rectangular lawn has a perimeter of 42 m and an area of 68 m². Find the length and width of the lawn.

Let the width be x, then since the perimeter is 42 m the length and width will add up to $\frac{1}{2}$ of 42 = 21 m, so the length will be $21 - x$. Hence:

$$\text{area} = 68\,\text{m}^2 = x(21 - x) \quad\quad = 21x - x^2$$
$$\Rightarrow \quad\quad\quad\quad x^2 - 21x + 68 = 0$$

Factorise to give:

$$(x - 17)(x - 4) = 0$$
$$\Rightarrow \quad x - 17 = 0 \quad \text{or} \quad x - 4 = 0$$
$$x = 17 \quad \text{or} \quad x = 4$$

Therefore the length $= 17$ m and the width $= 4$ m.

WORKED EXAMPLE 23   A picture measures 22 cm by 16 cm and the area of the uniform frame which surrounds it is 368 cm^2. Find the width of the frame.

Fig. 6.1

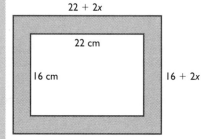

Let the frame be of width x, then the lengths of picture frame are $(22 + 2x)$ and $(16 + 2x)$, see Fig. 6.1. The total area of this rectangle is $(22 + 2x)(16 + 2x)$ which is equal to the area of the frame + area of picture $= 368 + (16 \times 22)$. So:

$$(22 + 2x)(16 + 2x) = 368 + (16 \times 22)$$

Multiply out to give:

$$352 + 76x + 4x^2 = 720$$

This rearranges to give:

$$4x^2 + 76x - 368 = 0$$

which will divide by 4 to give

$$x^2 + 19x - 92 = 0$$

which factorises to give:

$$(x + 23)(x - 4) = 0$$
$$\Rightarrow x + 23 = 0 \quad \text{or} \quad x - 4 = 0$$
$$\Rightarrow x = -23 \quad \text{or} \quad x = 4$$

Clearly x cannot be negative, so our solution is $x = 4$.

Exercise 7

▶   Read the questions carefully.
▶   Form your equations carefully.
▶   Find a suitable quadratic equation, and then solve it.
▶   Finally – don't forget to answer the question.

(a)   A room was 4 m longer than its width. The area was 221 m^2. Find the dimensions of the room.
(b)   A swimming pool measures 12 m by 5 m, and a path of uniform width runs along one side and one end. The total area of the pool and path is 120 m^2. Find the width of the path.

▶ **Simultaneous equations**   *Simultaneous equations* are pairs of equations that contain more than one variable and need solving at the same time. They are often linear, but they do not both need to be so. There are two basic techniques for solving them, the *elimination method* and the *substitution method*. Equations may appear in words instead of normal equations.

Elimination method

You eliminate one variable, solve the remaining equation then substitute back into one equation to find the final solution.

WORKED EXAMPLE 24

Solve simultaneously the equations $4x - 2y = 11$ (1)
$$3x + y = 12 \qquad (2)$$

Multiply equation (2) through by 2 to enable us to eliminate y:

$$4x - 2y = 11 \qquad (1)$$
$$6x + 2y = 24 \qquad (3)$$

Adding the two equations eliminates y; hence:

$$10x = 35$$
$$\Rightarrow \quad x = 3.5$$

'The elimination method'

Substitute $x = 3.5$ into equation (1):

$$14 - 2y = 11$$
$$\Rightarrow \quad 2y = 3$$
$$y = 1.5$$

It is usual to check the solution by substituting into the other equation, this time equation (2), to give $(3 \times 3.5) + 1.5 = 12$ which is correct; so the solution is $x = 3.5$, $y = 1.5$.

Exercise 8
Solve the pair of simultaneous equations: $2x + 3y = 10$
$$6x - y = 5$$

Substitution method

Let's use the same simultaneous equations as above:

$$4x - 2y = 11 \qquad (1)$$
$$3x + y = 12 \qquad (2)$$

Then from equation (2), $y = 12 - 3x$. Now substitute this into equation (1) to give:

$$4x - 2(12 - 3x) = 11$$
$$\Rightarrow \quad 4x - 24 + 6x = 11$$
$$\Rightarrow \quad 10x = 35$$
$$\Rightarrow \quad x = 3.5$$

'The substitution method'

and we are where we arrived at before. We now need to substitute $x = 3.5$ into one of the equations to complete the solution.

This method becomes more useful when only one equation is linear.

WORKED EXAMPLE 25

Solve the simultaneous equations $x^2 + y = 8$ (1)
$$x - 3y = 1 \qquad (2)$$

From equation (1), $y = 8 - x^2$, so substitute into equation (2) to give:

$$x - 3(8 - x^2) = 1$$
$$x - 24 + 3x^2 = 1$$
$$3x^2 + x - 25 = 0$$

which is a *quadratic* equation and can be solved by one of the previous methods to give $x = 2.72$ and $x = -3.06$ (2 decimal places). Substitute each into equation (1) which gives the final solution that:

$$x = 2.72; \, y = 0.60 \quad \text{and} \quad x = -3.06; \, y = -1.36$$

Exercise 9
Solve the simultaneous equations $x^2 - y = 5$ (1)
$$x^2 + 2y = 24 \qquad (2)$$

▶ **Algebraic fractions**

You really must be confident with normal fraction arithmetic to stand a chance of being successful with *algebraic fractions*. This is because you have to apply the normal fraction rules without being able to resort to 'common fractions'.

Adding and subtracting algebraic fractions

To add or subtract *algebraic fractions* we still follow those same rules for adding:

1. Find the lowest common multiple (LCM) of the denominator.
2. Write each fraction with this LCM.
3. Simplify the numerator.

WORKED EXAMPLE 26

Simplify $\frac{x}{2} + \frac{(x-2)}{5}$.

Recall how you would simplify $\frac{1}{2} + \frac{1}{5} = \frac{5+2}{10} = \frac{7}{10}$. The LCM of 2 and 5 is 10.

$$\frac{x}{2} + \frac{(x-2)}{5} = \frac{5x}{10} + \frac{2(x-2)}{10}$$
$$= \frac{(5x+2x-4)}{10}$$
$$= \frac{(7x-4)}{10}$$

WORKED EXAMPLE 27

'Solving fraction equations'

Solve $\frac{3x}{4} - \frac{2(x-3)}{5} = 2\frac{1}{4}$.

The LCM of 4 and 5 is 20.

$$\frac{3x}{4} - \frac{2(x-3)}{5} = \frac{15x}{20} - \frac{8(x-3)}{20} = 2.25$$
$$= \frac{(15x-8x+24)}{20} = 2.25$$
$$= \frac{(7x+24)}{20} = 2.25$$
$$7x + 24 = 2.25 \times 20 = 45$$
$$7x = 45 - 24 = 21$$
$$x = 3$$

WORKED EXAMPLE 28

Solve $\frac{1}{x-1} + \frac{3}{x+4} = 1$.

The LCM of the denominator is $(x-1)(x+4)$, so:

$$\frac{1}{x-1} + \frac{3}{x+4} = \frac{1(x+4)+3(x-1)}{(x-1)(x+4)} = 1$$
$$= \frac{x+4+3x-3}{(x-1)(x+4)} = 1$$
$$= \frac{4x+1}{(x-1)(x+4)} = 1$$
$$4x+1 = (x-1)(x+4) = x^2+3x-4$$

Hence $0 = x^2 - x - 5$ which solves to give $x = 2.79$ and $x = -1.79$.

Exercise 10

Solve the equations: (a) $5 + \frac{1}{x} = x$; (b) $\frac{1}{x-1} + \frac{2}{x+1} = 5$.

Multiplying

You must remember your cancelling technique, you can cancel any factor on the top with any factor on the bottom, e.g.:

$$\frac{\cancel{(x+1)}}{(x-3)\cancel{(x+1)}} = \frac{1}{x-3}$$

WORKED EXAMPLE 29

Factorise and simplify $\dfrac{x^2 - 5x + 6}{x^2 - 4}$.

Factorise numerator and denominator: $\dfrac{(x-2)(x-3)}{(x+2)(x-2)} = \dfrac{x-3}{x+2}$

Dividing

Remember the rule to turn the second fraction upside-down and multiply.

WORKED EXAMPLE 30

Solve $\dfrac{(x+1)}{3} \div \dfrac{4}{(x+1)} = 1.$

Turn the second fraction upside-down and multiply, which gives us:

$$\frac{(x+1)}{3} \times \frac{(x+1)}{4} = 1$$

$$\Rightarrow (x+1)^2 = 12$$
$$\Rightarrow x+1 = \sqrt{12} = 3.46 \text{ and } -3.46$$
$$x = (3.46 - 1) \text{ and } (-3.46 - 1)$$
$$x = 2.46 \text{ and } -4.46$$

Exercise 11

Find: (a) the product; (b) the quotient of $\dfrac{x+1}{x-1}$ and $\dfrac{x^2-1}{x^2+1}$.

▶ **Fractional indices**

'Do work all these out on the calculator with the correct buttons ... it's so much easier'

The use of the *fractional index* is used to denote a root, e.g.:

$$9^{1/2} = \sqrt{9} = 3 \quad \text{and} \quad -3$$
$$8^{1/3} = \sqrt[3]{8} = 2$$

Note: $8^{2/3} = (\sqrt[3]{8})^2 = 2^2 = 4 \quad$ or $\quad \sqrt[3]{8^2} = \sqrt[3]{64} = 4$

Use the $x^{1/y}$ button on your calculator to calculate the answers. For example, to calculate $9^{1/5}$, just press 9 followed by $x^{1/y}$, followed by 5 =, this should give you 1.55.

Similarly, if you need to calculate a cube root, maybe from a similar shape situation, then use the $x^{1/y}$ button on your calculator followed by a 3.

WORKED EXAMPLE 31

Which is the larger, $18^{2/3}$ or $8^{3/2}$?

$$18^{2/3} = (\sqrt[3]{18})^2 = 6.868$$
$$8^{3/2} = (\sqrt{8})^3 = 22.63$$

Hence $8^{3/2} > 18^{2/3}$

Exercise 12

Calculate: (a) $5^{2/5}$; (b) $\sqrt[3]{11}$; (c) $8^{-0.7}$

▶ **SOLUTIONS TO EXERCISES**

S1 $x - 3 = 3(x + 3) \implies x - 3 = 3x + 9$
$$\implies -3 - 9 = 3x - x$$
$$\implies -12 = 2x$$
$$\implies -6 = x \rightarrow x = -6$$

S2 (i) $(x + 6)(x + 4)$;   (ii) $(2m + 1)(m - 3)$;   (iii) $(2t + 5)(4t - 3)$

S3 (i) $(2m - 5)^2$;   (ii) $(2x + 3)(2x - 5)$;   (iii) $(6t - 7)(3t - 7)$

S4 (i) $(6x + 7)(3x + 7) = 0 \implies 6x + 7 = 0$ and $3x + 7 = 0$
$$\implies x = \tfrac{-7}{6} \quad \text{and} \quad x = \tfrac{-7}{3}$$
(ii) $25x^2 - 40x + 16 = 0 \implies (5x - 4)^2 = 0 \implies 5x - 4 = 0$
$$\implies x = \tfrac{4}{5}$$
(iii) $(2x - 3)^2 = 0 \implies 2x - 3 = 0 \implies 2x = 3$
$$\implies x = \tfrac{3}{2}$$
(iv) $8y^2 - 6y - 9 = 0 \implies (4y + 3)(2y - 3) = 0$
$$\implies 4y + 3 = 0 \quad \text{and} \quad 2y - 3 = 0$$
$$y = -\tfrac{3}{4} \quad \text{and} \quad y = \tfrac{3}{2}$$

S5 (a) $x^2 + 3x + \tfrac{5}{4} = 0 \implies x^2 + 3x = \tfrac{-5}{4} \implies (x + \tfrac{3}{2})^2 = \tfrac{-5}{4} + \tfrac{9}{4} = 1$
$$x + \tfrac{3}{2} = \pm 1 \implies x = -0.5 \quad \text{and} \quad -2.5$$
(b) $d^2 - \tfrac{5}{3}d - \tfrac{4}{3} = 0 \implies d^2 - \tfrac{5}{3}d = \tfrac{4}{3} \implies (d - \tfrac{5}{6})^2 = \tfrac{4}{3} + \tfrac{25}{36} = 2.027778$
$$d - \tfrac{5}{6} = \pm 1.424 \implies d = 1.424 + 0.8333 \quad \text{and} \quad -1.424 + 0.8333$$
$$= 2.26 \quad\quad\quad\quad \text{and} \quad -0.59$$

S6 (a) $(3t + 2p)(3t - 2p)$;   (b) $(2x^2 + 3y)(2x^2 - 3y)$

S7 (a) Let the width be x cm, then
$$x(x + 4) = 221 \implies x^2 + 4x - 221 = 0$$
This solves to give $x = 13$ or -17, we use the positive, hence the dimensions are 13 m, 17 m
(b) Let the width of the path be x, then
$$(x + 5)(x + 12) = 120 \implies x^2 + 17x + 60 = 120 \implies x^2 + 17x - 60 = 0$$
This factorises to $(x - 3)(x + 20) = 0$. Hence $x = 3$; the width of the path is 3 m.

S8 Eliminate y first to obtain $x = 1.25$, then substitute in one equation to give $y = 2.5$.

S9 From equation (1) $x = 5 + y$, substitute this into equation (2) to give:
$$(5 + y)^2 + 2y = 24$$
$$\implies 25 + 10y + y^2 + 2y = 24$$
$$\implies y^2 + 12y + 1 = 0$$
This will solve to give $y = -0.08$ and -11.9. So from equation (1) we can now give the full solution of:
$$x = 4.92, \quad y = -0.08$$
$$\text{and } x = -6.9, \quad y = -11.9$$

S10 (a) $5x + 1 = x^2 \Rightarrow x^2 - 5x - 1 = 0$
$\Rightarrow x = 5.19$ and -0.19

(b) $\dfrac{(x + 1) + 2(x - 1)}{(x - 1)(x + 1)} = 5$

$x + 1 + 2x - 2 = 5x^2 - 5$
$5x^2 - 3x - 4 = 0 \Rightarrow x = 1.24$ and -0.64

S11 (a) product $= \dfrac{(x + 1)}{(x - 1)} \times \dfrac{(x^2 - 1)}{(x^2 + 1)} = \dfrac{(x + 1)}{(x - 1)} \times \dfrac{(x + 1)(x - 1)}{(x^2 + 1)} = \dfrac{(x + 1)^2}{(x^2 + 1)}$

(b) quotient $= \dfrac{(x + 1)}{(x - 1)} \div \dfrac{(x^2 - 1)}{(x^2 + 1)} = \dfrac{(x + 1)}{(x - 1)} \times \dfrac{(x^2 + 1)}{(x + 1)(x - 1)} = \dfrac{(x^2 + 1)}{(x - 1)^2}$

S12 (a) Use calculator as $\boxed{5}$ $\boxed{x^y}$ $\boxed{0.4}$ (i.e. $\frac{2}{5}$) $\boxed{=}$ to get 1.9

(b) Use calculator as $\boxed{11}$ $\boxed{x^{1/y}}$ $\boxed{3}$ $\boxed{=}$ to get 2.22

(c) Use calculator as $\boxed{8}$ $\boxed{x^y}$ $\boxed{0.7}$ $\boxed{^{+/-}}$ $\boxed{=}$ to get 0.23

Do try to become familiar with the use of x^y and $x^{1/y}$ buttons on your calculator.

EXAMINATION QUESTIONS

▶ **Question 1** The ancient Babylonian stone tablet shown in Fig. 6.2 gives this formula for the length of the diagonal (d) of a rectangle. The longer side is l and the short w. The formula is only an approximation.

Fig. 6.2

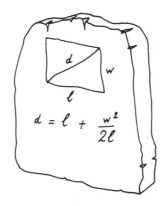

(a) What is the difference, to 3 decimal places, between the correct value of d and that given by the formula, when the rectangle measures (i) 6 cm by 5 cm, and (ii) 10 cm by 1 cm?

(b) Rearrange the formula to make w the subject.   (MEG)

▶ **Question 2**

Fig. 6.3

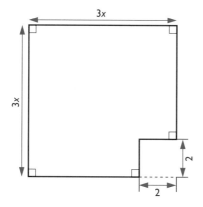

(a) Write down, in terms of x, an expression for the area of the shape in Fig. 6.3.

(b) Multiply out $(3x + 2)(3x - 2)$, giving your answer in its simplest form.

(c) By making one cut and reassembling, the shape in Fig. 6.3 can be made into a rectangle. Using your answers to (a) and (b), draw a diagram to show how this can be done. Mark the dimensions of the rectangle on your diagram.   (NEAB)

▶ **Question 3**   The cost, £C, of making n articles is given by the formula

$$C = a + bn$$

where a and b are constants. The cost of making 4 articles is £20 and the cost of making 7 articles is £29.

(a) Write down two equations in a and b.

(b) Solve these equations to find the values of a and b.   (London)

▶ **Question 4**   A rescue harpoon is fired horizontally from a cliff top, as shown in Fig. 6.4. The horizontal distance, x metres, it has travelled after t seconds is given by $x = 250t$. The distance of the harpoon below the cliff top, y metres, is given by $y = 5t^2$.

Fig. 6.4

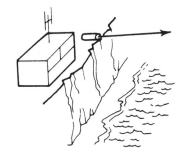

(a) (i) Write t in terms of x.

     (ii) Write an equation which connects y and x, but does not include t, in the form $y = \ldots$

(b) How many centimetres below the cliff top will the harpoon be when it is 50 metres horizontally from the firing gun?   (WJEC)

▶ **Question 5**   (a)   Evaluate $8^{1/3}$.

             (b) Write down $16^{1/4} \times 8^{-3}$ as a power of 2.

             (c) Given that $32^y = 2$, find the value of y.   (NEAB)

▶ **Question 6**   (a)   Multiply out $(2x + 3)(x - 4)$. Simplify your answer.

             (b) $x^2 - 8x + a = (x - b)^2$. Find the numerical value of a.

             (c) Write as a single fraction $\dfrac{1}{x - 3} + \dfrac{1}{x + 4}$.

             (d) The expression $\dfrac{1}{\sqrt{a}} = a^n$ is true for all values of a. Find the value of n.   (SEG)

▶ **Question 7**   Look at the number pattern in Fig. 6.5.

Fig. 6.5

```
 0   1   2   3   4   5   6   7   8   9
10  11  12  13  14  15  16  17  18  19
20  21  22  23  24  25  26  27  28  29
30  31  32  33  34  35  36  37  38  39
40  41  42  43  ...
```

Fig. 6.6

The section in Fig. 6.6 is called the **12L** because **12** is the middle number. To find the value of 12L you multiply the end numbers and add the middle number, as follows: $(2 \times 13) + 12$. Therefore the value of 12L is 38.

Fig. 6.7

(a) What is the value of the 27L section?
(b) (i) Write down the numbers missing from this L in Fig. 6.7 in terms of x.
    (ii) Find the value of this L in terms of x.
(c) Which L has a value of 998?   (WJEC)

▶ **Question 8**   The outer rectangle shown in Fig. 6.8 measures $(2x + 3)$ by $(x + 2)$.

Fig. 6.8

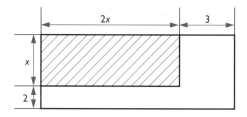

(a) Express the area of the shaded rectangle in terms of x.
(b) Express the area of the unshaded region in terms of x, in as simplified a form as possible.
(c) Calculate the value of x when the area of the shaded region is 2 square units less than the area of the unshaded region.   (NEAB)

▶ **Question 9**   Simplify (a) $2x^4 \times 4x^{-3}$;   (b) $8x^2 y \div 4x^4$;   (c) $x^{0.5} \times x^{2.5}$;   (d) $(x^{1/2})^{-4}$;

(e) $\dfrac{1}{2x} - \dfrac{1}{2x + 1}$

▶ **Question 10**   (a) Evaluate: (i) $8^{4/3}$;   (ii) 3^{-4}.
(b) Solve the equation $16^x = \frac{1}{4}$.

▶ **Question 11**   (a) Solve the equation $x^5 = 0.002\,43$.
(b) Once a year a scientist measured the mass of a certain piece of decaying radioactive element. His results are shown in the table.

Time (years)	0	1	2	3
Mass (kg)	20	18	16.2	14.58

    (i) Calculate the annual percentage decrease of the mass.
    (ii) Calculate the mass after 10 years.
    (iii) Estimate the half-life of the element (i.e. the time it takes to lose half of its mass).

▶ **Question 12**   (a) Work out $(a + b)(c + d)$.
(b) Jhoti wanted to use her calculator to work out the exact value of $537\,142 \times 612\,304$. Work this out on your calculator. Write down the display. Explain why this is not an exact result.
(c) Jhoti then wrote the problem as $(537\,000 + 142)(612\,000 + 304)$.
    (i) Using the result obtained in part (a), explain how she could find an exact answer to the problem.
    (ii) What is the exact answer?

▶ **Question 13** ABC is a right-angled triangle as shown. The total length of the sides is 12 cm. AC is 1 cm longer than AB, and $AB = x$ cm.

Fig. 6.9

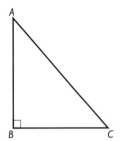

(a)   (i) Using Pythagoras' theorem for this triangle, show that $(11 - 2x)^2 + x^2 = (x + 1)^2$.
       (ii) Show that this simplifies to $2x^2 - 23x + 60 = 0$.
(b)   The equation in (a) (ii) has two solutions, one of which is a whole number. Find this solution by any suitable means.
(c)   The second solution to the equation lies between $x = 7$ and $x = 8$. Explain why this is an unacceptable solution for the triangle given.

▶ **Question 14**   Figure 6.10 shows a pile of bricks which are all the same size. They have been carefully placed so as to produce a pattern.

Fig. 6.10

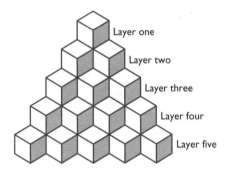

Layer one
Layer two
Layer three
Layer four
Layer five

(a)   Complete the table giving the number of bricks used to form the various layers.

Layer number	1	2	3	4	5
Number of bricks	1	3			

(b)   This pattern of bricks is continued so as to have one more layer beneath those shown in the drawing. How many bricks will there be in this new layer?
(c)   The number of bricks, N, in a certain layer, L, is given by the formula

$$N = aL^2 + bL \quad \text{where } a \text{ and } b \text{ are constants}$$

Use some of the information in the table above to form two simultaneous equations in a and b.
Solve your equations to find the exact formula.

▶ **Question 15**   A garden supplier regularly posts catalogues to his customers. There are two types of catalogue – a 'maxi' and a 'mini' version.
    At the post office he is charged £2.20 for posting 3 maxi and 2 mini catalogues to five customers. Later he is charged £2.42 for posting 2 maxi and 5 mini catalogues to seven customers.
    Work out the postal charge for sending each type of catalogue.

▶ **Question 16**   Three numbers x, y, z have the property that

$$(y - z) \times (z - x) \times (x - y) = 0$$

(a)   From this, **one** of the following statements can be deduced. State which and give a reason for your answer.
1.   At least one of x, y, z is zero.
2.   At least two of x, y, z are zero.
3.   The numbers x, y, z are all zero.
4.   At least two of x, y, z are equal.
5.   The numbers x, y, z are all equal.

(b)   You are given that three numbers x, y, z satisfy the equations

$$(y - z)(z - x)(x - y) = 0$$

and $x + 1 = 2y + 3 = 3z + 6$

There are three possible sets of values for x, y, z. Find them.   (OCSEB)

▶ **Question 17**   The equation $a^2 + b^2 = c^2$ gives the relation between the lengths of the sides of a right-angled triangle, c being the length of the hypotenuse and a and b the lengths of the other sides respectively. We wish to find integer values of a, b and c to satisfy the equation.

(a)   Show that the formulae $a = v^2 - u^2$, $b = 2uv$, and $c = u^2 + v^2$ may be used to find the required values.
(b)   How must u and v be chosen so that a, b and c have no common factor?   (WJEC)

▶ **Question 18**   Here are four consecutive numbers 13, 14, 15, 16.
If you multiply the middle pair, you get $14 \times 15 = 210$.
If you multiply the outer pair, you get $13 \times 16 = 208$.

(i)   Do a calculation like this for a different set of four consecutive numbers of your own choice.
(ii)   Repeat (i) twice more. You should notice a general rule. State this clearly in words.
(iii)   Use algebra to prove that your rule always works with any four consecutive numbers.
(iv)   Find a similar rule which works if you start with four consecutive odd numbers (such as 17, 19, 21, 23). Use algebra to prove this rule.   (OCSEB)

▶ **Question 19**   Two trains travel on parallel tracks towards each other at 60 mph and 80 mph respectively. At twelve o'clock they usually pass two points A and B respectively 80 miles apart.

(a)   Find where the trains pass each other.
(b)   One day, the slower train was late and passed the express train at a point 6 miles nearer to A than the usual passing point. Assuming the express train to be punctual and both trains to be travelling at the usual speeds, find how many minutes later than usual the slower train was that day.   (WJEC)

▶ ## EXAMINATION ANSWERS

A1   (a)   (i)   Actual value of $d = \sqrt{(6^2 + 5^2)} = 7.810\,25$.

Babylonian formula gives $d = 6 + \dfrac{25}{12} = 8.083\,333$. The difference is 0.273.

(ii)   Actual value of $d = \sqrt{(10^2 + 1^2)} = 10.049\,876$.

Babylonian formula gives $d = 10 + \dfrac{1}{20} = 10.05$. The difference is 0.000\,123\,79, which to 3 decimal places is 0.000.

(b)   From $d = l + \dfrac{w^2}{2l} \rightarrow d - l = \dfrac{w^2}{2l} \rightarrow 2l(d - l) = w^2$

$\rightarrow w = \sqrt{(2ld - 2l^2)}$

A2 (a) $9x^2 - 4$

(b) $9x^2 - 4$

(c) See Fig. 6.11. Either cut $------$ or cut $-\cdot-\cdot-$

Fig. 6.11

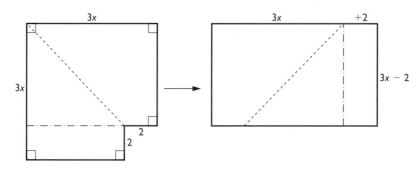

A3 (a) $20 = a + 4b$ and $29 = a + 7b$

(b) Solve the two simultaneous equations to give $b = 3$ and $a = 8$.

A4 (a) (i) $t = \dfrac{x}{250}$

(ii) $y = 5t^2 \rightarrow y = 5\left(\dfrac{x}{250}\right)^2 \rightarrow y = \dfrac{5x^2}{62\,500} = \dfrac{x^2}{12\,500}$

(b) When $x = 50$, $y = \dfrac{50^2}{12\,500} = 0.2$ metres $= 20\,$cm

A5 (a) 2

(b) $2 \times \tfrac{1}{2} = 1 = 2^0$

(c) $\tfrac{1}{5}$ or 0.2

A6 (a) $2x^2 + 3x - 8x - 12 = 2x^2 - 5x - 12$

(b) $(x - b)^2 = x^2 - 2bx + b^2$
Hence $2b = 8$, so $b = 4$, so $b^2 = a = 16$

(c) $\dfrac{(x + 4) + (x - 3)}{(x - 3)(x + 4)} = \dfrac{2x + 1}{(x - 3)(x + 4)}$

(d) $n = -\tfrac{1}{2}$

A7 (a) $(17 \times 28) + 27 = 503$

(b) (i) $(x - 10)$ and $(x + 1)$

(ii) $(x - 10)(x + 1) + x = x^2 - 9x - 10 + x$
$= x^2 - 8x - 10$

(c) When L $= 998$

then $x^2 - 8x - 10\quad = 998$
$\rightarrow x^2 - 8x - 1\,008 = \quad 0$

which will solve to give $x = 36$ and $x = -28$.
Here we need the positive solution of 36.

A8 (a) $2x^2$

(b) $(2x + 3)(x + 2) - 2x^2 = 2x^2 + 7x + 6 - 2x^2$
$= 7x + 6$

(c) This will be when $2x^2 + 2 = 7x + 6$.
Hence $2x^2 - 7x - 4 = 0$ which will solve to give $x = -0.5$ and $x = 4$.
Here we need the positive solution of $x = 4$.

A9   (a) $8x$;   (b) $\dfrac{2y}{x^2}$;   (c) x^3;   (d) $\dfrac{1}{x^2}$;   (e) $\dfrac{1}{2x(2x+1)}$

A10   (a) (i) $(\sqrt[3]{8})^4 = 2^4 = 16$;   (ii) $\dfrac{1}{3^4} = \dfrac{1}{81}$

(b) $16^x = \tfrac{1}{4} \;\Rightarrow\; 4^{2x} = 4^{-1} \;\Rightarrow\; 2x = -1 \;\Rightarrow\; x = -\tfrac{1}{2}$

A11   (a) $(0.002\,43)^{1/5} = 0.3 \Rightarrow x = 0.3$

(b) (i) $\dfrac{2}{20} \times 100 = 10\%$

(ii) $20 \times (0.9)^{10} = 6.97\,\text{kg}$
(iii) Find x where $20 \times (0.9)^x = 10$
$$\Rightarrow (0.9)^x = \tfrac{10}{20} = \tfrac{1}{2} = 0.5$$
By trial and improvement $x = 6.58$ years (6.6 is acceptable).

A12   (a) $ac + ad + bc + bd$
(b) $3.288\,942 \times 10^{11}$, not enough room on the calculator display to show all the figures.
(c) (i) Substitute the given values for a, b, c and d then add by 'long addition'.
(ii) Where $a = 537\,000$; $b = 142$; $c = 612\,000$; $d = 304$
$ac + ad + bc + bd = 328\,644\,000\,000 + 163\,248\,000 + 86\,904\,000 + 43\,168$
$$= 328\,894\,195\,168$$

A13   (a) (i) $AB = x$; $AC = x + 1$; $BC = 12 - (x + x + 1) = 11 - 2x$
since $BC^2 + AB^2 = AC^2$
then $(11 - 2x)^2 + x^2 = (x + 1)^2$
(ii) This expands to $121 - 44x + 4x^2 + x^2 = x^2 + 2x + 1$
$\Rightarrow 4x^2 - 46x + 120 = 0$ (divide through by 2)
$\Rightarrow 2x^2 - 23x + 60 = 0$
(b) $(2x - 15)(x - 4) = 0 \;\Rightarrow\; x = 4$ is the whole number
(c) Since then AC would be between 8 and 9. Yet the total perimeter has to be equal to 12, thus giving BC a negative value.

A14   (a)

Layer number	1	2	3	4	5
Number of bricks	1	3	6	10	15

(b) By looking at how the table builds up you can now predict adding 6 onto 15 to give 21.
(c) The simplest equations will be from layers 1 and 2:

$$a + b = 1 \qquad \text{(i) (layer 1)}$$
$$4a + 2b = 3 \qquad \text{(ii) (layer 2)}$$

Multiply equation (i) by 2 then eliminate b to give $a = \tfrac{1}{2}$.

Substitute $a = \tfrac{1}{2}$ into (i) to give $b = \tfrac{1}{2}$

Hence the formula is $N = \tfrac{1}{2}l^2 + \tfrac{1}{2}l$.

A15   Set up a pair of simultaneous equations:

$$3\,\text{max} + 2\,\text{min} = 220 \qquad (1)$$
$$2\,\text{max} + 5\,\text{min} = 242 \qquad (2)$$

Multiply equation (1) by 2 and equation (2) by 3 to give:

$$6 \text{ max} + 4 \text{ min} = 440 \qquad (3)$$
$$6 \text{ max} + 15 \text{ min} = 726 \qquad (4)$$

Eliminate 'max' by subtracting equation (3) from equation (4) to give:

$$11 \text{ min} = 286$$
$$\text{min} = 26$$

Substitute into equation (1) to give:

$$3 \text{ max} = 220 - 52 = 168$$
$$\text{max} = 56$$

Solution is max cost 56p and min cost 26p.

A16 (a) Conditions 1, 2, 3 and 5 are all special cases where the equation is satisfied. Since $(y - z)(z - x)(x - y) = 0$, then all we can deduce is that one of the brackets is zero, hence either $y = z$ or $z = x$ or $x = y$, hence at least two of x, y, z are equal. Condition 4 is satisfied.

(b) There are three possibilities for $(y - z)(z - x)(x - y) = 0$. These are that $y = z$, $z = x$ or $x = y$.

First, consider $y = z$. Then where:

$$x + 1 = 2y + 3 = 3z + 6$$
$$x + 1 = (2y + 3 = 3y + 6)$$
$$(2y + 3 = 3y + 6) \quad \Rightarrow \quad -3 = y$$

Hence $x + 1 = -6 + 3 = -3 \quad \Rightarrow \quad x = -4$

So $-4, -3, -3$, is a possible solution.

Next consider $z = x$. Then where:

$$x + 1 = 2y + 3 = 3z + 6$$
$$(x + 1) = 2y + 3 = (3x + 6)$$
$$(x + 1 = 3x + 6) \quad \Rightarrow \quad -5 = 2x \quad \Rightarrow \quad x = -2.5$$
$$\text{Hence} \qquad -2.5 + 1 = 2y + 3$$
$$\Rightarrow \quad -4.5 = 2y \Rightarrow y = -2.25$$

So $-2.5, -2.25, -2.5$, is another solution.

Lastly, consider $x = y$. Then where:

$$x + 1 = 2y + 3 = 3z + 6$$
$$(x + 1 = 2x + 3) = 3z + 6$$
$$(x + 1 = 2x + 3) \quad \Rightarrow \quad -2 = x$$
$$\text{Hence} \qquad -2 + 1 = 3z + 6 \rightarrow z = \frac{-7}{3}$$

So $-2, -2, \dfrac{-7}{3}$ is the third solution.

The three possible solutions to x, y, z are:

$$(-4, -3, -3); \quad (-2.5, -2.25, -2.5); \quad \left(-2, -2, \frac{-7}{3}\right)$$

A17 (a) From $a^2 + b^2 = c^2$, take the left-hand side where $a = v^2 - u^2$ and $b = 2uv$, then:

$$a^2 + b^2 = (v^2 - u^2)^2 + (2uv)^2$$
$$= v^4 - 2u^2v^2 + u^4 + 4u^2v^2$$
$$= v^4 + 2u^2v^2 + u^4$$

Take the right-hand side where $c = u^2 + v^2$, then:

$$c^2 = (u^2 + v^2)^2 = u^4 + 2u^2v^2 + v^4$$

It can now be seen that $a^2 + b^2 = u^4 + 2u^2v^2 + v^4 = c^2 \quad \Rightarrow \quad a^2 + b^2 = c^2$.

So the equations do hold on to the validity of $a^2 + b^2 = c^2$. Also, if we choose values of u and v to be integers, then so too will be v^2, u^2 and $2uv$, hence so too will be $v^2 - u^2$, $2uv$ and $v^2 + u^2$. So a, b and c will be integers in value.

(b) If a, b and c have a common factor, say x, then when $a = Ax$, $b = Bx$, $c = Cx$, A, B and C are integers and so we will have $Ax = v^2 - u^2$, $Bx = 2uv$, $Cx = u^2 + v^2$.

Hence, since A, B and C are integers then $\dfrac{v^2 - u^2}{x}, \dfrac{2uv}{x}, \dfrac{u^2 + v^2}{x}$ are also all integers.

Hence $(v^2 - u^2)$, $2uv$ and $(u^2 + v^2)$ are all multiples of x
  $\Rightarrow$ that both v^2 and u^2 are multiples of x
  $\Rightarrow$ both v and u are multiples of x.

If u and v are both odd or even, then $(v^2 - u^2)$ and $(v^2 + u^2)$ are both even as $2uv$ always is, hence a, b and c would all be multiples of 2.

So if we are to avoid a, b and c having common factors we must choose values of u and v that do not have common factors. Nor must the values be such that u and v are both even or both odd.

A18   (i) You could choose *any* four consecutive numbers, for example, 3, 4, 5, 6 is a simple one to start with, which gives

middle pair $= 4 \times 5 = 20$
outer pair $= 3 \times 6 = 18$

(ii) Choose two more sets (no need to choose large numbers, but you can if you wish). The general rule you should find is this: the product of the middle pair is always 2 more than the product of the outer pair.

(iii) If we let x be the first number, then the next three after that will be $x + 1$, $x + 2$, $x + 3$, to give the consecutive numbers:

x, $x + 1$, $x + 2$, $x + 3$

The product of the middle pair $= (x + 1)(x + 2) = x^2 + 3x + 2$
The product of the outer pair $= x(x + 3)$ $= x^2 + 3x$
The difference is $(x^2 + 3x + 2) - (x^2 + 3x) = 2$
So for all x, the difference is still 2.

(iv) Let x be the first odd number, then the four consecutive odd numbers will be:

x, $x + 2$, $x + 4$, $x + 6$

The product of the middle pair $= (x + 2)(x + 4) = x^2 + 6x + 8$
The product of the outer pair $= x(x + 6)$ $= x^2 + 6x$
So the difference is 8, giving the rule that 'the product of the middle pair of consecutive odd numbers is 8 more than the product of the outer pair.'
Note: This also works for consecutive even numbers.

A19

Fig. 6.12

(a) In Fig. 6.12 let distance d be the point where the trains pass. Then $t =$ time travelled in hours. The slower train will satisfy the equation $d = 60t$, while the faster train will satisfy the equation $d = 80 - 80t$.

So if d is when they pass, then

$60t = 80 - 80t$
$\Rightarrow 140t = 80$
$t = 0.5714$ hours

gives the time on passing at 34 minutes and the distance from A given by $60 \times 0.5714 = 34.3$ miles.

(b) If the trains passed 6 miles nearer to A, then they passed at a distance of 28.3 miles from A. As the express train was punctual, to find out how long it took that train to cover a distance of $(80 - 28.3)$ miles, we evaluate

$$\text{time} = \frac{\text{distance}}{\text{speed}} = \frac{51.7}{80} = 0.646\,25 \text{ hours} = 38.8 \text{ minutes}$$

The slower train took $\frac{28.3}{60} = 0.466\,7$ hours $= 28.3$ minutes to reach that point. The difference in time tells how late the first train was, which was 10.5 minutes late.

Grade checklist

For grade	You should be able to do the following:
B	Evaluate formulae, including the use of fractions or negative numbers. Manipulate algebraic formula, equations and expressions. Factorise quadratic expressions. Solve simultaneous equations.
A	Use rules of indices for negative and fractional values. Solve quadratic equations.
A*	Manipulate algebraic expressions in a variety of contexts.

▶ EXAMINATION QUESTION WITH STUDENT ANSWER

Question

A road tanker carries 30 tonnes of oil. When cold, the oil can be pumped out at a rate of x tonnes per minute.

(a)   Write down an expression for the time, in minutes, taken to empty the tanker.

Answer $\dfrac{30}{x}$

If the oil is heated then an extra 0.5 tonnes can be pumped out per minute.

'Good, clear and correct answers'

(b)   Write down an expression for the time taken to empty the tanker when the oil is heated.

Answer $\dfrac{30}{x + 0.5}$

If the oil has been heated then the time taken to empty the tanker is reduced by two minutes.

(c)   Show that the equation for x can be expressed in the form

'Correct and we can see what you have done'

$2x^2 + x - 15 = 0$ $\dfrac{30}{x} - \dfrac{30}{x + 0.5} = 2$ $\dfrac{30(x + 0.5) - 30x}{x(x + 0.5)} = 2$

$$30x + 15 - 30x = 2x^2 + x$$
$$15 = 2x^2 + x \quad \text{So } 2x^2 + x - 15 = 0$$

Solve this equation for x, and hence find the time taken to empty the tanker when the oil is cold.

'Good to see how you are trying to solve the equation'

 $(2x - 5)(x + 3) = 0$
So $x = 2.5$ and -3

Answer $x = 2.5$

'Correct final answer, but no mention has been made of why the negative answer of $x = -3$ has been rejected. This would lose a mark'

'A good answer showing algebraic manipulation has been clearly understood. You will get high marks for this answer'

SUMMARY

▷ **Transposition:** The rules for moving formulae and equations around are:
  (a) You can move any letter or number from one side of an equation to the other as long as it is operating on all the rest of that side.
  (b) Once the letter or number has moved, it must do the opposite operation on that side.

▷ **Equations**
  Linear equations, e.g. $2x + 3 = 7$ are solved by moving numbers around the equation to get the variable x on its own.
  Simultaneous equations are where we have a pair of equations (usually linear) that need solving at the same time. The usual way to do this is:
  (a) to combine the two equations in such a way as to eliminate one of the letters (variables);
  (b) to solve the resulting equation, then
  (c) to substitute this value into one of the original equations to complete the solution.
  You should always check the solution to a simultaneous equation by substituting both solutions into the other original equation.
  Quadratic equations, i.e. $ax^2 + bx + c = 0$ (a, b and c are constants) can be solved either by factorising into two brackets completing the square, or by the formula $x = \dfrac{-b \pm \sqrt{(b^2 - 4ac)}}{2a}$

▷ **Expansion of brackets**
  Numbers or expressions outside a bracket imply they are to be multiplied to all the inside of the bracket, e.g.:
$$3(x + 2y) = 3x + 6y$$
$$x(5x - 3y) = 5x^2 - 3xy$$
$$(x + 3)(x + 2) = x^2 + 2x + 3x + 6 = x^2 + 5x + 6$$

▷ **Factorisation** means putting the expression back into brackets, e.g.:
$$4t + 8 = 4(t + 2)$$
$$t^2 - 6t = t(t - 6)$$
$$x^2 + 7x + 10 = (x + 2)(x + 5)$$

▷ **Inequations** are equations with inequalities in them. Solve in the same way as normal equations, except take great care with those which involve powers.

▷ **Fractional indices,** e.g.:
  $x^{1/2}$ represents $\sqrt{x}$ and $x^{3/2}$ represents $(\sqrt{x})^3$

Graphs

► GETTING STARTED

For the highest grades of GCSE you must be able to draw a good graph from any of the equations given, and to recognise the type of equation a given graph will have. You will be expected to sort out your own sensible scales and to draw your graphs with accuracy. The accuracy needed in examinations is usually to the nearest millimetre.

Graphs will generally be drawn in order to find an algebraic solution, or a gradient or an area beneath the graph. Sometimes a graph will be drawn as an end in itself.

► Useful definitions

Cubic A cubic equation is one which has a cube as the highest power, e.g. $y^3 + 6y^2 + y = 5$.

Gradient The 'steepness' of a line. It is the tangent of the angle made with the horizontal.

Intercept Where a line crosses an axis.

Linear A *linear equation* is one which involves only single variables of power one, e.g. $2x + y = 5$. A *linear graph* will be a straight line.

Quadratic A *quadratic equation* is one which has a square as the highest power, e.g. $2x^2 + 4x = 3$. A *quadratic curve* is the graph of a quadratic equation and it is a symmetrical U shape.

Average speed (velocity) Gradient of the *chord* joining the points on a distance–time graph.

Instantaneous speed (velocity) Gradient of the *tangent* to a point on a distance–time graph.

Acceleration Gradient to a velocity–time graph. The rate of change of velocity (speed).

Distance travelled Area under a velocity–time graph.

► Topic chart

The following topic chart can be completed for each of the topics in 'Graphs'. Tick the appropriate box when you have first studied that topic. You can also keep a record of when you have revised that topic for the first and second time, etc.

London	MEG	NEAB	NICCEA	SEG	WJEC	IGCSE	TOPIC	STUDY	REVISION 1	REVISION 2
✓	✓	✓	✓	✓	✓	✓	Drawing graphs from equations			
✓	✓	✓	✓	✓	✓	✓	Graphs and their 'stories'			
✓	✓	✓	✓	✓	✓	✓	Distance–time graphs			
✓	✓	✓	✓	✓	✓	✓	Velocity–time graphs and acceleration			
✓	✓	✓	✓	✓	✓	✓	Area under a curve			
✓	✓	✓	✓	✓	✓	✓	Curved velocity–time graphs			
✓	✓	✓	✓	✓	✓	✓	Linear programming			
✓	✓	✓	✓	✓	✓	✓	Transformation of graphs			

▶ WHAT YOU NEED TO KNOW

▶ **Drawing graphs from equations**

There are four main types of equation for which you should be able to draw graphs.

Linear equations

A linear equation is of the form $y = mx + c$ where m and c are constants. This will always give a straight line, and the minimum number of points to plot is three. The easiest way to sketch or draw this type of equation is to find the x and y intercepts and one other point. Then draw the straight line that goes through all these points.

WORKED EXAMPLE I

Sketch the graphs of $5x + 2y = 7$.

Find the x-axis intercept by substituting $y = 0$, which gives $5x = 7$, $x = 1.4$. So one point is found as $(1.4, 0)$. Find the y-axis intercept by substituting $x = 0$, which gives $2y = 7$; $y = 3.5$. So another point is found as $(0, 3.5)$. Find another by substituting, say, $y = 2$, which gives $5x + 4 = 7 \rightarrow 5x = 3 \rightarrow x = 0.6$, hence the third point is found as $(0.6, 2)$. These can now be plotted and a straight line drawn through them, as shown in Fig. 7.1.

Fig. 7.1

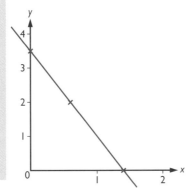

'You need to be able to sketch it then draw it accurately'

Exercise I
Sketch the graphs of $x + y = 8$ and $2x - y = 3$, stating the coordinate of intersection.

Quadratic equations

A *quadratic equation* is of the form $y = ax^2 + bx + c$, where a, b and c are constants. This will always give you a curved graph, and the interesting part usually asked for is this part that does a U-turn. See the two possible shapes in Fig. 7.2.

Fig. 7.2

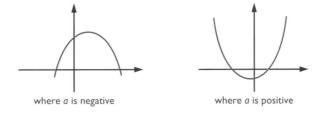

where a is negative　　　where a is positive

You will need quite a few points for plotting, especially around the 'dip' or 'hill top'. In an examination it is most likely that you will be told the range of values to plot and hence the dip will be among that range if the question requires it.

The main use of the dip is to tell you the least possible value that the function has, or, if it is the top of a hill, then the greatest possible value the function has.

WORKED EXAMPLE 2

Neil, a bit of a mathematician, reckoned that when he played golf and teed off with a 'one iron' then the path of the ball was given by the equation $y = \dfrac{3x(95 - x)}{200}$ where y is the vertical distance above the tee and x is the horizontal distance from the tee. With a one iron, Neil usually managed to hit the ball about 100 metres. Draw a graph of the path of the ball and find out its greatest height.

A table needs to be built up of values of x from 0 to 100. If we start with x going up in 20s to start with, we get Table 7.1.

Table 7.1

x	0	20	40	60	80	100
$3x$	0	60	120	180	240	300
$95 - x$	95	75	55	35	15	−5
$y = \dfrac{3x\,(95 - x)}{200}$	0	22.5	33	31.5	18	−7.5

This now lets us plot the points as in Fig. 7.3.

Fig. 7.3

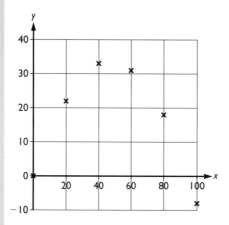

'Notice that I chose a scale that will fit the points on but not be too big'

We could do with finding a few more points near the top of the hill. This seems to be around $x = 50$. Hence, find the y ordinate at $x = 42, 45, 48$ and 50. Evaluating these gives us (42, 33.4), (45, 33.75), (48, 33.84), (50, 33.75). When we plot these points we get a much better picture of the solution and can now draw the graph as in Fig. 7.4, and the maximum height can be seen to be 33.8 metres.

Fig. 7.4

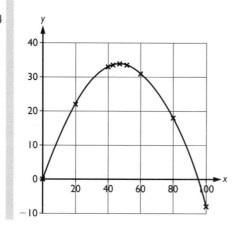

Exercise 2
Draw the graph of $y = x^2 + 3x + 4$ and find the least possible value of y. (Use values of x where $-3 \leqslant x \leqslant 1$.)

Solutions to quadratic equations
These can be found from their graphs. For example, the solutions of $ax^2 + bx + c = 0$ will be where the graph of $y = ax^2 + bx + c$ cuts the x-axis (i.e. where $y = 0$).

In general, the solution of $ax^2 + bx + c = d$ is where the graph of $y = ax^2 + bx + c$ cuts the line $y = d$.

WORKED EXAMPLE 3   Draw the graph of $y = x^2 + x - 4$ where $-3 \leqslant x \leqslant 3$ and hence find the solution to the equation $x^2 + x = 5$.

Construct the table of values for $-3 \leqslant x \leqslant 3$ as in Table 7.2.

Table 7.2

x	-3	-2	-1	0	1	2	3
x^2	9	4	1	0	1	4	9
-4	-4	-4	-4	-4	-4	-4	-4
$y = x^2 + x - 4$	2	-2	-4	-4	-2	2	8

This will give you the U-shaped curve as in Fig. 7.5.

Fig. 7.5

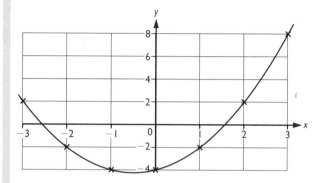

The solution to $x^2 + x = 5$ is given by $x^2 + x - 4 = 1$. (Check that this is the same equation.) Hence the solutions are where the graph of $y = x^2 + x - 4$ crosses $y = 1$, as in Fig. 7.6. The solutions are where $x = -2.8$ and $x = 1.8$.

Fig. 7.6

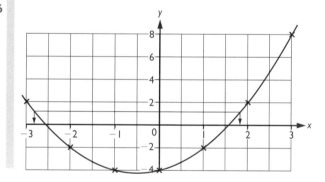

Reciprocal equations

A reciprocal equation is of the form $y = \dfrac{A}{x}$ where A can be any constant value not equal to zero. This will give a curved shape that has symmetry about the origin as you will see in the worked example.

WORKED EXAMPLE 4   Draw the graph of $y = \dfrac{6}{x}$ between $x = -3$ and $x = 3$ and fully describe all its symmetry.

First, construct the table of values for $-3 \leqslant x \leqslant 3$ as in Table 7.3. These points can now be plotted, as in Fig. 7.7. There are two symmetries of the drawn graph, for it has a line symmetry $y = -x$ and rotational symmetry of order 2. (If I had made the scale identical on both axes then $y = x$ would be another line of symmetry.)

Table 7.3

x	-3	-2	-1	0	1	2	3
$y = \dfrac{6}{x}$	-2	-3	-6	∞	6	3	2

Fig. 7.7

'Graph of a reciprocal equation'

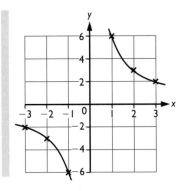

Exercise 3

Draw the graphs of $y = \dfrac{12}{x}$ and $y = x^2 - 2x + 1$ where $0 < x < 5$, and so state a solution of the equation $x^3 - 2x^2 + x = 12$.

Graphs of reciprocal equations in the form $y = \dfrac{a}{x^2}$

WORKED EXAMPLE 5   Draw a graph of the reciprocal equation $y = \dfrac{12}{x^2}$.

To draw this graph you need to find some values of x and y that fit the equation. Follow through the construction of the table of values below. (Notice we still cannot use $x = 0$.)

Table 7.4

x	−4	−3	−2	−1	1	2	3	4
x^2	16	9	4	1	1	4	9	16
$y = \dfrac{12}{x^2}$	0.75	1.33	3	12	12	3	1.33	0.75

Plot the values of x and y and join up the points with a smooth curve (Fig. 7.8).

Fig. 7.8

'Graph of a reciprocal equation involving a square term in the denominator'

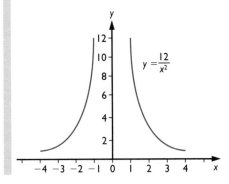

Notice again how the curve does not cross any axes.
Notice also the symmetry of the two 'branches'.
The two axes, namely $x = 0$ and $y = 0$, are the *asymptotes* of the curve.

Simultaneous equations

The last exercise had you solving a simultaneous equation by graph, by simply drawing the graph of each equation and then finding where both graphs cross. This can be a useful way of finding an approximate solution (especially if you need to find an approximate value for starting an *iterative solution*, which we looked at in Chapter 4). However, in general terms, it is always better to try to solve simultaneous equations by an algebraic method rather than by graph if you can, unless an examination question specifically says 'by graph'.

▶ **Graphs and their 'stories'**

The gradients of graphs and the area underneath them can have special meanings for particular graphs. You need to be fully aware of these.

Gradients of straight lines

The *gradient* of a straight line is a measure of its steepness. The gradient is defined as the vertical distance divided by the horizontal distance between any two points on that straight line. The gradient is often expressed as a fraction.

Fig. 7.9

'Gradient of a straight line'

Example

The gradient of the line *AB* in Fig. 7.9 is given by:

$$\frac{\text{vertical distance}}{\text{horizontal distance}} = \frac{3}{6} = \frac{1}{2}$$

We need to make a clear difference between the gradients of lines sloping in *opposite directions*.

Both *AB* and *PQ* in Fig. 7.10 have a gradient of $\frac{2}{3}$, yet they are clearly different.

We define a line sloping down from left to right (e.g. *AB*) as having a *negative gradient*.

We define a line sloping up from left to right (e.g. *PQ*) as having a *positive gradient*.

Fig. 7.10

'Negative and positive gradients'

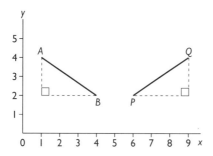

The gradient of *AB* is $-\frac{2}{3}$.

The gradient of *PQ* is $+\frac{2}{3}$ or $\frac{2}{3}$.

It will help if we can find a rule which will allow us to calculate the gradient of a line, including its sign.

Consider the gradient between two points $A(x_1, y_1)$ and $B(x_2, y_2)$ in Fig. 7.11.

Fig. 7.11

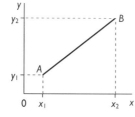
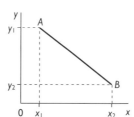

We can calculate the change in the *vertical distance* by the expression $(y_2 - y_1)$ and the change in the *horizontal distance* by the expression $(x_2 - x_1)$. The gradient in each case would be:

$$\frac{y_2 - y_1}{x_2 - x_1}$$

Notice the *negative gradient* in this case comes about when $(y_2 - y_1)$ is *negative*. Note that when you use this formula, you will get a negative gradient when either $(x_2 - x_1)$ or $(y_2 - y_1)$ is *negative*.

In short

The gradient between two points (x_1, y_1) and (x_2, y_2) is given by the equation:

'A rule for finding the gradient'

$$\text{gradient} = \frac{y_2 - y_1}{x_2 - x_1}$$

Exercise 4
Find the gradient of the straight line passing through (a) (1, 3) and (5,5);   (b) (3, 2) and (5, −7).

'These practical situations need understanding and remembering, they will be asked in the exam'

Making sure your x_2 is always the biggest of the x coordinates will give you a *positive* denominator, so that when $y_2 > y_1$, your gradient is positive (uphill) and when $y_2 < y_1$, the gradient is negative (downhill).

Look through the examples of axes, lines and gradients shown in Fig. 7.12 to gain the feel for changing axis units to gradient units.

Fig. 7.12

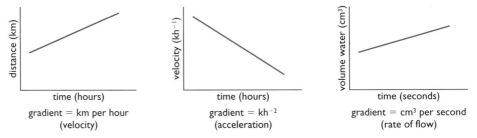

gradient = km per hour   gradient = kh⁻²   gradient = cm³ per second
(velocity)   (acceleration)   (rate of flow)

The first two examples in Fig. 7.12 are the most common ones that you will meet in the examination, where the gradient of a distance–time graph is always the *velocity*, and the gradient of a velocity–time graph is always the *acceleration*.

If you have the equation of the straight line, which can always be put into the form of $y = mx + c$ where m and c are some constants, then the *coefficient of x*, namely m, will always be equal to the *gradient* of the graph of that equation.

Equation of the straight line joining two points

Given any two points, A and B, we can join them together with a straight line. We then find the gradient, m of this line and use the equation $y = mx + c$ to calculate c. We now have enough information to write down the equation of the line.

WORKED EXAMPLE 6

Find the equation of the line joining the point (2, 7) to the point (5, 16).

The gradient of the line joining (2, 7) to (5, 16) is given by:

$$\text{gradient} = \frac{16 - 7}{5 - 2}$$
$$= \frac{9}{3}$$

The equation of the line is $y = 3x + c$.
To find c we substitute into this equation the coordinates of any one of the two given points. For example we can substitute (2, 7) into the equation to give:

'Always use the coordinates of the point with smaller numbers to substitute into the equation'

$$7 = 3 \times 2 + c$$
$$7 = 6 + c$$
$$\rightarrow c = 1$$

Hence the equation will be $y = 3x + 1$.

WORKED EXAMPLE 7

Find the equation of the line joining the points $A(-3, 4)$ and $B(2, -1)$.

The gradient is given by $\dfrac{-1 - 4}{2 - (-3)} = \dfrac{-5}{5} = -1$.

Hence the equation of the line is $y = -x + c$.
Now substitute (2, −1) into this equation to give:

$$-1 = -2 + c$$
$$2 - 1 = c = 1$$

hence $y = -x + 1$

Exercise 5
(a)   Find the equation of the straight line passing through the points (7, 1) and (1, 3).
(b)   Calculate the equation of the line parallel to $y = 3x - 1$ and passing through the point (2, 4).

▶ **Distance–time graphs**

Fig. 7.13

Many of the distance–time graphs that you have met would have used straight lines, as in Fig. 7.13.

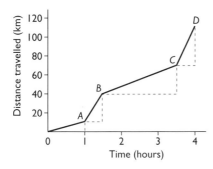

'Remember: gradient

$$= \frac{\text{vertical distance}}{\text{horizontal distance}}$$

The graph shows the journey of a coach in four stages.
The *gradient* of each stage represents the *speed* of the coach.
From Fig. 7.13 we can work out these gradients.

Example

From O to A; speed = gradient = $\dfrac{10\,\text{km}}{1\,\text{hour}}$ = 10 kph

From A to B; speed = gradient = $\dfrac{30\,\text{km}}{\frac{1}{2}\,\text{hour}}$ = 60 kph

From B to C; speed = gradient = $\dfrac{30\,\text{km}}{2\,\text{hours}}$ = 15 kph

From C to D; speed = gradient = $\dfrac{40\,\text{km}}{\frac{1}{2}\,\text{hour}}$ = 80 kph

In Fig. 7.13 the speed has changed on only 4 occasions, and is constant throughout each of the 4 stages of the journey.

When the speed of an object is *continually* changing, then the distance–time graph is a *curved line*.

We can still use the idea of a gradient to find the average speed between any two times, and the speed at any particular instant of time.

Figure 7.14 shows another coach's journey over a four-hour period from 12 noon to 4 pm. This time the graph is a curved line.

Fig. 7.14

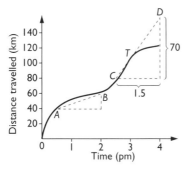

Average speed

The *average speed* between time t_1 and time t_2 is found by calculating the *gradient of the chord* joining the points on the curve that correspond to those times.

For example, to find the average speed between 12.30 pm and 2.00 pm, we draw the chord AB.

average speed = gradient of AB = $\dfrac{20\,\text{km}}{1.5\,\text{h}}$ = 13.3 kph

Instantaneous speed

The *instantaneous speed* is constantly changing along a curved line. However, at any given time, T, the instantaneous speed is given by the gradient of the tangent to the distance--time curve at that exact time, T.

To find this speed, the tangent of the curve at that point has to be drawn and the gradient calculated.

For example, to find the instantaneous speed at 3.00 pm, we draw the tangent to the curve at $T = 3.00$ pm. This is shown as CD in Fig. 7.14. The gradient of CD will give the instantaneous speed.

$$\text{Instantaneous speed} = \text{gradient of } CD = \frac{70 \text{ km}}{1.5 \text{ hours}} = 47 \text{ kph (rounded to nearest whole number)}$$

Note: The gradient can have a positive or negative sign. Here we can give the *absolute value* of the gradient and ignore any negative signs. For example, a negative gradient (Fig. 7.15) simply means the speed on the *return* journey.

WORKED EXAMPLE 8   A woman drives to the airport to pick up her son, and then drives him back home. The graph in Fig. 7.15 shows her journey. Calculate:

(a)   the average speed between 1.04 pm and 1.30 pm;
(b)   the actual (instantaneous) speed at 1.52 pm.

Give your answers in kph.

Fig. 7.15

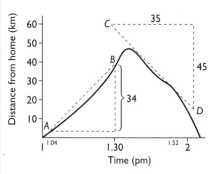

(a)   Find the gradient of AB, from 1.04 pm to 1.30 pm:

$$\text{average speed} = \text{gradient} = \frac{34 \text{ km}}{26 \text{ min}}$$
$$= 1.308 \times 60 \text{ kph}$$
$$= 78.5 \text{ kph}$$

(b)   Find the gradient of the tangent CD at 1.52 pm:

$$\text{speed} = \text{gradient} = \frac{45 \text{ km}}{35 \text{ min}}$$
$$= 1.286 \times 60 \text{ kph}$$
$$= 77.2 \text{ kph}$$

Exercise 6
A stone was thrown off a cliff and out to sea. After t seconds, its height was h metres above the ground, as shown in Table 7.5.

Table 7.5

t	0	0.5	1	1.5	2	2.5	3	3.5	4	4.5	5
h	20	27	30	32	30	27	20	10	0	-14	-30

Draw the graph of h against t, and use your graph to help you calculate:

(a)   the average speed of the stone from: (i) $t = 0.5$ to 2;   (ii) $t = 4.5$ to 5;
(b)   the speed of the stone when: (i) $t = 1$;   (ii) $t = 3.5$.

▶ **Velocity–time graphs and acceleration**

When we plot the velocity of a moving object against the time taken, we can find two very useful pieces of information.

▶   The *gradient* of the velocity–time graph at any time T, will give the *acceleration* of the object.
▶   The *area* under the graph between t_1 and t_2 (i.e. the area enclosed by the graph and the horizontal axis) will give the *distance travelled* between those times.

WORKED EXAMPLE 9   Look at the velocity–time graph in Fig. 7.16. Identify and describe the periods of constant velocity and of acceleration. Also work out the distance travelled over the various periods of time.

Fig. 7.16

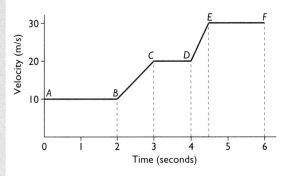

The graph shows the following:

▶   Three periods of constant velocity:
    AB   10 m/s
    CD   20 m/s
    EF   30 m/s

▶   Two periods of positive acceleration (increasing velocity):
    BC   acceleration = gradient

$$= \frac{10 \text{ m/s}}{1 \text{ s}} = 10 \text{ m/s/s} = 10 \text{ m/s}^2$$

    DE   acceleration = gradient

$$= \frac{10 \text{ m/s}}{\frac{1}{2}} = 20 \text{ m/s/s} = 20 \text{ m/s}^2$$

'Note that the unit for acceleration m/s/s is written as m/s²'

▶   The distance travelled during various periods of time.
The area under the section of the graph *AB* represents the distance travelled at 10 m/s for 2 seconds = 20 m.
(Notice that the area under *AB* will also be 10 × 2 = 20 m.)
The area under *BC*, which is a trapezium, gives an area of $\frac{1}{2}(10 + 20) = 15$ m
The area under *CD* = 20 × 1 = 20 m

'Here area is the distance travelled'

The area under $DE = \dfrac{0.5}{2} \times (20 + 30) = 12.5$ m

The area under *EF* = 30 × 1.5 = 45 m
The *total area* under the graph is therefore:

    20 + 15 + 20 + 12.5 + 45 = 112.5 m

Exercise 7
Figure 7.17 shows the speed of a bird over 12 seconds.

(a)   Calculate the acceleration:
    (i) over the first two seconds;
   (ii) after 10 seconds.
(b)   Calculate the total distance the bird has travelled in these 12 seconds.

Fig. 7.17

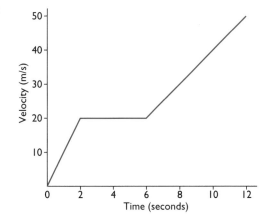

▶ **Area under a curve**

We can only *estimate* the *area* under most curves. The best way to do this is to split the region up into trapeziums and then find the area of each trapezium.

WORKED EXAMPLE 10

Find the area under the curve shown in Fig. 7.18.

Fig. 7.18

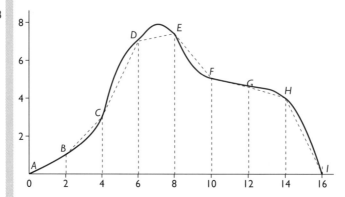

'At the ends of the curve we may use *triangles* rather than trapeziums'

Notice that we split the area under the curve at regular intervals into

▶   triangles at either end, and
▶   trapeziums in the middle.

Notice also that for some of these strips we will get an area *less* than the actual area under the curve. On the other hand, some strips will give us an area *greater* than the actual area under the curve.

These differences usually balance out when we make the *total* estimation of area under the curve.

In this example, the *total area* will be estimated by summing the areas under the following lines:

$AB + BC + CD + DE + EF + FG + GH + HI$

'The area of a trapezium is found by taking the average of the lengths of the two parallel sides and multiplying by the distance between them'

$$= (\frac{2}{2} \times 1) + \frac{2}{2}(1 + 3.4) + \frac{2}{2}(3.4 + 7) + \frac{2}{2}(7 + 7.5) + \frac{2}{2}(7.5 + 5.2) + \frac{2}{2}(5.2 + 3.3)$$

$$+ (\frac{2}{2} \times 3.3)$$

$$= 1 + 4.4 + 10.4 + 14.5 + 12.7 + 8.5 + 3.3$$
$$= 54.8 \text{ sq. units}$$

We can also summarise this to the trapezium rule if we divide the area under the curve into strips of equal length as shown in Fig. 7.19. The total area is:

$$\frac{1}{2}h(y_0 + y_1) + \frac{1}{2}h(y_1 + y_2) + \frac{1}{2}h(y_2 + y_3) + \frac{1}{2}h(y_3 + y_4)$$

$$= \frac{1}{2}h\{(y_0 + y_4) + 2(y_1 + y_2 + y_3)\}$$

Fig. 7.19

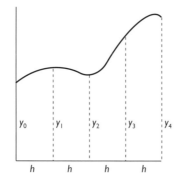

In general, if you divide the area into *n* strips of equal width, then

$$\text{total area} = \frac{1}{2}h\{(y_0 + y_n) + 2(y_1 + y_2 + y_3 + \dots + y_{n-1})\}$$

▶ **Curved velocity– time graphs**

To be realistic, more situations give us *curved* velocity–time graphs than straight ones. Hence more thought and care has to be taken when finding information from these curves.

▶ The *acceleration* at any point will be found by first drawing a tangent at that point on the curve and then *calculating the gradient*.

▶ The *distance travelled* over part (or all) of the journey will be estimated by calculating *the area under the curve*.

WORKED EXAMPLE 11

In a race, Graham's velocity was recorded at different times. The velocity–time graph for the race is given in Fig. 7.20. Calculate:

(a) the acceleration after 15 seconds exactly;
(b) the length of the race.

Fig. 7.20

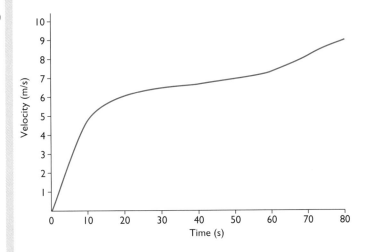

(a) Acceleration after 15 seconds is found by first drawing the tangent to the curve at 15 s and then by calculating the gradient of the tangent (Fig. 7.21).

Fig. 7.21

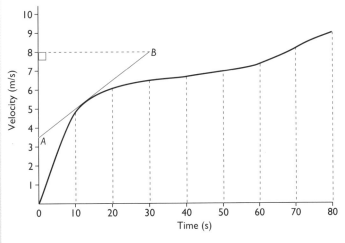

$$\text{Acceleration} = \text{gradient } AB = \frac{4.6 \text{ m/s}}{30 \text{ s}}$$

$$= 0.153 \text{ m/s}^2$$

(b) The length of the race is the area under the whole curve. We have split the region into 8 strips. The areas under these strips are as follows:

$$\frac{1}{2}(10 + 4.5) + \frac{10}{2}(4.5 + 6) + \frac{10}{2}(6 + 6.3) + \frac{10}{2}(6.3 + 6.4) + \frac{10}{2}(6.4 + 6.6)$$

$$+ \frac{10}{2}(6.6 + 7.1) + \frac{10}{2}(7.1 + 8.3) + \frac{10}{2}(8.3 + 9)$$

$$= 22.5 + 52.5 + 61.5 + 63.5 + 65 + 68.5 + 77 + 86.5$$
$$= 497$$

I would estimate that the race was a 500 m race.

Exercise 8

1. The speed of a cyclist is observed at 10-second intervals over one minute. The observations are as follows:

Table 7.6

time (s)	0	10	20	30	40	50	60
speed (m/s)	0	5	14	26	34	38	40

(a) Plot the points on a speed–time graph and join them together with a smooth curve.
(b) Estimate the acceleration (i) after 30 seconds;   (ii) when the speed is 35 m/s.
(c) Estimate the total distance covered by the cyclist over the minute.

2. Gillian, who was learning to drive, was practising by driving along quiet country lanes. Over the first 4 hours she drove with a speed v kilometres per hour, varying with time, t hours, given by the equation $v = t^3 - 4t^2 + 3t + 20$. Find the total distance covered in these 4 hours.

▶ Linear programming

Linear programming is a way of modelling real situations to enable you to see a possible range of solutions and then come to the most suitable solution to a particular problem.

Graphing linear inequalities

To draw the region $y \leqslant 3x + 1$ is best done in two parts.

(a) Draw the line $y = 3x + 1$.
This is a linear equation and hence is a straight line. Three points will define this line. Check that (0, 1), (1, 4) and (2, 7) are all points on the line $y = 3x + 1$.
The line through these points can be drawn.
(b) Decide which side of the line to shade, by shading out the region we do *not* want.
A simple way of doing this is to choose a simple point such as (0, 0) or (1, 1) and see if it is in the required region or not.
For example, try (0, 0), substitute $x = 0$, $y = 0$ into $y \leqslant 3x + 1$ to get $0 \leqslant 1$. This is *true*, hence the region with (0, 0) in is the required region so we shade out the other region. The unshaded region is the region $y < 3x + 1$. The line is the region $y = 3x + 1$.
Hence the unshaded region in Fig. 7.22 *AND* the line define the region $y \leqslant 3x + 1$.

Fig. 7.22
Solution for $y \leqslant 3x + 1$

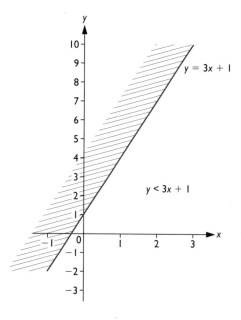

If the region $y < 3x + 1$ was to be shown we should show this where the dotted line indicates that the line itself is *not* part of the solution (Fig. 7.23).

Fig. 7.23

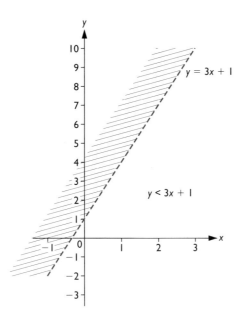

'Use a dotted line to indicate when it is *not* part of the solution'

Exercise 9
Draw diagrams to illustrate the following regions. (Shade out the region you do not want.)
(a) $y \le x$;   (b) $y > x + 3$;   (c) $y \le 6 - x$.

Solution sets

When we are asked to find a region that satisfies two or more inequalities we call this the *solution set*.

WORKED EXAMPLE 12 Show on a graph the region which is the solution set of the inequalities:

$$2x + y < 6 \text{ and } y - x \le 3$$

We need to shade out the *unwanted regions* of both inequalities.

▶ Draw the line $2x + y = 6$ (dotted since we do not want the line in the solution). Use the points (0, 6), (2, 2) and (3, 0) to define the line.
▶ Check if (0, 0) fits the inequality $2x + y < 6$.
 Yes, it does, hence we shade out the region *not* including the origin (right-hand side of line).
▶ Draw the line $y - x = 3$ (continuous line, since the line is part of the solution). Use the points (3, 6), (2, 5) and (0, 3) to define the line.
▶ Check if (0, 0) fits the inequality $y - x \le 3$.
 Yes, it does, hence we shade the region *not* including the origin (left-hand side of line). The solution set is therefore the unshaded region of Fig. 7.24 and the solid line $y - x = 3$.

Fig. 7.24

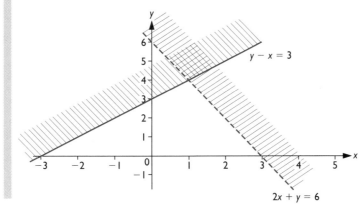

Exercise 10
Illustrate the solution sets of the following inequalities by shading out the unwanted regions:
$3x + 2y \geqslant 15$ and $4x - 3y \geqslant 12$.

WORKED EXAMPLE 13   Show on a graph the region which gives the solution set of the inequalities

$$y - x \leqslant 2; \quad 2x < 5; \quad 3y > -2x$$

▶ Draw the solid line $y - x = 2$ (solid because the line contains solutions).
$0 - 0 \leqslant 2$ is correct, hence $(0, 0)$ is *in* the region $y - x \leqslant 2$, so shade out the left-hand side of $y - x = 2$.

▶ Draw the dotted line $2x = 5$, i.e. $x = 2.5$ (dotted because the line is not part of the solution).
Shade out the right-hand side of $x = 2.5$.

'$(0, 0)$ cannot be used here'

▶ Draw the dotted line $3y = -2x$, i.e. $y = -\frac{2}{3}x$.
Test the point $(1, 1)$: is $3 \times 1 > -2 \times 1$? Yes, so $(1, 1)$ is in the region we want, so shade out the left-hand side of $y = -\frac{2}{3}x$.

Fig. 7.25

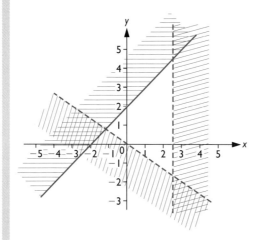

The unshaded region gives the solution set for all points which satisfy all three inequalities.

Exercise 11
Draw diagrams to illustrate the solution sets for the following. (Shade out the unwanted regions.)

$$x + y < 5; \quad y - x \leqslant 3; \quad x \geqslant 0; \quad y \geqslant 0$$

Linear programming in practice

Problems involving inequalities often occur in industry and in ordinary life. Many of these problems can be solved by drawing graphs to show solution sets and, from these, possible answers can be determined.

WORKED EXAMPLE 14   It is decided to spend £1 on small prizes for a party. The choice of suitable prizes at a local shop is: small lollipops 6p each or candy sticks 8p each.
There must be at least 6 of each type, and each of the 13 children at the party must get at least one prize. How can the £1 be spent?

(The first thing is to sort out the information and write down some inequalities.)

Let the number of lollipops be L and the number of candy sticks be K, then since there is 100p to be spent and each lollipop is 6p with each candy stick 8p, we can write:

$$6L + 8K \leqslant 100$$

Since there must be at least six of each type, then:

$$L \geqslant 6 \quad \text{and} \quad K \geqslant 6$$

since each of the 13 children must get a prize, then:

$$L + K \geqslant 13$$

These can now be drawn on a graph, Fig. 7.26.

Fig. 7.26

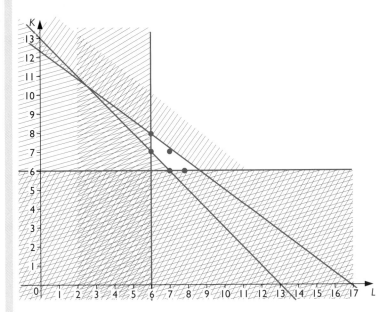

Notice the possible solutions are the *integer values* in the solution set, shown by the heavy dots in the diagram. So the possible prizes that can be bought are:

Lollipops		Candy sticks
6	and	7
6	and	8
7	and	6
7	and	7
8	and	6

Often a further piece of information is required, such as what is the least cost or the greatest number of prizes that can be bought. These answers can either be found by intelligent trial and error on the values in the solution set, or by using what can be called a solution line.

WORKED EXAMPLE 15

From the party above what is the greatest number of prizes that can be won?

(Yes, we can see the solution is 14 by intelligent trial and error, but follow through this method of solution as it is useful when you have a lot more possibilities.)

The number of prizes bought is $L + K$, hence we want the largest value of N where $L + K = N$.

From Fig. 7.27 you will see that all the lines $L + K = N$ will be parallel to each other.

Our solution is found by using a ruler parallel to the lines $L + K = N$ and finding the solution line which is as far to the right as possible on Fig. 7.26. This is in our solution set.

You will find on Fig. 7.26 that this solution line is $L + K = 14$ which gives the three possible solutions on it:

Lollipops	Candy sticks
6	8
7	7
8	6

Fig. 7.27

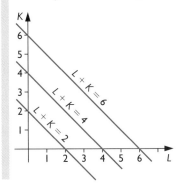

WORKED EXAMPLE 16

A market stall holder is to spend up to £1 100 buying up to 500 T-shirts. He has the choice of two kinds: one at £1 each, the other at £3 each.
The profit on the dearer type is twice that on the cheaper.
How many of each kind should he buy to give himself the greatest possible profit?

Let him buy x of the cheaper T-shirts and y of the expensive T-shirts. The inequalities to be satisfied then are:

$$x + y \leqslant 500; \quad x + 3y \leqslant 1\,100; \quad x \geqslant 0; \quad y \geqslant 0$$

Figure 7.28 shows the solution set.

Fig. 7.28

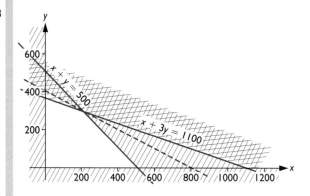

Letting P = profit, the profit line is $x + 2y = P$.
Find a line in this family; say $x + 2y = 400$, then find the line parallel to this but as far to the right as possible.
This solution line is the dotted line on Fig. 7.28, which gives the greatest profit at (200, 300).
The solution of greatest profit, then, is:

200 of the cheaper T-shirts and 300 of the expensive T-shirts

Exercise 12
A manager buys two types of printer, a dot matrix and an ink injection. The dot matrix would need a working space of 3 000 cm² and costs £200. The ink injection would need a working space of 2 000 cm² and costs £600. The manager has only 40 000 cm² of working space available, and can spend up to £4 500. What is the greatest number of printers he can buy?

▶ **Transformation of graphs**

At the highest level of GCSE you need to be able to sketch graphs of simple transformations from a given initial graph.

WORKED EXAMPLE 17

Figure 7.29 is a sketch graph of $y = \dfrac{a}{x}$ where a is any integer.

Fig. 7.29

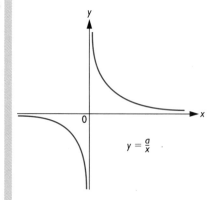

$y = \dfrac{a}{x}$

This is a *reciprocal graph* of the type already seen on page 92.
Note: we use the word *asymptote* to refer to a situation where the curve gets nearer and nearer to a straight line (usually an axis) but never quite touches that line. In Fig. 7.29, each

of the two curves (one for positive and one for negative values of x and y) has an asymptote at the x-axis and an asymptote at the y-axis.

Draw sketch graphs of (a) $y = \dfrac{a}{x+b}$; (b) $y = \dfrac{a}{x} + c$; (c) $y = \dfrac{a}{x+b} + c$ where a, b and c are integers.

(a)   It is $x = 0$ which 'causes' the two asymptotes on the y-axis in the initial diagram (Fig. 7.29). In the new situation, the two asymptotes on the y-axis will occur around $x + b = 0$, which is $x = -b$. So the sketch graph is as shown in Fig. 7.30.

(b)   For each value of x, the value of y is now $+c$ greater than in the initial diagram (Fig. 7.29). The two asymptotes on the x-axis will now occur around $y = +c$ (instead of $y = 0$ as previously), as shown in Fig. 7.31.

Fig. 7.30   **Fig. 7.31**

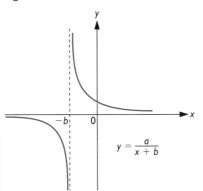

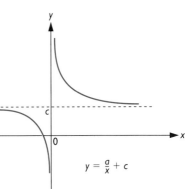

(c)   Putting the aspects of (a) and (b) together, we get the two asymptotes on both the y-axis and the x-axis moved as shown in Fig. 7.32.

Fig. 7.32

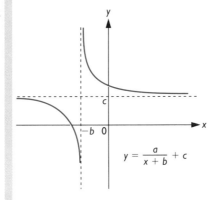

WORKED EXAMPLE 18   Figure 7.33 is a sketch graph of $y = ax^2$.

Fig. 7.33

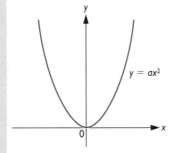

Draw sketch graphs of the following:
(a) $y = a(x + t)^2$;   (b) $y = ax^2 + v$;   (c) $y = a(x + t)^2 + v$

(a)   The initial graph (Fig. 7.33) is a quadratic with a U-shaped curve (since a is positive) and a zero intercept on the y-axis.

The lowest value of y occurs in Fig. 7.33 when $x = 0$. Now the lowest value of y occurs where $(x + t) = 0$, i.e. when $x = -t$. So the sketch graph is as shown in Fig. 7.34.

(b)   The initial graph (Fig. 7.33) has a value of $y = 0$ when $x = 0$, i.e. $y = 0$ is the lowest (minimum) value of y. Now the (lowest) value of y when $x = 0$ is $+v$, as shown in Fig. 7.35.

Fig. 7.34

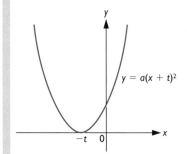

Fig. 7.35

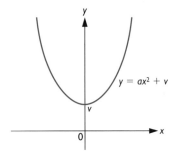

(c)   Putting the aspects of (a) and (b) together, we get the lowest value of y at $(-t, v)$, as shown in Fig. 7.36.

Fig. 7.36

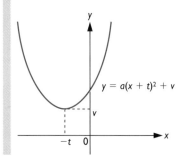

SOLUTIONS TO EXERCISES

S1

Fig. 7.37

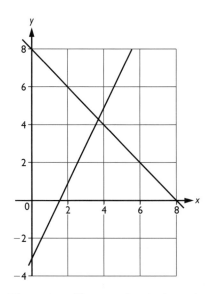

The point of intersection is the point (3.7, 4.3), as shown in Fig. 7.37.

S2   You should have a table of values and a graph, as shown in Table 7.7 and Fig. 7.38.

Fig. 7.38

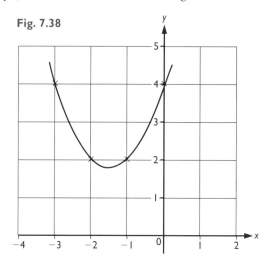

Table 7.7

x	-3	-2	-1	0	1
x^2	9	4	1	0	1
$3x$	-9	-6	-3	0	3
4	4	4	4	4	4
$y = x^2 + 3x + 4$	4	2	2	4	8

The dip looks to be at about $x = -1.5$. We can then find this value by substituting $x = -1.5$ into $y = x^2 + 3x + 4$ to get $y = 1.75$, which seems to be confirmed by the graph. So the least possible value of y is 1.75.

S3   You should have tables as shown in Tables 7.8 and 7.9.

Table 7.9

Table 7.8

x	1	2	3	4	5
$y = \dfrac{12}{x}$	12	6	4	3	2.4

x	0	1	2	3	4	5
x^2	0	1	4	9	16	25
$-2x$	0	-2	-4	-6	-8	-10
1	1	1	1	1	1	1
$y = x^2 - 2x + 1$	1	0	1	4	9	16

You should then see which gaps needed filling in. These would be chiefly on the $y = x^2 - 2x + 1$ graph around the dip, at $x = \frac{1}{2}$ and $x = 1\frac{1}{2}$. The solution of the equation $y = x^3 - 2x^2 + x = 12$ is given by the intersection of the two curves as from

$$y = \frac{12}{x} = x^2 - 2x + 1 \quad \Rightarrow \quad 12 = x^3 - 2x^2 + x$$

This point of intersection is at the point $x = 3$ (which you can see from the tables).

S4   (a)   gradient $= \dfrac{5-3}{5-1} = \dfrac{2}{4} = \dfrac{1}{2}$

   (b)   gradient $= \dfrac{-7-2}{5-3} = \dfrac{-9}{2} = -4.5$

S5   (a)   gradient $= \dfrac{3-1}{1-7} = \dfrac{2}{-6} = \dfrac{-1}{3}$

   It passes through (1, 3), hence $3 = -\dfrac{1}{3} \times 1 + c \quad \Rightarrow \quad c = \dfrac{10}{3}$

   Hence equation is $y = -\dfrac{1}{3}x + \dfrac{10}{3}$ which simplifies to $3y = 10 - x$

   (b)   gradient $= 3$; c given by: $4 = 3 \times 2 + c$
   $$\Rightarrow c = -2$$
   Equation is $y = 3x - 2$

S6   (a)   (i)   Find the gradient of the line from $t = 0.5$ to 2 on the graph: 3 m/s.
   (ii)   Similarly, 32 m/s.
   (b)   Find the gradients of the tangents at each point to give: (i) 5 m/s;   (ii) 20 m/s.

S7 (a) (i) Gradient of the line is 10 m/s².
      (ii) Gradient at $t = 10$ is the same as the line it is on: 5 m/s².
(b) Total area under the graph adds up to 310 m.

S8 1. (b) (i) Gradient of the tangent at (i) $t = 30$ is 1.15 m/s², and at
          (ii) speed = 35 is 0.65 m/s².
      (c) Total area under the graph adds up to 1370 m.
    2. You need to draw the graph then find the area underneath. You should end up with a
        table of values as in Table 7.10.

Table 7.10

t	0	1	2	3	4
v	20	20	18	20	32

As you see, you would really need to know what value v has when $t = \frac{1}{2}$. This is
$v = 20.625$. The graph can now be drawn as in Fig. 7.39, and can be split into the four
strips as shown. Using the trapezium rule we would end up with:

$$\text{total area} = \tfrac{1}{2}\{20 + 2(20 + 18 + 20) + 32\} = 84$$

Fig. 7.39

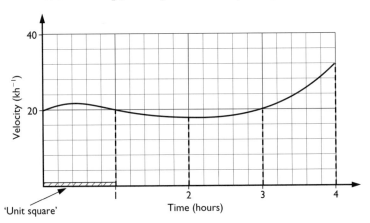

'Unit square'

The 'unit square' has been 1 kh⁻¹ for 1 hour, which is a distance of 1 kilometre. So the
total distance covered by Gillian while practising her driving would be 84 kilometres.

S9

Fig. 7.40 (a)

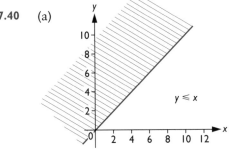

(b)

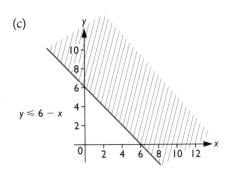

(c)

S10

Fig. 7.41

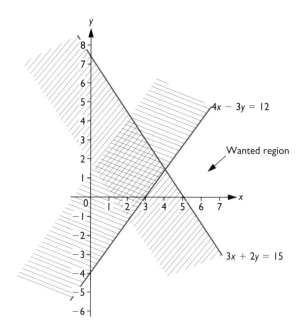

$4x - 3y = 12$

Wanted region

$3x + 2y = 15$

S11

Fig. 7.42

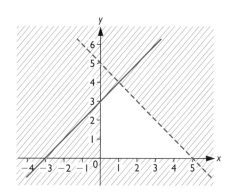

S12   From the floor space, we get the equation:

$$3\,000d + 2\,000i \leqslant 40\,000 \quad \Rightarrow \quad 3d + 2i \leqslant 40$$

From the cost, we get the equation

$$200d + 600i \leqslant 4\,500 \quad \Rightarrow \quad 2d + 6i \leqslant 45$$

These two give the solution set shown in Fig. 7.43.

Fig. 7.43

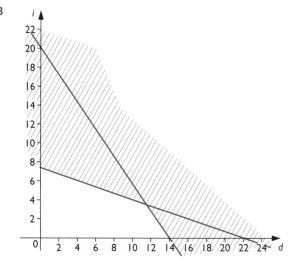

The biggest value of $d + i = 14$ (to nearest whole number).
Hence the largest number of printers he can buy is 14.

EXAMINATION QUESTIONS

▶ **Question 1**   Given that $3x + 4y + 7 = 0$:

(a)   write this equation in the form $y = mx + c$;
(b)   what is the gradient of the straight line represented by this equation?   (NEAB)

▶ **Question 2**   Huw observes a bird flying directly away from a bird box. He starts his watch and finds out
how far the bird is from the box at different times.

Fig. 7.44

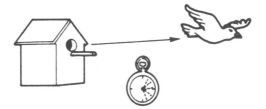

The graph shown in Fig. 7.45 was drawn from his results.

(a)   How far is the bird from the box when Huw starts his watch?
(b)   How fast is the bird flying?
(c)   Write down a formula for the distance, d, the bird is from the box in terms of time, t.
                                                                                (WJEC)

Fig. 7.45

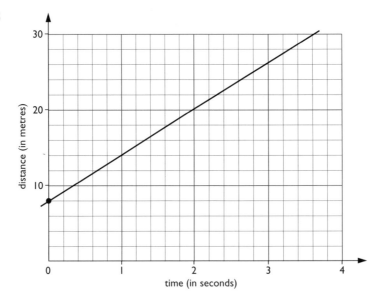

▶ **Question 3**   A school inspector uses his own car to visit schools. He can claim travel expenses each week
on one or other of two schemes.
Scheme A: For distances up to 100 miles, 40 pence per mile. For distances over 100 miles,
40 pence per mile for the first 100 miles then 10 pence per mile for each mile after the first
100 miles.
Scheme B: A basic allowance of £10 plus 20 pence per mile travelled.

(a) Copy and complete the table for scheme A (shown in Table 7.11):

Table 7.11

Miles travelled (x)	0	50	100	150	200	250	300	350	400
Expenses claimed (£y)	0		40		50			65	

(b) On graph paper, using scales of 2 cm to 50 miles travelled and 2 cm to £10 expenses claimed, draw a graph for scheme A for distances travelled up to 400 miles in one week.

(c) On the same axes, draw a graph for scheme B for distances travelled up to 400 miles in one week.

(d) (i) Use your graphs to find the two values of x (miles travelled) for which scheme A and scheme B produce equal values of £y (expenses claimed).

(ii) For what range of values of x (miles travelled) does scheme A produce the greater value of £y (expenses claimed)?

(iii) When the distance travelled is 400 miles, find how much more can be claimed using scheme B than by using scheme A.

(iv) Find the values of x for which the amount claimed using one scheme is £10 more than the amount claimed using the other scheme.   (London)

▶ **Question 4**   On the grid in Fig. 7.46, indicate, by shading out the region not required, the solution of the inequality $2x + 3y \geqslant 6$.   (MEG)

Fig. 7.46

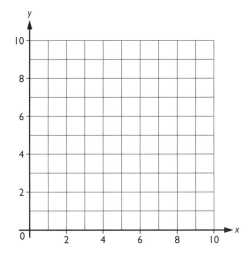

▶ **Question 5**   The values in Table 7.12 are based on the performance figures for a Datsun Bluebird car as it accelerates from rest.

Table 7.12

Time (s), t	0	2	4	6	8	10
Velocity (m/s), v	0	10	18	23.5	27.5	31

(a) Draw the graph of v against t.

(b) By drawing the tangent to the curve at (4, 18), estimate the gradient of the curve at this point, and state the significance of this value.

(c) Estimate the area of the region bounded by the curve, the t-axis and the line $t = 10$ by approximating this area to a triangle and four trapezia. State the significance of this value.   (NEAB)

▶ **Question 6**   The graph in Fig. 7.47 is of $y = x^2 - 2x - 5$.

Fig. 7.47

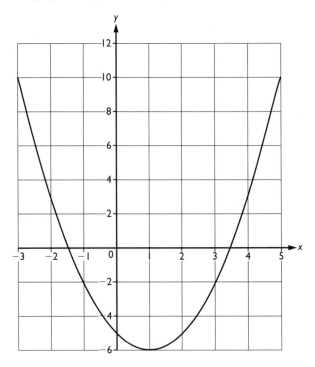

(a)   Using the same axes, draw the line whose equation is $y = x - 1$.
(b)   Write down the solution set to $x^2 - 2x - 5 = x - 1$.
(c)   Show that $x^2 - 2x - 5 = x - 1$ can be written as $x^2 - 3x - 4 = 0$.
(d)   By drawing a suitable line, using the same axes, solve the equation $x^2 - x - 11 = 0$.
(WJEC)

▶ **Question 7**   A pebble is thrown upwards from the edge of a seaside cliff and eventually falls into the sea. The height of the pebble above the sea after t seconds is h metres, where h is given by the formula $h = 24 + 8t - 2t^2$.

Table 7.13

t	0	1	2	3	4	5	6
h							

(a)   Copy and complete Table 7.13 for the values of h.
(b)   Using a scale of 2 cm for 5 m on the h-axis and 2 cm for 1 second on the t-axis, draw a graph of h against t for $0 \leqslant t \leqslant 6$.
(c)   Find:
　(i)   the height of the cliff;
　(ii)   how high the pebble rises above the level of the cliff-top;
　(iii)   after how many seconds the pebble lands in the sea;
　(iv)   by drawing a suitable line, an estimate for the speed of the pebble after 5 seconds.
(London)

▶ **Question 8**   A rectangular block shown in Fig. 7.48 has a square base of side x cm and a height of h cm. The total surface area of the block is 72 cm².

Fig. 7.48

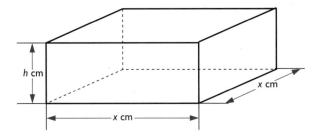

(a) Express h in terms of x.

(b) Show that the volume, $V\,\text{cm}^3$, of the block is given by $V = 18x - \dfrac{x^3}{2}$.

(c) Copy and complete Table 7.14 to show corresponding values of x and V.

Table 7.14

x	0	1	2	3	4	5	6
V	0			40.5	40		0

'Use the scale they've given you or you will lose marks'

(d) Using a scale of 2 cm to represent 1 unit on the x-axis and 2 cm to represent 10 units on the V-axis, draw the graph of $V = 18x - \dfrac{x^3}{2}$ for values of x from 0 to 6 inclusive.

(e) A block of this type has a volume of $30\,\text{cm}^3$. Given that $h > x$, find the dimensions of the block.   (MEG)

▶ **Question 9** The number of bacteria in a colony doubles every 30 minutes.

(a) Complete Table 7.15 to show the number of bacteria for the first four hours. The colony starts with 25 bacteria.

Table 7.15

Time (hours)	0	$\frac{1}{2}$	1	$1\frac{1}{2}$	2	$2\frac{1}{2}$	3	$3\frac{1}{2}$	4
No. of bacteria	25	50							

(b) (i) Draw a graph to represent these figures, forming the points with a smooth curve.
     (ii) From the graph find the time when there will be 2 500 bacteria.
(c) If the number continues to double every 30 minutes, calculate how many bacteria there would be after 10 hours.   (MEG)

▶ **Question 10**

Fig. 7.49

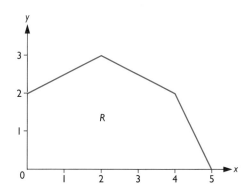

The region R shown in the diagram is bounded by five straight lines.

(a) R is defined by five inequalities, three of which are

$$x \geqslant 0; \quad y \geqslant 0; \quad x + 2y \leqslant 8$$

Find the other two inequalities.
(b) For the points (x, y) in R, find:
     (i) the greatest possible value of $x + y$ and the coordinates of the point at which this greatest possible value occurs,
     (ii) the least possible value of $x - 2y$ and the coordinates of one point at which this least possible value occurs.   (MEG)

▶ **Question 11**   On each of the grids in Fig. 7.50 the graph of $y = x^2$ is drawn.

Fig. 7.50

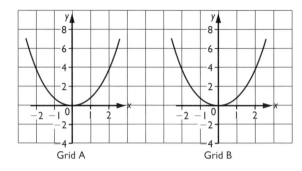

Grid A   Grid B

(a)   On grid A, sketch the graph of $y = x^2 - 1$.
(b)   On grid B, sketch the graph of $y = (x - 1)^2$.

▶ **Question 12**

Fig. 7.51

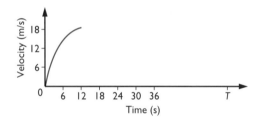

Figure 7.51 represents part of a velocity–time graph for a car moving between two sets of traffic lights.

(a)   Calculate an estimate of the maximum acceleration during the first 12 seconds of the motion.
After the first 12 seconds, the car maintains a constant velocity of 18 m/s for the next 20 seconds.

(b)   Continue the velocity–time graph to show this stage of the journey.

It then slows down with constant deceleration until it comes to rest at time T seconds. The total distance travelled is approximately 630 m.

(c)   Find the value of T.   (London)

▶ **Question 13**   On the graph in Fig. 7.52, the line PQ has the equation $y = ax + b$.

Fig. 7.52

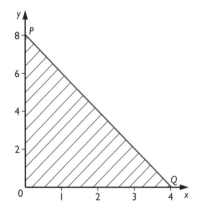

(a)   Write down the value of b.
(b)   Find the value of a.
(c)   Write down the three inequalities which together define the region shaded.   (NEAB)

▶ **Question 14**   Figure 7.53 shows the graph of $y = x^2 - \dfrac{1}{x}$.

Fig. 7.53

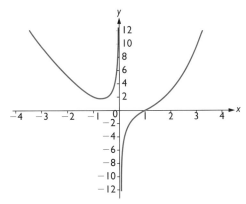

(a)   From this graph write down (correct to the nearest integer) the solutions of the equation

$$x^2 - \frac{1}{x} = 10$$

The solutions of $x^2 - \dfrac{1}{x} = 10$ may also be found by iteration.

(b)   One method is to rewrite the equation as $x = \sqrt{\left(10 + \dfrac{1}{x}\right)}$, and use the iteration

$$u_{n+1} = \sqrt{\left(10 + \frac{1}{u_n}\right)}$$

  (i)   Using this iteration with $u_1 = 3$, find u_2 and u_3, writing down all the figures shown on your calculator.
  (ii)   Hence write down, correct to 2 decimal places, one solution of the equation.

(c)   (i)   Show that the equation may also be rewritten as:

$$x = \frac{1}{x^2 - 10}$$

  (ii)   Use the iteration $u_{n+1} = \dfrac{1}{u_n{}^2 - 10}$ to find a second solution, correct to 2 decimal places, of the equation.

(d)   Use a modification of the iteration in (b) to find the third solution, correct to 2 decimal places, of the equation.

▶ **Question 15**   The consumption of electricity in a house is measured by the number of rotations of the disc in the electricity meter. One unit of electricity is equivalent to 150 revolutions of the disc.

(a)   When an immersion heater is switched on, the disc rotates at a constant rate of 12 revolutions every minute. Calculate the number of units of electricity used in one hour.

(b)   Figure 7.54 shows the speed of rotation of the disc, ω, in revolutions per minute (rpm) over a three-hour period, where t is the time in hours after 7 pm.

  The curved part of the graph is given by the equation $\omega = \dfrac{15}{t} - t$.

  (i)   From the graph, estimate the value of t when the disc is rotating at 8 rpm.
  (ii)   Use this estimate and the iterative formula $t_{n+1} = \frac{1}{8}(15 - t_n{}^2)$ to calculate this time to the nearest minute.

(c)   (i)   Estimate, as accurately as possible, the area of the region between the graph and the t-axis from $t = 0$ to $t = 3$.
  (ii)   Electricity is charged at 6p per unit. Use your answer to part (c) (i) to estimate the cost of electricity used between 7 pm and 10 pm.   (MEG)

Fig. 7.54

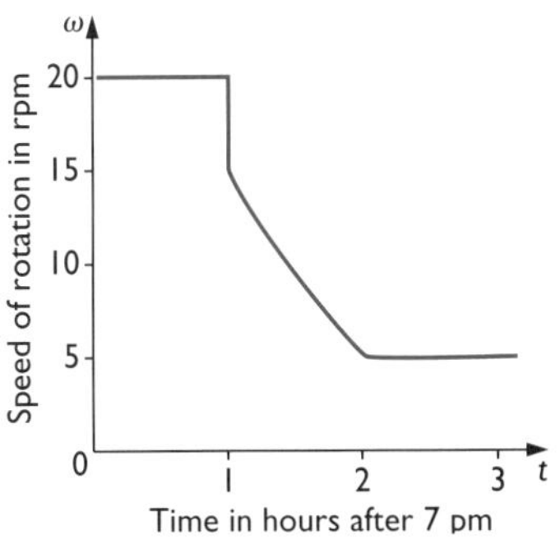

ω

Speed of rotation in rpm

20
15
10
5
0

1   2   3   t

Time in hours after 7 pm

▶ **Question 16**   A fishtank of dimensions 40 cm × 40 cm × 90 cm contained two types of tropical fish: Dwarf Gourami (which have average length of 5 cm) and Climbing Perch (which have average length 20 cm). The Dwarf Gourami require 0.1 g of fish food each day whereas the Climbing Perch need 0.5 g each day.

(a) To exist in harmony it is assumed that each fish needs a volume equal to the cube of twice the average length. The number of Dwarf Gourami is x and the number of Climbing Perch is y. Show that x and y satisfy the inequality

$$x + 64y \leqslant 144$$

(b) Each day 2 g of fish food is available. Show that

$$x + 5y \leqslant 20$$

(c) (i) Using x-axis from 0 to 30. Draw the lines whose equations are:
$x + 5y = 20$, and $x + 64y = 144$.
(ii) In each case clearly identify which side of the line corresponds to the required inequalities.

(d) There must be at least one of each type of fish in the tank. What is the maximum possible number of fish in the tank?   (SEG)

▶ **Question 17**   Figure 7.55 shows how the speed of a car changes as it comes to rest.

Fig. 7.55

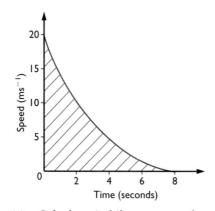

(a) Calculate, in kilometres per hour, the speed of the car when $t = 0$.
(b) The area under the curve gives the distance travelled by the car in coming to rest. This area is shaded on the graph.
Divide the area into four strips of equal width. Calculate an estimate of the distance travelled by the car as it comes to rest.   (NEAB)

▶ **Question 18**

Fig. 7.56

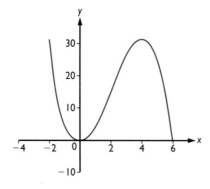

Figure 7.56 shows the graph of $y = x^2(6 - x)$ for $-2 \leqslant x \leqslant 6$.
(a) Making your method clear, find the gradient of this graph at the point $(-1, 7)$.
(b) Using the given graph together with a straight line which is to be drawn in the diagram, solve the equation

$$x^2(6 - x) = 8(2 - x) \quad \text{for } x \text{ in the range } -2 \leqslant x \leqslant 6 \qquad \text{(MEG)}$$

▶ **Question 19**   (a) An open-air swimming pool is filled through a pipe. The rate of flow is 10 000 litres per hour from noon until 7 pm, and it is increased to 15 000 litres per hour from 7 pm until 9 pm. This is shown on the graph in Fig. 7.57.

Fig. 7.57

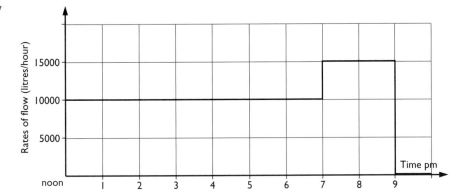

Show that the total amount of water put into the pool is measured by the area under the graph.

(b)   At midnight it starts to rain. The graph in Fig. 7.58 shows the rate at which the rain falls on the pool.

Fig. 7.58

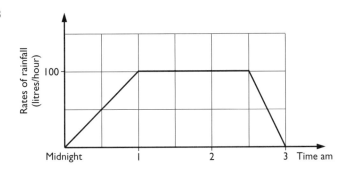

(i)   Describe in words how the rainfall varies between midnight and 3 am.
(ii)   Assuming that the total amount of rain that falls into the pool is measured by the area under the graph, calculate this amount in litres.
(iii)   When the pool was filled through the pipe the previous day, the average depth of the water was 2 metres. How much does the water level rise as a result of the rain?

(c)   Between 8 am and 9 am there is a thunderstorm. The graph in Fig. 7.59 shows the rate at which rain falls on the pool during the storm.

Fig. 7.59

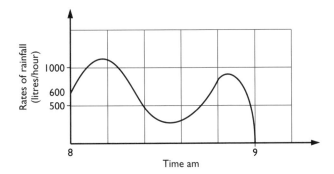

Use an approximate method to estimate how much rain falls on the pool during the storm.

(OCSEB)

▶ **Question 20**   John is trying to design a more efficient speedboat. He has designed the hull of the boat and tested it. He recorded the drag d (the resistance of the water), measured in Newtons at various velocities (V).

Table 7.16

Velocity, V (m/s)	0.50	1.00	1.50	2.00	2.50	3.00
Drag, d (Newtons)	0.52	1.15	2.41	4.07	5.88	8.53

(a) Explain how John can tell from the table of values in Table 7.16 that the graph of (V, d) is not a straight line.

(b) He wanted to test whether the drag would satisfy a formula of the type $d = aV^2 + b$ where a and b are constants. He made a new table to show the values of V^2 and d.

Table 7.17

V^2	0.25	1.00				
d	0.52	1.15	2.41	4.07	5.88	8.53

Complete the new Table 7.17 to show the values of V^2 and d obtained from Table 7.16 above.

(c) (i) When John graphed this table, why do you think he would be satisfied?
     (ii) Deduce the formula that John is likely to declare satisfies the performance of his speedboat.

▶ **EXAMINATION ANSWERS**

A1 (a) $3x + 4y + 7 = 0 \Rightarrow 4y = -3x - 7$
         $\Rightarrow y = -\frac{3}{4}x - \frac{7}{4}$

     (b)   The gradient is the coefficient of x which is $-\frac{3}{4}$.

A2 (a)   8 metres (it is the point on the graph where $t = 0$).

     (b)   The gradient of the line which is found from two points $(0, 8)$ and $(3, 26)$ to give
$$\frac{26 - 8}{3 - 0} = \frac{18}{3} = 6 \text{ m/s.}$$

     (c)   The equation is of the form $y = mx + c$ where m is the gradient and c the y-axis intercept. So here it will be $d = 6t + 8$.

A3 (a)   See Table 7.18.

Table 7.18

Miles travelled (x)	0	50	100	150	200	250	300	350	400
Expenses claimed (£y)	0	20	40	45	50	55	60	65	70

(b)   See Fig. 7.60.

Fig. 7.60

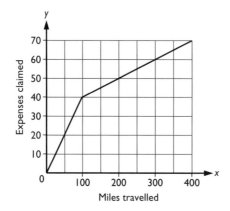

(c) See Fig. 7.61.

Fig. 7.61

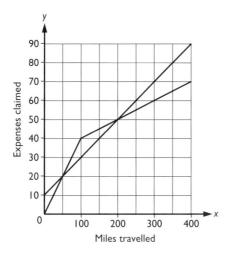

(d) (i) Where the graphs intersect is $x = 50$ and $x = 200$
(ii) $50 < x < 200$
(iii) $£90 - £70 = £20$
(iv) Look at the graph to see where the vertical difference is worth just £10. This happens when $x = 0$, $x = 100$, $x = 300$, although I don't think the school inspector would claim when $x = 0$. So the two values would be just $x = 100$ and $x = 300$.

A4 Draw the line $2x + 3y = 6$ first, which is a straight line as illustrated in Fig. 7.62. Then consider any point, say, (0, 0), substitute it into the inequality and you get $0 + 0 \geqslant 6$. This is not true hence this is the region we do *not* want, and therefore in this question the one that needs shading out (see Fig. 7.63). Do not *touch* the line $2x + 3y = 6$, as this line is included in the region wanted.

Fig. 7.62

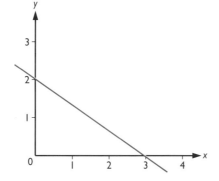

Fig. 7.63

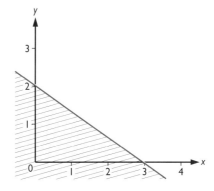

A5 (a) Your graph should look like that in Fig. 7.64.

Fig. 7.64

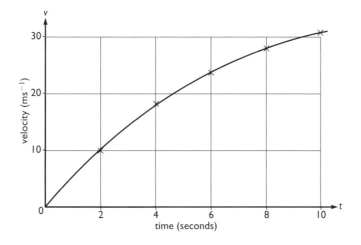

(b) The gradient of the straight line in Fig. 7.65 is $28 \div 8 = 3.5$ and the significance of this is that this represents the actual acceleration of the car after 4 seconds.

Fig. 7.65

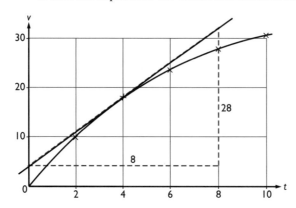

(c) In Fig. 7.66, estimating the area by the trapezium method gives us:

$$\text{area} = \frac{2}{2}\{0 + 2(10 + 18 + 23.5 + 27.5) + 31\}$$

$$\text{area} = 189$$

Fig. 7.66

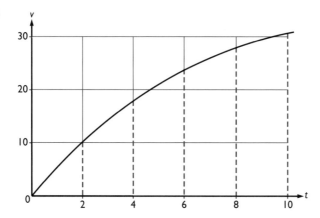

The significance of this is that it represents the total distance covered over the 10 seconds which will be 189 metres.

A6   (a) See Fig. 7.67.

Fig. 7.67

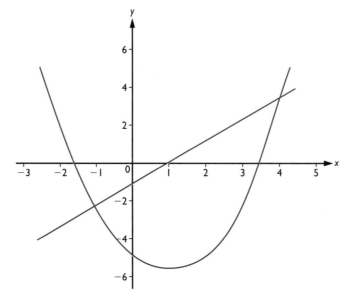

(b) The solution set is found at points where the intersection of these curves occurs, which is the point where $x = -1$ and the point where $x = 4$.

(c) $x^2 - 2x - 5 = x - 1 \Rightarrow x^2 - 2x - x - 5 + 1 = 0$
$\Rightarrow x^2 - 3x - 4 = 0$

(d) You need to evaluate $(x^2 - 2x - 5) - (x^2 - x - 11) = -x + 6 = 6 - x$.
Now, from the given equation $x^2 - x - 11 = 0$, we see that adding $6 - x$ to both sides
gives $(x^2 - x - 11) + (6 - x) = 6 - x$.
$\Rightarrow x^2 - 2x - 5 = 6 - x$
You now need to draw the line $y = 6 - x$ and find its point of intersection with
$y = x^2 - 2x - 5$. Doing this will give you the solutions $x = 3.9$ and $x = -2.8$.

A7 (a) The missing heights are 24, 30, 32, 30, 24, 14, 0, respectively.

(b) Your graph should look something like Fig. 7.68.

Fig. 7.68

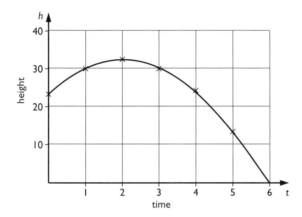

(c) (i) Height of the cliff is where the graph starts on the y-axis, 24 metres.
(ii) Up to 32 metres, 8 metres higher than the cliff-top.
(iii) Hits the sea when $h = 0$, this is when $t = 6$, i.e. after 6 seconds.
(iv) You need to draw a tangent to the curve at $t = 5$, which will give you a straight line
of gradient $= \dfrac{-36}{4} = -9$ metres per second, but this is velocity, and the speed is
the velocity with no sign, so the speed is 9 metres per second.

A8 (a) Surface area given by $2 \times (hx + hx + x^2) = 4hx + 2x^2$, and since the total surface area
is 72 cm^2, then $4hx + 2x^2 = 72 \Rightarrow 4hx = 72 - 2x^2$, i.e.:

$$h = \frac{72 - 2x^2}{4x} = \frac{18}{x} - \frac{x}{2}$$

(b) volume = length × breadth × height
$= x \times x \times h$

$$= x^2 \left(\frac{18}{x} - \frac{1}{2}x \right) = 18x - \frac{1}{2}x^3$$

(c) The table should be completed as in Table 7.19.

Table 7.19

x	0	1	2	3	4	5	6
V	0	17.5	32	40.5	40	27.5	0

(d) The graph will look like Fig. 7.69.

Fig. 7.69

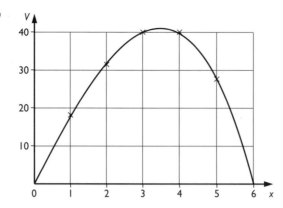

(e) Read from the graph above when $V = 30$ metres. There are two values, $x = 1.8$ and 4.8; but since we are told that $h > x$, then from where

$$h = \frac{18}{x} - \frac{x}{2} \text{ then } \frac{18}{x} - \frac{x}{2} > x \quad \Rightarrow \quad \frac{18}{x} > \frac{3x}{2}$$

$$\Rightarrow \quad 12 > x^2$$
$$\Rightarrow \quad x < 3.5$$

So the solution we seek is $x = 1.8$ cm (from the graph), hence $h = 9.1$ cm.

A9 (a) See Table 7.20.

Table 7.20

Time (hours)	0	$\frac{1}{2}$	1	$1\frac{1}{2}$	2	$2\frac{1}{2}$	3	$3\frac{1}{2}$	4
No. of bacteria	25	50	100	200	400	800	1 600	3 200	6 400

(b) (i) The graph will be like that in Fig. 7.70.

Fig. 7.70

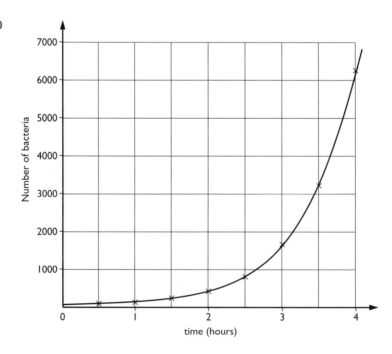

(ii) Read from the graph when the bacteria reach 2 500 — it is after 3.3 hours (3 hours 18 minutes).

(c) After 10 hours the number has doubled 20 times, hence 25×2^{20}, which will be 26 214 400 or 26 million.

A10 (a) The 'first line' from (0, 2) to (2, 3), has gradient $\frac{1}{2}$ and passes through (0, 2) hence from $y = mx + c$ where $m = \frac{1}{2}$ and $c = 2$ the equation is $y = \frac{1}{2}x + 2$. So the region on and under the line is $y \leqslant \frac{1}{2}x + 2$.

The 'second line' line from (2, 3) to (4, 2) has gradient $-\frac{1}{2}$ and will pass through y-axis at 4, hence the equation is $y = -\frac{1}{2}x + 4 \Rightarrow 2y = 8 - x$ which is the one given.

The 'third line' from (4, 2) to (5, 0) has a gradient -2.
Substitute (5, 0) into $y = -2x + c \Rightarrow c = 10$.
Hence the equation of the line is $y = -2x + 10$.
So the region on and under the line is $y \leqslant 10 - 2x$.

  (b) (i) 6 at (4, 2)
        (ii) -4 at (0, 2) or $(1, 1\frac{1}{2})$ or (2, 3)

A11

Fig. 7.71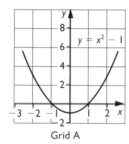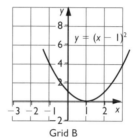

Grid A   Grid B

A12 (a) The steepest slope is at the beginning, the gradient of this line is $\frac{18}{8} = 2.25$ m/s².
  (b) You should draw a straight line for 20 seconds horizontal at $V = 18$.
  (c) The area under the graph up to 32 seconds is 474 m, which leaves 156 m to cover. The last part of the journey is a triangle where $\frac{1}{2} \times t_1 \times 18 = 156 \Rightarrow t_1 = 17.3$, hence T will be $32 + 17 = 49$.

A13 (a) The y-axis intercept, 8.

  (b) The gradient, $\dfrac{-8}{4} = -2$.

  (c) $x > 0$; $y > 0$; $y < 8 - 2x$.

A14 (a) Where $y = 10$; $x = -1$ $x = 3$ $x = -3$ (to the nearest integer)
                                                      (note that 0 is not an integer)

  (b) (i) $u_2 = \sqrt{\left(10 + \dfrac{1}{3}\right)} = 3.214\,550\,3$

        $u_3 = \sqrt{\left(10 + \dfrac{1}{u_2}\right)} = 3.211\,087\,9$

      (ii) The solution is $x = 3.21$

  (c) (i) From $x^2 - \dfrac{1}{x} = 10$ $\Rightarrow$ $x^2 - 10 = \dfrac{1}{x}$ $\Rightarrow$ $x = \dfrac{1}{x^2 - 10}$
      (ii) Start with $u_1 = -1$ then

$$u_2 = \frac{1}{(-1)^2 - 10} = -0.111\,111\,11$$

$$u_3 = \frac{1}{(u_2)^2 - 10} = -0.100\,123\,6$$

$$u_4 = \frac{1}{(u_3)^2 - 10} = -0.100\,100\,3$$

Hence solution is $x = -0.10$

(d)   Let $u_1 = -3$ then

$$u_2 = \sqrt{\left(10 + \frac{1}{-3}\right)} = -3.109\,126\,4 \qquad \text{(note we use the negative)}$$

$$u_3 = \sqrt{\left(10 + \frac{1}{u_2}\right)} = -3.111\,007\,3$$

The solution is $x = -3.11$

A15   (a) $12 \times 60 \div 150 = 4.8$ units

(b)   (i)   1.575

(ii) $t_2 = \frac{1}{8}(15 - 1.575^2) = 1.564\,921\,9$

$$t_3 = \frac{1}{8}(15 - t_2^2) = 1.568\,877\,4$$

$$t_4 = \frac{1}{8}(15 - t_3^2) = 1.567\,327\,9$$

Solution is 1.57 (2 decimal places) which is 1 hour 34 minutes.

(c)   (i)   area $= (20 \times 60) + \frac{30}{2}(14 + 8.5) + \frac{30}{2}(8.5 + 5.5) + (5.5 \times 60)$

$= 2077.5$ (note we used minutes as our unit)

(ii)   2077.5 represents the number of revolutions in the 3 hours.

$$\text{cost} = \frac{2077.5}{150} \times 6 = 83.1$$

estimated cost $= 83$p

A16   (a) $(2 \times 5)^3 x + (2 \times 20)^3 y \leqslant 40 \times 40 \times 90$

$\Rightarrow 1\,000x + 64\,000y \leqslant 144\,000$ (divide through by 1 000)

$\Rightarrow x + 64y \leqslant 144$

(b) $0.1x + 0.5y \leqslant 2$ (multiply through by 10)

$x + 5y \leqslant 20$

(c)

Fig. 7.72

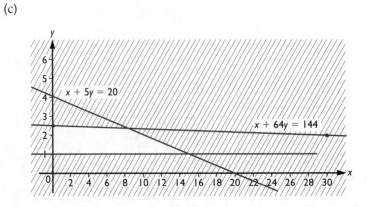

(d)   The maximum number of fish is 16: 1 Perch and 15 Gourami.

A17   (a)   Read from the graph: speed = 20 m/s

       (b)   area = $\frac{2}{2}(20 + 10) + \frac{2}{2}(10 + 5) + \frac{2}{2}(5 + 2) + \frac{1}{2}(2 \times 2)$

              = 54 m

A18   (a)   Find the gradient of the tangent at $(-1, 7)$: $-\frac{21}{7} = -3$

       (b)   Draw the line $y = 8(2 - x)$ and the solutions are the x ordinates of the intersections: $x = -2$ and $x = 1.2$.

A19   (a)   10 000 litres per hour for 7 hours = 70 000 litres
               15 000 litres per hour for 2 hours = 30 000 litres
               Giving a total of 100 000 litres.

               Looking at the graph, if we calculate the area of the two rectangles as in Fig. 7.73, the area = $(10\,000 \times 7) + (2 \times 15\,000) = 100\,000$, the same as above. So the area beneath the graph is the amount of water put into the pool.

Fig. 7.73

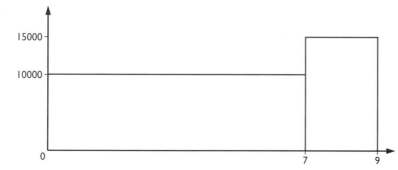

       (b)   (i)   From midnight the rainfall steadily increased until 1 am. From 1 am to 2.30 am, it was a continuous downpour, then it gradually decreased until at 3 am it had stopped raining.

             (ii)   The shape is a trapezium of area $\frac{100}{2}(1\frac{1}{2} + 3) = 225$ litres.

            (iii)   Height of water, h metres $\propto$ amount of water put in, w litres, i.e. $h \propto w$.
                   Hence $h = Kw$ (K being a constant).
                   When $w = 100\,000$, $h = 2 \to 2 = 100\,000\,K \to K = 0.000\,02$.
                   So when $w = 225$, representing the extra water put in, the rise in height will be given by:

                   $h = 0.000\,02 \times 225$ m
                      = 0.0045 m = 0.45 cm

Fig. 7.74

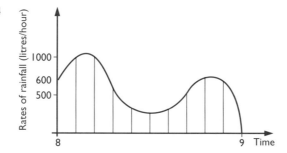

(c) Split the shape up into trapeziums as in Fig. 7.74, then using the trapezium rule width of $2\frac{1}{2}$ little squares, which will represent a time of 0.1 hour. The area will be given by:

$$\text{area} = \frac{0.1}{2}\{600 + 2(1050 + 1100 + 700 + 300 + 250 + 300 + 600 + 800 + 850) + 0\}$$

$$= 625 \text{ litres}$$

A20 (a) Since the differences of V are all the same (0.50), then if the relationship between V and d gave a straight line the differences between d would also be constant. Here they are 0.63, 1.26, 1.66, 1.81, 2.65, gradually increasing and *not* constant. So the graph of (V, d) is *not* going to be a straight line.

(b) See Table 7.21.

Table 7.21

V^2	0.25	1.00	2.25	4.00	6.25	9.00
d	0.52	1.15	2.41	4.07	5.88	8.53

(c) (i) Because if you draw the graph V^2 against d you do get points that look as if they lie in a straight line, and so this shows that the relationship is of the form $d = aV^2 + b$, where a will be the gradient of that straight line, and b the d-axis intercept.

(ii) Where gradient $= \dfrac{8.75}{8.01} = 1.09$ and d-axis intercept $= -0.32$.

Hence $d = 1.09\,V^2 - 0.32$.

Grade checklist

For grade	You should be able to do the following:
B	Locate regions given by linear inequalities. Interpret graphs which describe real-life situations and contexts. Know the shapes of simple functions: e.g. quadratic, cubic, reciprocal.
A	Solve equations using graphical methods. Calculate gradients of curves. Understand what distance/time graphs tell us. Understand what speed/time graphs tell us.
A*	Find the area between a curve, the axis and two limits, and interpret the result.

▶ **EXAMINATION QUESTION WITH STUDENT ANSWER**

(a) Copy and complete the table for values of y where:

$$y = 2x - 7 + \frac{10}{x}$$

'Good, correct answers, rounded off to a suitable degree of accuracy'

x	1	1.5	2	2.5	3	3.5	4
y	5	2.7	2	2	2.3	2.9	3.5

(b) Draw an x-axis, using a scale of 4 cm to 1 unit. Draw a y-axis using a scale of 2 cm to 1 unit.
Plot the points from your table and draw the graph of

$$y = 2x - 7 + \frac{10}{x}$$

'Points plotted correctly, but the curve is rubbish! Here is a bump! It should be a smooth curve'

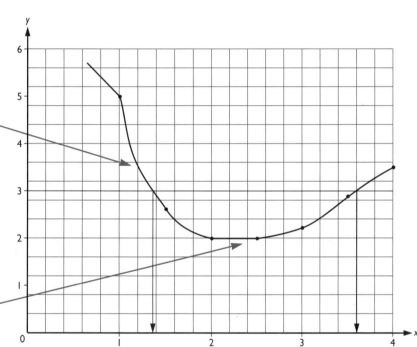

'A poor flat bottom! This should have been rounded to give a smooth, curved bottom'

(c) Use the graph to find the minimum value of $2x - 7 + \frac{10}{x}$ for values of x between 1 and 4.

'Answer wrong because of the flat bottom. Unlikely to be given any credit here at all'

answer 2

(d) By drawing a suitable straight line on your graph parallel to the x-axis, find the approximate solutions of

$$2x + \frac{10}{x} = 10$$

'Excellent, well done, drawn in the correct line of $y = 3$ and found the intersection with the curve accurately from your graph'

x = 1.35   x = 3.59

'You are obviously a good student, but have thrown marks away with a sloppy curve. Would still score well with this answer'

SUMMARY

▷ **Drawing graphs**   The questions will almost always either give you a pair of axes to start with or tell you what scale to use. Make sure you use it, make sure that you plot the points accurately and make the graph go through each point if it should. If it should be a straight line, then draw this with a ruler.
If it should be curved, then draw a smooth curve with no straight bits or extra bumps.

▷ **Recognising graphs**   Make sure you can recognise and sketch the following graphs.

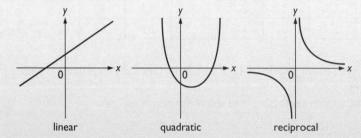

linear   quadratic   reciprocal

▷ **Gradients**   The gradient of a straight line is found by drawing a right-angled triangle on the line, with the line itself the hypotenuse. The gradient is found by dividing the height of the triangle by the length of the base. If it slopes uphill (left to right) it is a positive gradient, if it slopes downhill (left to right) it is a negative gradient.

The gradient of a point on a curved graph is found by the gradient of the tangent to the curve at that point.

▷ $y = mx + c$ This is the general equation of all straight lines, where m is the gradient and c is the y-axis intercept.

▷ **Distance/time graphs**   Time on the horizontal axis and distance on the vertical axis. This can be used to find the speed at any time (gradient of the line), and average speed of the journey by total distance divided by total time travelled.

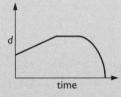

▷ **Velocity/time graphs**   The gradient of these graphs is the acceleration, while the area underneath the graph is the total distance covered.

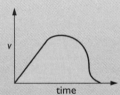

▷ **Graphing inequalities**   When you graph inequalities, then you shade in a whole region.

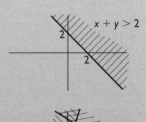

When solving linear programming problems then you would shade out the regions you do not want, to leave you with a blank area as the solution set.

Chapter

8

Geometry

GETTING STARTED

At the higher level of mathematics, the knowledge of *geometrical facts* is expected. These will often have been explored during coursework in school or college, but they do need *learning* for the examination. In the exam it is how you *apply* your knowledge of geometrical facts that gains you marks. So be familiar with the 'rules of the geometrical game'. These will then give you the confidence to search through a geometrical problem to find the correct solution.

▶ Useful definitions

Allied	Supplementary angles on one side of a transversal, facing each other.
Complementary	Angles that add up to 90°.
Diagonal	A line joining two corners of a geometrical shape.
Edge	The line where two faces meet.
Equilateral	Having same lengths.
Euler's rule	$V + F - E = 2$, i.e. number of vertices + number of faces − number of edges = 2, in a polygon.
Face	The surface of a solid shape bounded by edges.
Polygon	A plane shape with many straight lines.
Rhombus	A parallelogram with all its sides the same length.
Subtend	Two lines that meet and form an angle.
Supplementary	Angles adding up to 180°.
Tessellation	A plane shape that will fill a complete plane and leave *no* spaces.
Transversal	A straight line that crosses through at least two parallel lines.
Vertex	A point where two lines or edges meet.

▶ Topic chart

The following topic chart can be completed for each of the topics in 'Geometry'. Tick the appropriate box when you have first studied that topic. You can also keep a record of when you have revised that topic for the first and second time, etc.

London	MEG	NEAB	NICCEA	SEG	WJEC	IGCSE	TOPIC	STUDY	REVISION 1	REVISION 2
✓	✓	✓	✓	✓	✓	✓	Angles			
✓	✓	✓	✓	✓	✓	✓	Congruent triangles			
✓	✓	✓	✓	✓	✓	✓	Geometrical drawing			
✓	✓	✓	✓	✓	✓	✓	Loci			

WHAT YOU NEED TO KNOW

▶ **Angles**   There are a lot of geometrical facts involving *angles*. You are advised to learn them all. This will then arm you with the weapons necessary for problem-solving and for recognising the different situations that these geometrical facts apply to.

Polygons (having N sides)

The total of the exterior angles is *always* 360°.
The total of the interior angles is 180 (N − 2)°.

Regular polygons (having N sides)

A *regular polygon* is one that has all its sides the same length and where each exterior angle is equal. Then:

the size of each *exterior* angle is given by $\dfrac{360°}{N}$

the size of each *interior* angle is given by $180° - \dfrac{360°}{N}$

Isosceles triangle

An *isosceles triangle* has two sides the same length, and the angles opposite to these equal sides are always equal (see Fig. 8.1). The vertical angle bisector will also be the perpendicular bisector of the opposite side as shown here. This will give us two congruent triangles, as shown in Fig. 8.2.

Fig. 8.1      Fig. 8.2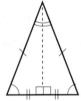

Trapezium

A *trapezium* is a quadrilateral that has two sides parallel as shown in Fig. 8.3. The pairs of angles made with each transversal are *allied* angles, that is they add up to 180° (e.g. $a + b = 180° = c + d$).

Fig. 8.3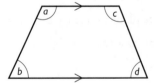

Circles

From any chord in a *circle*, all the angles subtended on the same arc are equal (see Fig. 8.4). From any chord in a circle, the angle subtended at the centre is double any angle subtended at the arc of the circle in the same segment (see Fig. 8.5).

Fig. 8.4   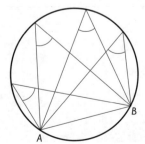   Fig. 8.5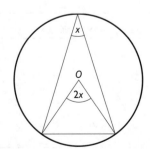

Any quadrilateral drawn so that its four vertices touch the circumference of the same circle is said to be *cyclic*. The opposite angles will add up to 180°, e.g. in Fig. 8.6, $a + c = 180°$, $b + d = 180°$. Any quadrilateral that has its opposite angles adding up to 180° will be cyclic and so a circle can be drawn around the vertices.

If any triangle is drawn in a *semi-circle* with one side the diameter and its opposite angle on the arc (as in Fig. 8.7), then this angle made at the arc is a right angle.

Fig. 8.6

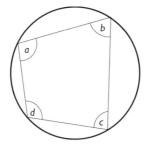

Fig. 8.7

Tangents to a circle will be perpendicular to the radius of the circle. Intersecting tangents form an isosceles triangle (see Fig. 8.8).

Fig. 8.8

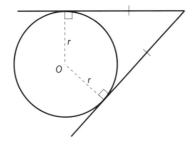

Where OT is a tangent at T, then the angles indicated (x) are equal, this being called the *alternate segment* theorem (see Fig. 8.9).

Fig. 8.9

'Now see how many of these facts you've remembered'

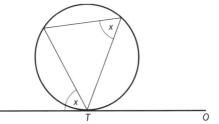

▶ **Congruent triangles**

Congruent triangles are exactly the same in shape, lengths and angles (although one may be a reflection of the other).

There are four possible conditions for two triangles which will determine whether both triangles are congruent. Meeting any *one* condition will result in the triangles being congruent.

'The conditions that will lead to congruent triangles are listed here. Any one condition will do'

- ▶ All three sides are known and correspond.
- ▶ Given two sides and the angle between them all correspond.
- ▶ Given all the angles and a particular side correspond.
- ▶ Given a right angle, the longest side and one other length all correspond.

It is *impossible* to draw more than one triangle if we know any of the facts in the situations above.

Hence, if we are given two triangles and *any* of the above situations fits *both* triangles, then we can say that these triangles are *congruent*.

The four rules can be abbreviated to help us remember them:

1. **The corresponding sides of both triangles are equal**
Side, Side, Side – SSS
triangle $ABC \equiv$ triangle XYZ

Fig. 8.10

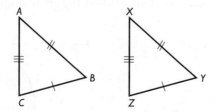

2. **Two sides and the included angle of both triangles are equal**
Side, Angle, Side – SAS
triangle $ABC \equiv$ triangle DEF

Fig. 8.11

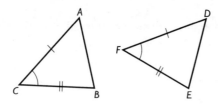

3. **Two angles and a corresponding side of both triangles are equal**
Angle, Angle, Side – AAS, or Angle, Side, Angle – ASA
triangle $ABC \equiv$ triangle PQR

Fig. 8.12

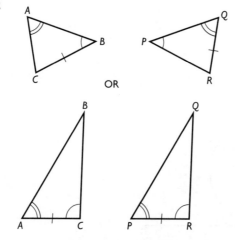

4. **Both triangles have a right angle with equal hypotenuse and corresponding side**
Right angle, Hypotenuse, Side – RHS
triangle $ABC \equiv$ triangle LMN

Fig. 8.13

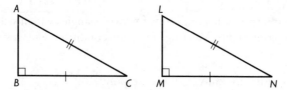

WORKED EXAMPLE 1   The triangles in Fig. 8.14 are congruent: triangle $ABC \equiv$ triangle MLN.
Reason: SSS.
     Notice how we say $ABC \equiv MLN$
     since angle A matches up with angle M
         angle B matches up with angle L
         angle C matches up with angle N

Fig. 8.14

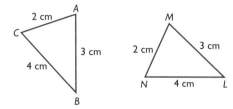

WORKED EXAMPLE 2   The triangles in Fig. 8.15 are congruent: triangle $ABC \equiv$ triangle PQR.
Reason: ASA.
Note: you are expected to be able to find the third angle if you are given the first two.

Fig. 8.15

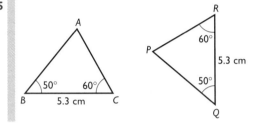

WORKED EXAMPLE 3   The triangles in Fig. 8.16 are *not* congruent since we cannot match the triangles with each other *and* since we cannot fit any one of the four rules to the situation.
Note: if we know that two sides of two triangles are the same then the known angle must be between them if we are to identify them as congruent.

Fig. 8.16

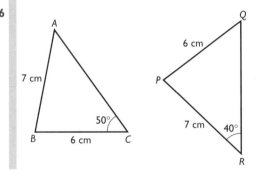

Exercise 1
(a)   Draw a rectangle (not a square!) *ABCD*. Draw in the diagonals *AC* and *BD*. Let the diagonals intersect at *X*. Which triangles are congruent?
(b)   Draw an equilateral triangle *ABC*. Draw in the angle bisectors *AM*, *BN* and *CP*. Which triangles are congruent?

▶ **Geometrical drawing**   Even at the highest level of GCSE mathematics you are quite likely to be asked to draw or construct a particular plane shape. It could be to find out a result or to solve some problem by a scale drawing.
    You need to be confident about drawing to scale information about a particular bearing by the use of a protractor, remembering always to start by drawing in your *North* line.

WORKED EXAMPLE 4   From home, Jenny flew a plane 30 km on a bearing of 150°, then flew at a bearing of 060° until landing at Cleethorpes Airport. She flew straight back on a bearing of 260°. How far is her home from Cleethorpes Airport?

If we use a scale drawing of 1 cm to represent 10 km then we can easily draw Jenny's journey to Cleethorpes (Fig. 8.17), except as yet we do not know where she stopped.
    Now, since home is a bearing of 260° from Cleethorpes, then Cleethorpes must be on a bearing of $260 - 180 = 80°$ from home. Draw this line in to give us the situation in Fig. 8.18. We can now see where Cleethorpes Airport is and measure the distance. It will be 8.9×10 km $= 89$ km.

Fig. 8.17

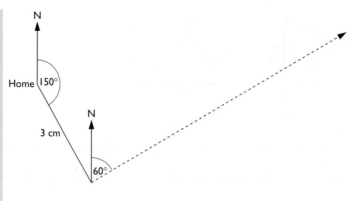

Fig. 8.18

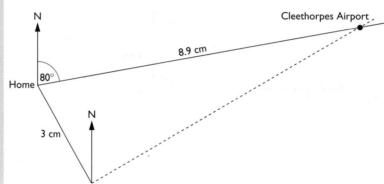

Constructions

You need to be able to perform the following constructions with confidence.

Line bisector

Make two arcs from either end of the line and draw a straight line through the points of intersection. Figure 8.19 illustrates this method of bisecting the line *CD*. It is worth noting that this line is properly called the *perpendicular bisector*.

Fig. 8.19

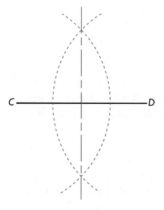

Angle bisector

From the vertex of the angle, draw an arc through both sides of the angle. Then from these points of intersection, arc into the middle of the space between the angles. Where these two arcs cross over join to the vertex of the angle for the angle bisector. This is illustrated in Fig. 8.20.

Fig. 8.20

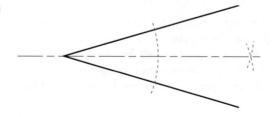

Right angle at a point
From the point *P* where the right angle needs to be drawn, arc on both sides. (You may need to extend the line to be able to do this.) From these two arcs, just construct a line bisector. This will be a perpendicular line at the point where you want it. This is illustrated in Fig. 8.21.

Fig. 8.21

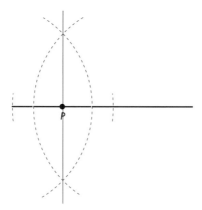

Fig. 8.22

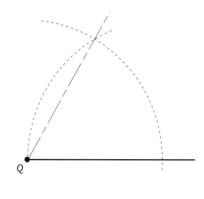

60° angle
From the point *Q* where you want the 60°, arc a quarter turn to just intersect with the line where you want the angle. Then from that intersection, with the same size arc, arc a quarter turn to go from your original point to intercept with the previous quarter-turn. Join this point of intersection with the original point to give 60°. This is shown in Fig. 8.22.

Perpendicular from a point, R, to a line
From the given point, *R*, draw an arc big enough to cut the line twice. Then from these cuts, construct on the other side of the line, a perpendicular bisector between them; join this up to the given point *R* and you have your perpendicular. This is illustrated in Fig. 8.23.

Fig. 8.23

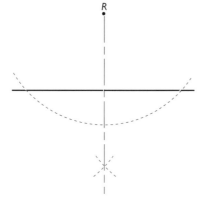

▶ **Loci**   *Loci* are the paths of moving points that usually have some pattern to them. You are quite likely to be asked to find the locus of a point, but there are some locus situations with which you ought to be familiar to start off with.

The *locus* of a point moving so that it is a constant distance from:

▶   a point *A*, is a circle (see Fig. 8.24).

Fig. 8.24

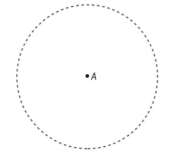

▶ two fixed points, *A* and *B*, is the perpendicular bisector of the line joining those two
   points (see Fig. 8.25).
▶ a line *AB*, is a 'racetrack' shape, made up of two parallel lines and two semi-circles (see
   Fig. 8.26).

Fig. 8.25

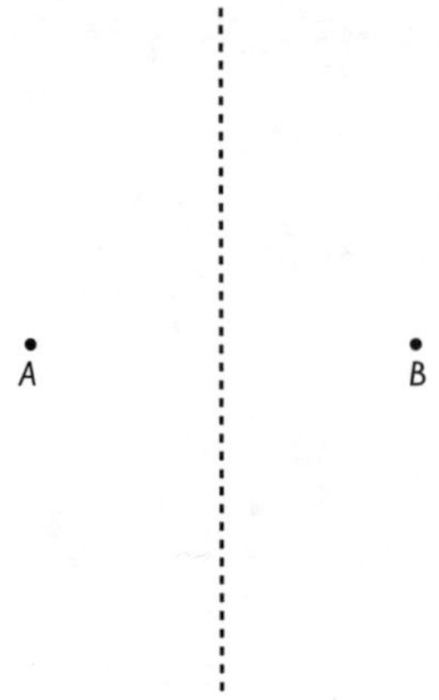

Fig. 8.26

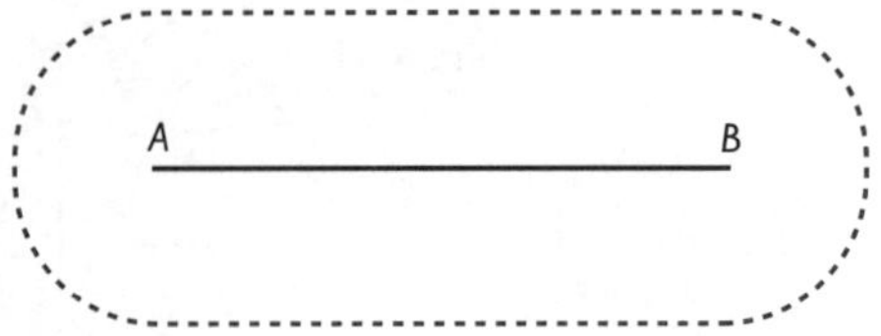

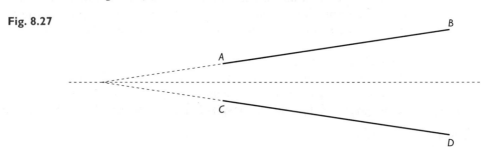

▶ two lines *AB* and *DC*, is the angle bisector of the angle that both lines subtend to (see
   Fig. 8.27).

Fig. 8.27

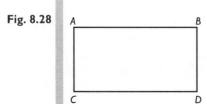

WORKED EXAMPLE 5 Draw the locus of the point *P* which is always 1 cm away from the rectangle *ABCD* in
Fig. 8.28.

Fig. 8.28

You can see from Fig. 8.29 that the distances easily worked out are those vertically
perpendicular 1 cm from the straight edges.

Fig. 8.29   **Fig. 8.30**

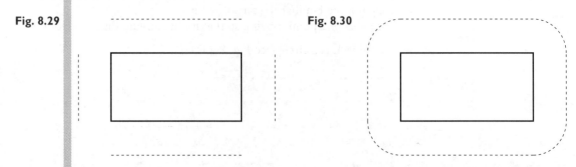

We then need to consider the point, *P*, 1 cm away from each vertex *A*, *B*, *C* and *D*. These
will be quarter-circles joining the given straight lengths already to give the final locus as in
Fig. 8.30.

Exercise 2
Construct an equilateral triangle of side 4 cm, then draw the locus of the point, *P*, which is 1 cm away from the triangle (and not inside it).

SOLUTIONS TO EXERCISES

S1   (a)   There are three different sets:
      (i)   *ABC*, *DCB*, *CDA* and *BAD*
      (ii)   *ABX*, *DCX*
      (iii)   *ADX*, *BCX*
    (b)   There are two different sets:
      (i)   *AXC*, *AXB*, *BXC*
      (ii)   the six little triangles *AXN*, *CXN*, *CXM*, *BXM*, *BXP* and *AXP*

S2   You will have a shape looking something like Fig. 8.31. With three straight sides of length 4 cm, each parallel to one side of the equilateral triangle, then the curved parts are each arcs of circles with radius 1 cm having the centres the vertices of the triangle.

Fig. 8.31

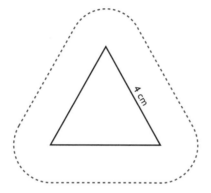

EXAMINATION QUESTIONS

▶ **Question 1**   In Fig. 8.32 angle *EAD* = 40° and angle *AFB* = 60°. Calculate the size of angle *AED*, giving reasons for each step of your calculation.   (NEAB)

Fig. 8.32

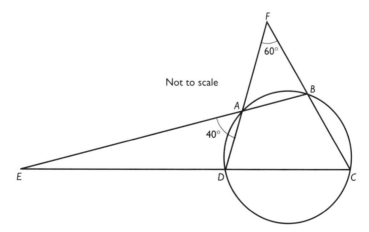

▶ **Question 2**   In this question you must give valid reasons for your answers. Numbers on their own will not be sufficient. Figure 8.33 shows the cross-section of a tunnel. The tunnel is circular with a platform *DC* in it. The platform is held by five rods *AB*, *AD*, *BC*, *BD* and *AC*. Rods *AB*, *AD* and *BC* are all the same length. The angle between *AC* and *BC* is 30°.

Fig. 8.33

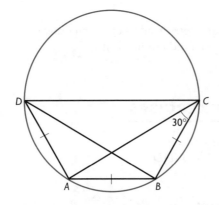

(a)   Find: (i) ∠ADB;   (ii) ∠ABD;   (iii) ∠DBC;   (iv) ∠BDC.
(b)   (i) Explain how you know that platform *DC* must be parallel to rod *AB*.
       (ii) What does the answer to (a) (iii) tell you about *DC*?   (WJEC)

▶ **Question 3**   Figure 8.34 shows the location of a television transmitter (*T*) in relation to two towns Amburg (*A*) and Beetown (*B*).

Fig. 8.34

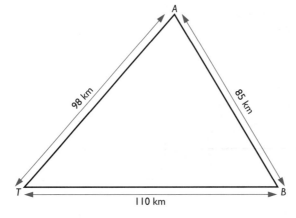

'Use your pair of compasses for the curve to be accurate'

(a)   Using a scale of 1 cm to represent 10 km, draw an accurate scale diagram of the triangle *TAB*.

(b)   The transmitter has a range of 80 km. Draw accurately, on your scale drawing, the curve which represents the limiting range of the transmitter.

It is planned to build a repeater station, *R*, which is an equal distance from both Amburg and Beetown.

(c)   On your drawing, construct accurately the line on which the repeater station must be built.

The repeater station is to be built at the maximum range of the transmitter.

(d)   (i) Mark with the letter *R* the position of the repeater station on your diagram.
       (ii) Find the minimum transmitting range of the repeater stations so that programmes can be received in Amburg. Give your answer in km, to the nearest km.

(London)

▶ **Question 4**   Figure 8.35 shows the outline of a 50p piece. *O* is the centre.   **Fig. 8.35**
(a)   (i) Work out the sizes of the angles marked *x* and *y*.
       (ii) Correct your answers to the nearest degree.
(b)   Work out *x* + 2*y* using your answers to (a) (ii).
(c)   Explain why the answer to (b) is not 180°.

(MEG)

▶ **Question 5**   Figure 8.36, which is drawn to scale, shows a wheel, centre *A*, of radius 25 cm, which rolls along the ground and then mounts a step of height 15 cm. Draw the resulting locus of *A* as the wheel approaches the step, mounts it and then moves on.   (NEAB)

Fig. 8.36

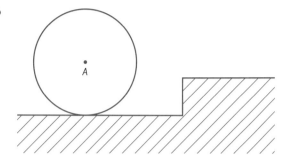

▶ **Question 6**   (a)   The tile *ABEFGHCD* in Fig. 8.37 is made up of a square *ABCD* attached to a regular hexagon *BEFGHC* along their common side *BC*. What is the size of (i) ∠*ABC*; (ii) ∠*EBC*;   (iii) ∠*ABE*?

Fig. 8.37   **Fig. 8.38**

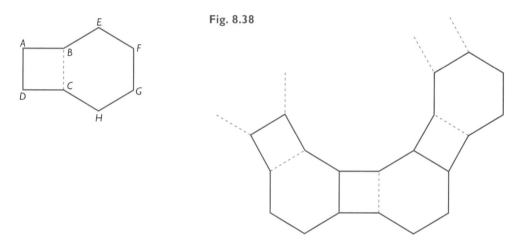

(b)   Tiles of the same shape as *ABEFGHCD* are placed in the pattern shown in Fig. 8.38.
  (i) Without drawing the completed figure, explain why the tiles will form a closed shape if the pattern is continued.
  (ii) The completed shape encloses a regular polygon. How many sides has this polygon?   (WJEC)

▶ **Question 7**   Figure 8.39 shows a cyclic quadrilateral *ABCD* with *AB* parallel to *DC*. The line *TAS* is the tangent to the circle at *A*. Angle *DAT* = 47° and angle *BAS* = 52°.

Fig. 8.39

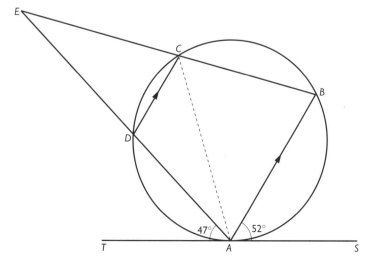

(a) Find the size of: (i) angle *ACB*; (ii) angle *DCA*; (iii) angle *CBA*.

The lines *BC* and *AD* are produced to meet at *E*.

(b) Show that the triangle *EBA* is isosceles.

The triangles *ECD* and *EBA* are similar such that $EC : CB = 2 : 3$.

(c) Calculate the value of $\dfrac{\text{area of triangle } ECD}{\text{area of triangle } EBA}$.   (London)

▶ **Question 8**   Two rods pivoted at *P* (Fig. 8.40) are touching a cylinder at points *A* and *B*.
(a) Use congruent triangles to show that $PA = PB$.
(b) Show that the angle between the radii *OA* and *OB* is equal to the angle θ.   (MEG)

Fig. 8.40

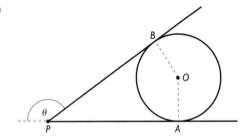

▶ **Question 9**   (a) The country of Futuria is one vast horizontal plain. As part of its national defences, a straight electronic strip, 20 km long and of negligible width, is built along the ground. This emits delta-rays, which causes radio jamming anywhere within 10 km of any point of the strip. Draw, on a scale of 1 cm to 4 km, the region on the ground that is affected by the jamming.
(b) The influence of the strip also extends into the atmosphere, so that there is a region above the ground affected by the radio jamming. Describe the shape of this region in words, using the names of mathematical figures.
(c) Foreign aircraft are required to fly across Futuria horizontally at a height of 8 km above the ground. The Ministry of Aviation issues charts showing the region affected by the jamming at this height. Draw, on the same scale as (a), the shape of this region.
(d) In another part of the country there is a strip with similar properties in the shape of a letter L, each arm of the L being 10 km long. Draw, on the same scale as (a), the region on the ground affected by jamming from this strip.   (OCSEB)

▶ **Question 10**   (a) Figure 8.41 shows the proposed vertices of a planar network (that is, a network in which no edges cross over one another). Also, each vertex is to be joined to each other vertex by one edge (but not more than one). Draw this network, and answer the following questions about it:
      (i)   What are the values of *V*, *R* and *E*, the numbers of vertices, regions and edges? (Do not forget to count the outside region.)
      (ii) What is the degree of each vertex?
'Euler's rule'   (iii) Check that $V + R - E = 2$. (This is called Euler's rule.)
      (iv) How many edges are there on the boundary of each region?
(b) The problem in this part of the question is to draw a different planar network: each vertex is to be joined to exactly three other vertices, and there are to be four edges on the boundary of each region.

Fig. 8.41

      (i)   Give a reason why *E* must be equal to $\dfrac{3}{2}V$.

      (ii) Give a reason why *E* must be equal to 2*R*.
      (iii) Use Euler's rule to calculate the values of *V*, *R* and *E*.
      (iv) Make a drawing of this network.

Fig. 8.42

• •
•   •
•

(c) Now consider the problem of drawing a planar network in which each vertex is joined to exactly four other vertices, and in which there are five edges on the boundary of each region.
  (i) Write down equations connecting E with V, and E with R.
  (ii) Use Euler's rule to calculate the values of V, R and E.
  (iii) What do you deduce about this network?
(d) Figure 8.42 shows how a doodler marked five points on a sheet of paper, and tried to join each vertex to each other vertex by one edge, in such a way that no edges crossed over one another. Prove that, however he tried to do it, he would not be successful.

(OCSEB)

▶ **Question 11** (a) Mark two points A and B on your paper, 8 cm apart. By choosing various pairs of numbe (not necessarily both whole numbers) which multiply together to give 20, plot a number of points P on your paper with the property that $PA \times PB = 20$, (where both PA and PB are measured in centimetres). Hence draw as accurately as you can, the locus of points with this property.
(b) Starting again with a new pair of points A and B, still 8 cm apart, draw the locus of points with the property $PA \times PB = 16$.
(c) Repeat (b) with the property $PA \times PB = 15$.
(d) The three loci which you have drawn should all look different, but they all have the same kinds of symmetry. Name, with reference to the points A and B,
  (i) any lines of reflective symmetry,
  (ii) the centre and order of any rotational symmetry, for all three loci.
  Describe a simple shape which has the same symmetry as these loci.
(e) All the loci in (a), (b) and (c) have a property of the form $PA \times PB = K$, where K is a number. For some values of K, there are points where the locus cuts the line between A and B. Suppose that it does this at a point P where $PA = x$ cm.
  (i) What is the length PB in terms of x?
  (ii) Show that x satisfies the quadratic equation $x^2 - 8x + K = 0$.
  (iii) For the values $K = 16$ and $K = 15$, solve this equation for x.
  (iv) Show that, if $K = 20$, the equation has no solution for x.
  (v) Use these results to explain why the loci have different forms for these three values of K.

(OCSEB)

▶ **EXAMINATION ANSWERS**

A1 You should work it out on the diagram first, then state the route that gets you to the answer in the shortest (but correct) way.
$BAF = 40° \dots$ opposite angles equal.
$BAD = 140° \dots$ angles on a line add up to 180°.
$BCD = 40° \dots$ cyclic quadrilateral, opposite angles add up to 180°.
$FDC = 80° \dots$ angles in a triangle add up to 180°.
$ADF = 100° \dots$ angles on a line add up to 180°.
$AED = 40° \dots$ angles in a triangle add up to 180°.
Hence $AED = 40°$.

A2 (a) (i) $ADB = 30°$. From the same chord AB that angle ACB is from, hence $ADB = ACB$.
        (ii) $ABD = 30°$ since triangle ABD is isosceles and so $ABD = ADB$.
        (iii) Since $DAB = 120°$, angles in a triangle add up to 180°, then $DCB = 60°$, because opposite angles in a cyclic quadrilateral add up to 180°.
            Also $BAC = 30°$, since ABC is an isosceles triangle where $BAC = BCA$.
            Hence $CDB = 30°$, it is from the same chord BC that angle BAC is from.
            Finally $DBC = 90°$ since DBC, BCD and CDB add up to the angles of a triangle and hence 180°.
        (iv) $BDC = 30°$, having found it on the way to DBC.
     (b) (i) Because the angles DCB and CBA add up to 180° and in their position are allied angles, meaning that BC is the transversal, so DC and AB are parallel.
        (ii) That DC is the diameter of the circle.

A3   Your final diagram should look like Fig. 8.43.

Fig. 8.43

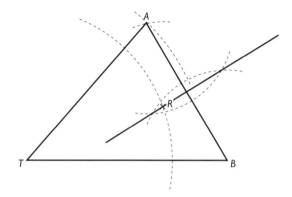

(d)   (ii) The minimum range is the distance from A to the point R which is 45 km.

A4   (a)   (i) $x = 360 \div 7 = 51.43°$; $y = \frac{1}{2}(180 - 51.43) = 64.29°$
              (ii) $x = 51°$; $y = 64°$
         (b) $x + 2y = 51 + 2 \times 64 = 179$
         (c)   Because both x and y have been rounded down.

A5   The locus will follow the dotted line shown in Fig. 8.44.

Fig. 8.44

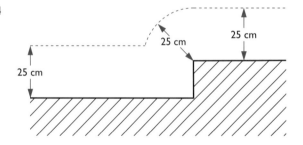

You do need to find the centre when the wheel has just touched the step for the first time, since that is where the locus changes from the straight line to the curve, with the centre being the top vertex of the step.

A6   (a)   (i) 90°;   (ii) $180 - \left(\dfrac{360}{6}\right) = 120°$;   (iii) $360° - (90 + 120) = 150°$

         (b)   (i) Because they fit together forming a regular shape where the inside edges are a regular polygon of exterior angles shown in Fig. 8.45, and 30 is a factor of 360, hence they will all fit together with $360 \div 30 = 12$ so 12 edges are needed, hence 6 tiles are being used.
              (ii) The polygon has $360 \div 30 = 12$ sides.

Fig. 8.45

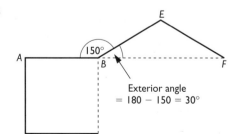

A7 (a) (i) 52° (alternate segment theorem)
 (ii) 47° (alternate segment theorem)
 (iii) $180 - (52 + 47) = 81°$ (*CBA* and *BCD* being allied angles)
(b) Angle $DAB = 180 - (52 + 47) = 81°$ (angles on a line add up to 180). Hence angle $DAB =$ angle CBA, and triangle EBA is isosceles.
(c) If $EC : CB = 2 : 3$ then $EC : (EC + CB) = 2 : 5$. So the ratio of the lengths of $\triangle ECD$ and $\triangle EBA$ is $2 : 5$, and the ratio of the triangles is $2^2 : 5^2 = 4 : 25$, hence:

$$\frac{\text{area of } \triangle ECD}{\text{area of } \triangle EBA} = \frac{4}{25}$$

A8 (a) Consider triangles *POB* and *POA*.
both $\angle B$ and $\angle A$ are right angles (*PB* and *PA* being perpendicular to radii); both *OB* and *OA* are radii, hence equal.
PO is common to both triangles.
Hence Right Angle, Side, Side illustrate congruent triangles.
Hence $PA = PB$ (corresponding sides).
(b) $\angle BPA + \theta = 180°$ (angles on a line); $\angle BPA + \angle BOA = 180$ $(360° - 90 - 90)$
hence $\angle BPA + \theta = \angle BPA + \angle BOA \rightarrow \angle BOA = \theta$.

A9 (a) See Fig. 8.46.

Fig. 8.46

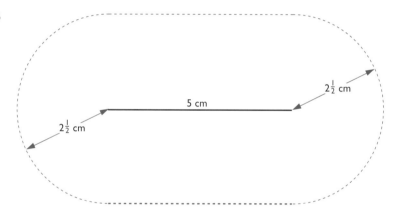

(b) At each end the shape will be one half of a hemisphere of radius 10 km, then between them will be half a cylinder with regular cross-section being a semi-circle of radius 10 km.
(c) Consider the semi-circle cross-section of the middle, shown in Fig. 8.47. The dotted line represents the limit of the unsafe area.

Fig. 8.47

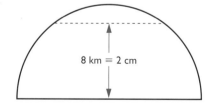

Consider the front elevation of the atmospheric 'shape' shown in Fig. 8.48. Again the dotted line indicates the limit of the unsafe area.

Fig. 8.48

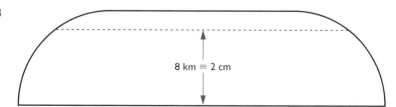

So on the plan of the shape, by using the end and front elevations, you can fix the bounds of this region, as shown in Fig. 8.49.

Fig. 8.49

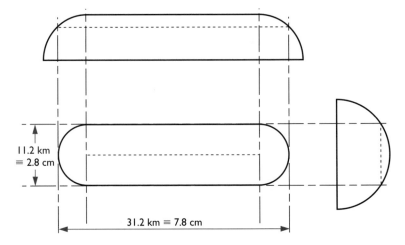

11.2 km ≡ 2.8 cm

31.2 km ≡ 7.8 cm

(d) See Fig. 8.50.

Fig. 8.50

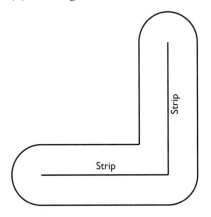

Strip

Strip

A10 (a) See Fig. 8.51.
(i) $V = 4, R = 4, E = 6$; (ii) 3; (iii) $4 + 4 - 6 = 2$. Yes; (iv) 3

Fig. 8.51

(b) (i) Each vertex has 3 edges coming from it, so you would have $E = 3V$, but each edge is joined to 2 edges, hence you halve the total number of edges, so $E = \dfrac{3V}{2}$ (see Fig. 8.52).

Fig. 8.52

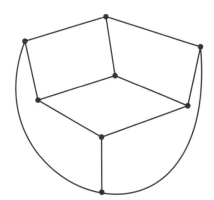

(ii) Since 4 edges bound each region, then this would give $E = 4R$, but each edge is used to form two regions, hence $E = \dfrac{4R}{2}$ which gives $E = 2R$.

(iii) Using $V + R - E = 2$ and $E = \dfrac{3V}{2} \rightarrow V = \dfrac{2E}{3}$

and $E = 2R \rightarrow R = \tfrac{1}{2}E$

Substitute for V and R to give:

$$\frac{2E}{3} + \frac{1E}{2} - E = 2 \quad \Rightarrow \quad \frac{7E}{6} - E = 2 \quad \Rightarrow \quad \frac{E}{6} = 2 \quad \Rightarrow \quad E = 12$$

If $E = 12$, then $V = 8$ and $R = 6$.

(iv) This is the drawing given to start with, which is possibly the best way to start the problem!

(c) (i) By following the pattern found in the last part, here you would get

$$E = \frac{4V}{2} \Rightarrow E = 2V \quad \text{and } E = \frac{5R}{2}$$

(ii) From Euler's rule $V + R - E = 2$.

Substitute $V = \dfrac{E}{2}$ and $R = \dfrac{2E}{5} \Rightarrow \dfrac{E}{2} + \dfrac{2E}{5} - E = 2 \Rightarrow E = -20$

If $E = -20$, then $V = -10$ and $R = -8$.

(iii) That it is impossible to draw.

(d) Trying to do that is to try to make (i) each vertex join exactly 4 other vertices and so each region would be bounded by 3 edges.

This will imply the relationship $E = \dfrac{4V}{2}$ and $E = \dfrac{3R}{2}$.

So solving $V + R - E = 2$ when $E = 2V$ and $E = \dfrac{3R}{2}$ gives $V = \dfrac{1E}{2}$ and $R = \dfrac{2E}{3}$.

Substituting gives us $\dfrac{1E}{2} + \dfrac{2E}{3} - E = 2 \Rightarrow \dfrac{7E}{6} - E = 2 \Rightarrow E = 12$.

$E = 12$ means that $R = 8$ and $V = 6$.
So you need 6 vertices to do this, and so it is impossible with only 5.

A11 (a) Using pairs of numbers like $(2, 10)$, $(10, 2)$, $(4, 5)$, $(5, 4)$, $(2\tfrac{1}{2}, 8)$, $(8, 2\tfrac{1}{2})$, etc. you should end up with a locus like Fig. 8.53.

Fig. 8.53

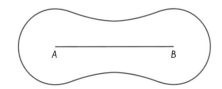

(b) See Fig. 8.54.

Fig. 8.54

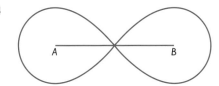

(c)   See Fig. 8.55.

Fig. 8.55

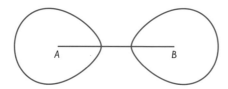

(d)   (i) All have 2 lines of symmetry, one along the line *AB*, the other along the perpendicular bisector of *AB*.
      (ii) Rotational symmetry of order 2 about the midpoint of line *AB*.
      (All rectangles (that are not squares) have the same properties.)

(e)   (i) $8 - x$.
      (ii) Since $PA \times PB = K$, where $PA = x$ and $PB = 8 - x$
      Then $x(8 - x) = K \Rightarrow 8x - x^2 = K$
      So $x^2 - 8x + K = 0$.
      (iii) When $K = 16$,
      $x^2 - 8x + 16 = 0 \Rightarrow (x - 4)(x - 4) = 0$
      $\Rightarrow x = 4$
      When $K = 15$,
      $x^2 - 8x + 15 = 0 \Rightarrow (x - 3)(x - 5) = 0$
      $\Rightarrow x = 3$ and $x = 5$
      (iv) When $K = 20$,
      $x^2 - 8x + 20 = 0$

      If we tried to solve by using the formula $x = \dfrac{-b \pm \sqrt{(b^2 - 4ac)}}{2a}$

      where $a = 1$, $b = -8$, $c = 20$, then $x = \dfrac{8 \pm \sqrt{(64 - 80)}}{2}$

      But note $\sqrt{-16}$ is impossible, hence there is no solution.
      (v) The solutions to $x^2 - 8x + K = 0$ are the possible distances *AP* where *P* is the point that the loci cross *AB*.
      Each different value of *K* here gives a different type of quadratic equation.
      When $K = 16$, the equation has only one solution, hence the loci only cross *AB* once.
      When $K = 15$, the equation has two solutions, hence the loci cross *AB* twice.
      When $K = 20$, the equation has no solutions, hence the loci do not cross *AB* at all.

Grade checklist

For grade	You should be able to do the following:
B	Remember the angle rules and which equal which! Recognise loci.
A	Understand congruent triangles.
A*	Know and use angle and tangent properties of circles.

> ## EXAMINATION QUESTION WITH STUDENT ANSWER

Question

The diagram, which is drawn to a scale of 1 cm to represent 1 m shows a rod *OA* of length 3 m which is pivoted at a point *O* on a horizontal table so that it can rotate in a vertical plane. A light is positioned at *L*, 5 m vertically above *O*, as a result of which the rod casts a shadow *OP* on the table.

When the size of angle *LOA* is $x°$, the length of the shadow *OP* is *y* metres.

By drawing different positions of *OA* and measuring, construct a table of possible values of *y* against *x* for $0 \leqslant x \leqslant 90$. Draw a graph to show how *y* varies as *x* increases from 0 to 90 and hence determine the greatest possible value of *y*.

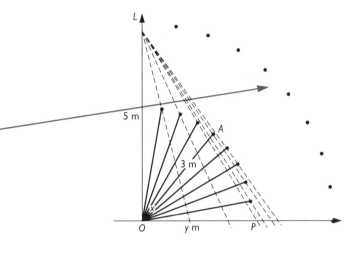

'Good to see the systematic approach of measuring every 10°'

'The table confirms the correct approach to the problem, but the accuracy could be better, as the graph indicates'

x	0	10	20	30	40	50	60	70	80	90
y	0	1.4	2.5	3.2	3.8	3.9	4.0	3.7	3.4	3.0

'From this graph the answer is correct and would gain credit'

biggest y is 4

'The points have been plotted correctly and the axes are just what was asked for – well done. The slight dip at x = 50° should have indicated an error and this particular piece of data should have been checked'

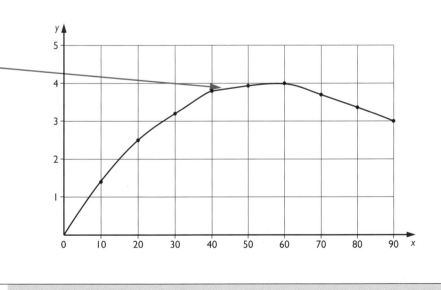

'Poor drawing resulted in wrong information being used and lost marks. (The correct answer should be 3.75 cm, try and show this to yourself)'

SUMMARY

▷ **Parallels**   A line cutting a pair of parallel lines is called a transversal, and it creates equal angles called *alternate angles*

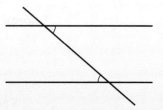

▷ **Plane figures**   You should be able to draw and label equal sides, equal angles and special angles in each of the following shapes:

isosceles triangle   parallelogram
equilateral triangle   rhombus
rectangle   trapezium
kite

▷ **Polygons**   You should be able to write down the names of all the polygons from three sides to ten sides. You should also know that:

(a)   all the exterior angles add up to 360°
(b)   the angle sum of an *n*-sided polygon is given by $180(n - 2)$

You should be familiar with the angle facts of a regular *n*-sided polygon:

(a)   the exterior angle is equal to $360 \div n$
(b)   the interior angle is $180 -$ exterior angle

▷ **Circles**   There are four facts that you should know about angles in circles:

(a)   angles from the same chord
(b)   angles at the centre
(c)   angles in a semi-circle
(d)   cyclic quadrilateral

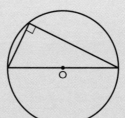
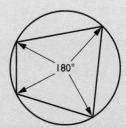

▷ **Congruency**   Two shapes are congruent if they are exactly the same shape and size.

▷ **Similarity**   Two shapes are mathematically similar if one shape is an enlargement of the other. in which case the ratios of the corresponding lengths are all equal to the scale factor of the enlargement.

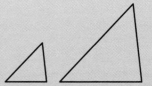

▷ **Loci**   The locus of a point *K* cm from a point is a circle of radius *K* cm from the point.

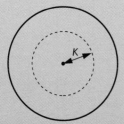

A locus is a collection of points that all obey some given rule.

▷ **Bearings**   You must be familiar with cardinal bearings, e.g. north, south, and three-figure bearings measured clockwise from north.

Mensuration

 GETTING STARTED

This topic is all about calculating lengths, areas and volumes of given shapes and solids, or even distances from one place to another. It is a vital link between arithmetic and algebra. In the vast majority of cases you will need a *formula* to substitute into. These formulae are best learned, then you will have the confidence that you are armed with the right equipment for problem solving. At the higher level of GCSE mathematics a lot of the problems to solve are 3D situations in which you have to think abstractly about the situation.

There will be many questions set in your mathematics examination that relate to this chapter.

▶ Useful definitions

Arc	Part of the circumference of a circle.
Area	Flat space included in a boundary.
Adjacent	The side of a triangle next to the angle concerned and the right angle.
Depression (angle of)	The angle measured below the horizon.
Elevation (angle of)	The angle measured above the horizon.
Hypotenuse	The longest side of a right-angled triangle.
Opposite	The side of a triangle opposite the angle concerned.
Perimeter	The length around all the outside of a flat shape.
Sector	The area of a circle bounded by two radii and the circumference.
Volume	The space inside a 3-dimensional shape.

▶ Topic chart

The following topic chart can be completed for each of the topics in 'Mensuration'. Tick the appropriate box when you have first studied that topic. You can also keep a record of when you have revised that topic for the first and second time, etc.

London	MEG	NEAB	NICCEA	SEG	WJEC	IGCSE	TOPIC	STUDY	REVISION I	REVISION 2
✓	✓	✓	✓	✓	✓	✓	Perimeter			
✓	✓	✓	✓	✓	✓	✓	Area			
✓	✓	✓	✓	✓	✓	✓	Volume			
✓	✓	✓	✓	✓	✓	✓	Surface area			
✓	✓	✓	✓	✓	✓	✓	Pythagoras			
✓	✓	✓	✓	✓	✓	✓	Trigonometry			
✓	✓	✓	✓	✓	✓	✓	Trigonometrical graphs			
✓	✓	✓	✓	✓	✓	✓	Sine rule			
✓	✓	✓	✓	✓	✓	✓	Cosine rule			

▶ WHAT YOU NEED TO KNOW

▶ **Perimeter**   It is essential that you understand the meaning of *perimeter*: it is the total outside length of a flat shape. The one formula you must learn is the perimeter of a circle, which is given by:

circumference = $\pi \times$ diameter of circle   or $C = \pi D$

▶ **Area**   You must *learn* the following facts set out in Figs 9.1–9.6.

Fig. 9.1   Rectangle   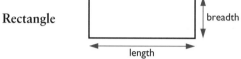   area is length × breadth

Fig. 9.2   Parallelogram      area is length × height

'Some useful formulae for area'

Fig. 9.3   Triangle   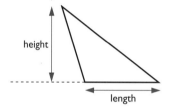   area is $\frac{1}{2}$ × base length × height

Fig. 9.4   Trapezium   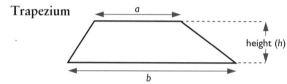   area is $\frac{1}{2}$ × height × sum of parallel lengths $= \dfrac{h}{2}(a + b)$

Fig. 9.5   Circle      area is πr^2

Fig. 9.6   Sector   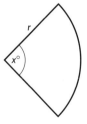   area is $\dfrac{x}{360}\pi r^2$

'Do try to learn them, it saves a lot of time and helps you to see the solution more clearly'

Although some of these will be on a formula sheet, it will give you much more confidence if you know them and are familiar with them all.

▶ **Volume**   You should be familiar with the following two formulae for finding *volumes*. In an examination a formula might well be given, but it will help you to have more confidence and to see what is the appropriate method to use if you actually know these formulae yourself.

Prisms

Many of our regular mathematical shapes are *prisms*, and the volume of any prism is found by:

$$\boxed{\text{volume} = \text{length} \times (\text{regular cross-sectional area})}$$

In a prism, the regular cross-section is the same as the area of the end, hence the formula is perhaps better remembered as volume = length × end area.

Pyramids

The volume of any pyramid or cone is given by:

$$\boxed{\text{volume} = (\text{height} \times \text{base area}) \div 3}$$

WORKED EXAMPLE 1

The cone shape in Fig. 9.7 is full of water. The water is poured into the cup shown next to it. What will be the depth of water in the cup?

Volume of water in the cone $= \frac{1}{3} \times 8 \times$ end area $= \frac{1}{3} \times 8 \times \pi \times 3^2 = 24\pi$ (I keep it in terms of π as I do not want to have to do any rounding off until the very end of the question.) The volume of water inside the cup is given by:

$$(\text{end area}) \times \text{height} = \pi \times 2.5^2 \times h$$

but as the volume we are interested in is 24π, we can set up the equation

$$\pi \times 2.5^2 \times h = 24\pi$$

$$h = \frac{24\pi}{\pi \times 2.5^2} = 3.84$$

Hence the depth of water will be 3.8 cm.

Fig. 9.7

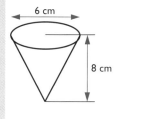

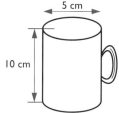

Sphere

The volume of a sphere of radius r (see Fig. 9.8) is given by

$$\boxed{\text{volume} = \frac{4}{3}\pi r^3}$$

Fig. 9.8

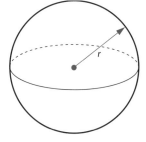

Fig. 9.9

Exercise 1

A sphere of ice cream of diameter 5 cm was placed into a cone-shaped cornet of diameter 5 cm and height 12 cm (Fig. 9.9). The ice cream melted, yet all stayed inside the cone. What depth of the cone was filled with the melted ice cream? (Assume the melted ice cream will have the same volume as the frozen ice cream.)

▶ **Surface area**   There is no regular pattern to follow here, so use your mathematical wits and common sense, being sure to remember the surface areas of the tops and bottoms. Outlined in Figs 9.10–9.12 are some particular solids and how to find their total surface area.

Fig. 9.10   Cylinder

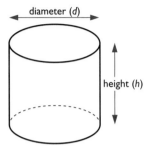

curved surface area $= \pi dh$
area of ends $= 2\pi r^2$ (2 ends)
total surface area $= 2\pi r^2 + \pi dh$

Fig. 9.11   Sphere

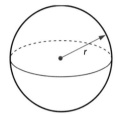

surface area $= 4\pi r^2$

Fig. 9.12   Cone

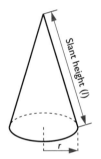

curved surface area $= \pi r l$
area of end $= \pi r^2$
total surface area $= \pi r^2 + \pi r l$

Exercise 2
The Earth has a diameter of 12 762 km. Two-thirds of the earth is covered by water. What will be the total surface area of all the water in the seas and lakes of the world?

▶ **Pythagoras**   You should be familiar with the theory of Pythagoras, which is illustrated in Fig. 9.13.

Fig. 9.13

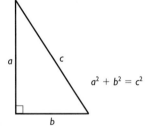

$a^2 + b^2 = c^2$

WORKED EXAMPLE 2   The regular octagon in Fig. 9.14, of side 13 cm, was being cut out of a square piece of card. What is the smallest sized piece of card that this could be?

Fig. 9.14

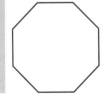

Fig. 9.15

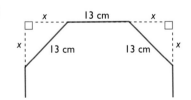

Consider one end of the card, the corners cut off form a right-angled triangle with the hypotenuse 13 cm and the smaller sides the same length of x, as in Fig. 9.15. Hence:

$$x^2 + x^2 = 13^2; \quad 2x^2 = 169; \quad x^2 = 84.5; \quad x = 9.2 \, \text{cm}$$

So the length of the square will be $13 + (2 \times 9.2) = 31.4 \, \text{cm}$.

Exercise 3
Draw a right-angled triangle and then construct a semi-circle on each side, as in Fig. 9.16.

Fig. 9.16

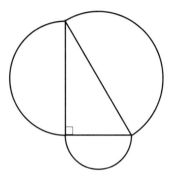

(a)   See if the areas of the two smaller semi-circles add up to the area of the large one.
(b)   Do you think that this will always be the case?

▶ **Trigonometry**

Fig. 9.17

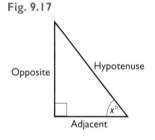

You must be familiar with the simple trig ratios found in right-angled triangles, illustrated in Fig. 9.17.

$$\tan x = \frac{\text{opposite}}{\text{adjacent}}; \quad \sin x = \frac{\text{opposite}}{\text{hypotenuse}}; \quad \cos x = \frac{\text{adjacent}}{\text{hypotenuse}}$$

Note, we use the abbreviated form of the trigonometrical ratios of:

tan   …for tangent
sin   …for sine
cos   …for cosine
(and trig …for trigonometry)

'No-one gets a grade A without being able to do trigonometry, so do try to take it all in and learn as much off by heart as you can'

You must be able to recognise when trig is needed and be able to recognise quickly which of the trig ratios – tan, sin or cos – to use. You will need to use trig if you wish to find:

▶   angles from information about lengths, or
▶   lengths from information about angles and length.

You need to be familiar with the above trig ratios to enable you to go straight to the correct one. Try the following way of spotting which is needed from the involved sides:

No hypotenuse (Fig. 9.18) … use tan

Fig. 9.18

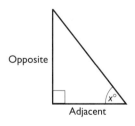

Fig. 9.19

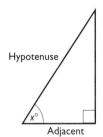

Angle 'cosy' (between two sides – Fig. 9.19) …use cos

Side next to angle (adjacent) not involved (Fig. 9.20) …use sin

Fig. 9.20

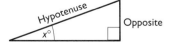

Adopt any method of being able to recognise which to use, but do find one that *you* can remember. (Try 'Tommy On A Ship Of His Caught All Herring'.)

The way that you set out your trig questions can lose you marks, so do be careful; set out correctly, use correct trig statements, and unless told otherwise 'round off to one more significant figure than the given information'.

WORKED EXAMPLE 3   In Fig. 9.21, calculate x.

Fig. 9.21

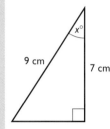

$\cos x = \dfrac{7}{9} = 0.777$. (Use inv cos or $\cos^{-1}$ on your calculator.)

$x = 39°$

WORKED EXAMPLE 4   In Fig. 9.22, find x.

Fig. 9.22

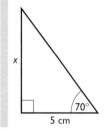

$\dfrac{x}{5} = \tan 70° \Rightarrow x = 5 \tan 70$

$x = 13.7$ cm.

WORKED EXAMPLE 5   In Fig. 9.23, find x.

Fig. 9.23

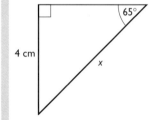

$\dfrac{4}{x} = \sin 65° \rightarrow \dfrac{4}{\sin 65°} = x$

$x = 4.41$ cm.

Note the kind of information that you need to write down as your solution, it's not much but it's vital to be correct. At this high level, you will lose marks for not writing down your trig statements as above ... be warned!

Exercise 4
A regular pentagon is drawn inside a circle of radius 8 cm. Find the length of one straight edge of the pentagon.

Special trig facts

You may have discovered the following facts in your coursework; if not, then try now to show that they are true:

$$\tan x = \frac{\sin x}{\cos x} \quad \text{and} \quad (\sin x)^2 + (\cos x)^2 = 1$$

At this stage, these facts do not have a lot of use, but they do 'come into their own' at A-level – look out for them.

▶ **Trigonometrical graphs**   You need to be able to recognise the special features about the *graph* of each trig function, so that you can sketch them when necessary.

Sine curve

In Fig. 9.24, see how the sine of angles between 0 and 180° are positive, and the sine of angles between 180° and 360° are negative.

Fig. 9.24

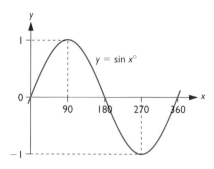

WORKED EXAMPLE 6   Solve the equation $\sin x = 0.5$ $(0 < x < 180)$.

Using $\sin^{-1} x$ on the calculator gives $x = 30°$, but look at the graph and you will see that there are two angles with a sine of 0.5. One is 30° (check with the calculator). Now, from the symmetry of the graph you can see that the other angle will be $(180 - 30)$ which is 150°. Hence:

$$x = 30° \quad \text{and} \quad x = 150°$$

Check then from the graph that:

$$\text{for } 0 < x \leqslant 180 \qquad \sin(180 - x) = \sin x$$
$$\text{for } 180 < x \leqslant 360 \quad \sin(180 + x) = -\sin x$$

Play about with these two facts on your calculator and show to yourself that they are true. They are difficult facts to learn, but if you learn the shape of the sine curve and its main points then you can always work them out again for yourself.

WORKED EXAMPLE 7   Sketch the graph of $y = \sin 3x$ $(0 < x < 180)$.

A table of values can be built as in Table 9.1.

Table 9.1

x	0	30	60	90	120	150	180
$3x$	0	90	180	270	360	450	540
$y = \sin 3x$	0	1	0	-1	0	1	0

Sketched smoothly this gives Fig. 9.25.

Fig. 9.25

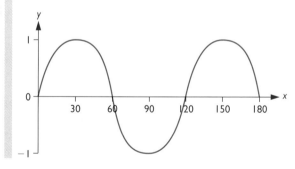

Exercise 5
Sketch the graph of $y = 3 \sin x$.

Similar facts and statements can be made about cos and tan. Follow them through now.

Cosine curve

In Fig. 9.26, see how the cosine of angles between 0 and 90, or 270 and 360 are positive, and of angles between 90 and 270 are negative.

Fig. 9.26

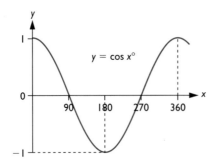

From the symmetry of the graph:

$$\cos(180 - x) = -\cos x$$
$$\cos(180 + x) = -\cos x$$
$$\cos(360 - x) = \cos x$$

Note: the sine curve and the cosine curve are exactly the same shape: the graph of $\cos x$ is just $\sin x$ moved down (i.e. to left) $90°$.

Tangent curves

Notice that Fig. 9.27 is a series of parallel curves with what we call *asymptotes* at $x = 90°$ and $270°$. (More of that at A-level.) It is quite different from the sin and cos curves, yet it still has symmetry to enable us to see that:

Fig. 9.27

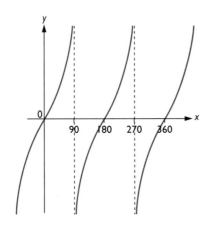

$$\tan(180 - x) = -\tan x$$
$$\tan(180 + x) = \tan x$$

Exercise 6
Sketch the graphs of $y = \cos 2x$ and $y = \tan x$ to estimate a solution to $\cos 2x = \tan x$ $(0 < x < 180)$.

Angles bigger than 90°

To find the trig ratio of angles bigger than $90°$ just press the correct buttons on your calculator. However, when given a ratio and you are asked for possible angles, then most calculators will not tell you. You need either to remember the above rules or to sketch the graph to remind you.

WORKED EXAMPLE 8 Solve the equation $\cos x = 0.8$ $(0 < x < 360)$.

On the calculator $\cos^{-1} 0.8 = 36.9°$.
Also, $\cos(360 - x) = \cos x$, hence where $x = 36.9°$; another solution is $(360 - 36.9)$, which is $323.1°$. So $x = 36.9°$ and $323.1°$.
(You can always easily check the solutions by the use of cos on the calculator.)

Exercise 7
Solve the equation $\tan x = 2$ $(0 < x < 360)$.

▶ **Sine rule**   You may also have come across the *sine rule* as a piece of coursework; it is a very simple but useful fact.

Fig. 9.28

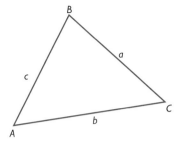

For *any* triangle (label as in Fig. 9.28), then:

'Learn the sine rule'

$$\frac{a}{\sin A} = \frac{b}{\sin B} = \frac{c}{\sin C} = 2R$$

where R is the radius of the circumscribed circle, that is the circle that will touch each vertex of the triangle ABC.

Sometimes it is more useful to look at the rule the other way round, that is:

$$\frac{\sin A}{a} = \frac{\sin B}{b} = \frac{\sin C}{c} = \frac{1}{2R}$$

You use the *sine rule* when:

▶   you have *not* got a right angle;
▶   you have information about one side and its opposite angle;
▶   you have information about either one more side or angle.

WORKED EXAMPLE 9   In Fig. 9.29, find x.

Use the sine rule and start with what it is you are looking for:

Fig. 9.29

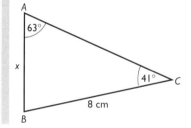

$$\frac{x}{\sin C} = \frac{a}{\sin A} \quad \Rightarrow \quad \frac{x}{\sin 41°} = \frac{8}{\sin 63°}$$

$$\Rightarrow x = \frac{8 \times \sin 41°}{\sin 63°} = 5.9 \text{ cm}$$

WORKED EXAMPLE 10   In Fig. 9.30, find angle x.

Fig. 9.30

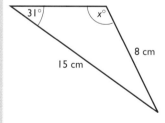

Apply the sine rule to give:

$$\frac{\sin x}{15} = \frac{\sin 31°}{8}$$

$$\Rightarrow \sin x = \frac{15 \sin 31°}{8} = 0.9657$$

$$\Rightarrow x = 74.9° \text{ or } (180 - 74.9)$$
$$x = 74.9° \text{ or } 105.1°$$

Note: there are sometimes two possible solutions from the sine rule.

WORKED EXAMPLE 11   In Fig. 9.31, find $x°$.

Fig. 9.31

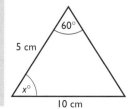

We cannot go straight to x here but we can go to the other unknown angle, let's call it y, then apply the sine rule:

$$\frac{\sin y}{5} = \frac{\sin 60}{10}$$

$$\Rightarrow \sin y = \frac{5 \sin 60}{10} = 0.4330$$

$$\Rightarrow \quad y = 25.7 \text{ or } (180 - 25.7) = 154.3$$

Since one angle is already given as 60°, then another angle cannot be 154.3, since $60 + 154.3 > 180$. Hence $y = 25.7$ and so $x = 180 - (60 + 25.7)$, i.e.:

$$x = 94.3°$$

Exercise 8
In Fig. 9.32, find the length of the side marked x.

Fig. 9.32

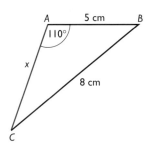

Area of triangles by sine rule

Fig. 9.33

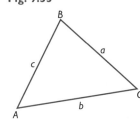

The *area* of any triangle (see Fig. 9.33) can be found by one of the following formulae:

area $= \frac{1}{2}ab \sin C$

area $= \frac{1}{2}bc \sin A$

area $= \frac{1}{2}ac \sin B$

You can use the sine rule for area of a triangle when you know two sides and the angle between them (the *included* angle).

WORKED EXAMPLE 12   In Fig. 9.34, find the area of triangle *ABC*.

Use the sine rule as: area $= \frac{1}{2} \times 4 \times 5 \times \sin 120 = 8.7 \text{ cm}^2$.

Fig. 9.34

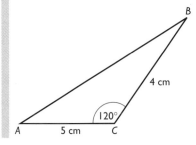

Exercise 9
Find the area of the triangle *ABC* in Fig. 9.35.

Fig. 9.35

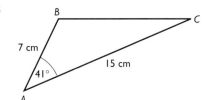

▶ **Cosine rule**

'Don't use this on a right-angled triangle, it's too heavy!'

This rule appears in two different forms and we use each one depending on whether we are calculating a side or an angle.

I To find a side

If, as in the 'sine area rule', we are given two sides and the included angle, then, labelling the triangle as in Fig. 9.36, we can use the *cosine rule* as:

Fig. 9.36

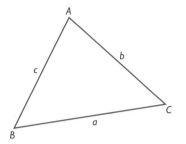

$a = \sqrt{(b^2 + c^2 - 2bc \cos A)}$, or

$b = \sqrt{(a^2 + c^2 - 2ac \cos B)}$, or

$c = \sqrt{(a^2 + b^2 - 2ab \cos C)}$

(Look at the pattern of what is given and how you use it.)

WORKED EXAMPLE 13   In Fig. 9.37, find x.

Fig. 9.37

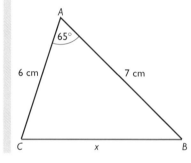

Use the cosine rule as:

$x = \sqrt{(6^2 + 7^2 - 2 \times 6 \times 7 \times \cos 65°)}$

$\quad = \sqrt{49.5}$

$x = 7.0 \text{ cm}$

WORKED EXAMPLE 14   In Fig. 9.38, find x.

Fig. 9.38

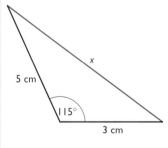

Use the cosine rule as:

$x = \sqrt{(3^2 + 5^2 - 2 \times 3 \times 5 \times \cos 115°)}$

$\quad = \sqrt{46.678548}$

$x = 6.8 \text{ cm}$

(Note the cos 115° was negative, but should have caused no problems.)

Exercise 10
In Fig. 9.39, find x.

Fig. 9.39

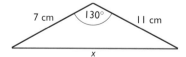

2 To find an angle

When you know *all* the three sides of a triangle you can use this form of the cosine rule to find any angle. From Fig. 9.40:

Fig. 9.40

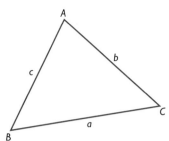

'Using the cosine rule to find an angle'

$$\cos A = \frac{b^2 + c^2 - a^2}{2bc}, \text{ or}$$

$$\cos B = \frac{a^2 + c^2 - b^2}{2ac}, \text{ or}$$

$$\cos C = \frac{a^2 + b^2 - c^2}{2ab}$$

(Look at the pattern of each one and learn the pattern.)

WORKED EXAMPLE 15 In Fig. 9.41, find the size of angle A.

Fig. 9.41

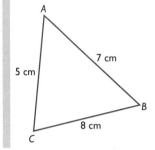

Use the cosine rule to give $\cos A = \dfrac{5^2 + 7^2 - 8^2}{2 \times 5 \times 7} = 0.1429$

$$\Rightarrow A = 81.8° = 82°$$

WORKED EXAMPLE 16 In Fig. 9.42, find the size of angle B.

Fig. 9.42

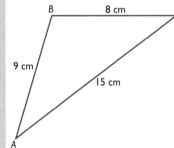

Use the cosine rule to give $\cos B = \dfrac{9^2 + 8^2 - 15^2}{2 \times 9 \times 8} = -0.5556$

$$\Rightarrow B = 123.7° = 124°$$

(Note that if the cosine works out to be negative, the angle will be obtuse.)

Exercise 11
In the triangle *ABC* in Fig. 9.43 calculate the size of:
(a) the smallest angle; (b) the largest angle.

Fig. 9.43

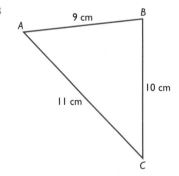

▶ **SOLUTIONS TO EXERCISES**

S1   The volume of ice cream is given by $\frac{4}{3}\pi r^3 = \frac{4}{3}\pi \times (2.5)^3 = 65.4 \text{ cm}^3$.

The volume of the cone is given by $\frac{1}{3}\pi r^2 h = \frac{1}{3}\pi \times (2.5)^2 \times 12 = 78.5 \text{ cm}^3$.

So the ratio of volume between the melted ice cream and the cone is given by $65.4 : 78.5$ which is $0.8331 : 1$.

Fig. 9.44

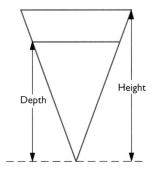

The two volumes are similar shapes (see Fig. 9.44) with volume ratio of $0.8331 : 1$, hence a length ratio of $\sqrt[3]{0.8331} : 1$ which is $0.941 : 1$.
So the depth of ice cream will be $12 \times 0.941 = 11.3$ cm.

S2 Surface area of Earth given by $4\pi r^2 = 4 \times \pi \times (6\,381)^2$.
So two-thirds will be given by $\frac{2}{3} \times 4 \times \pi \times (6\,381)^2 = 3.4 \times 10^8$ km^2.

S3 (a) Yes, they should do;   (b) Yes, it will always be the case.

S4 If the pentagon is divided into triangles, then the angle of each triangle at the centre, O, of the circle will be $360 \div 5 = 72°$ (see Fig. 9.45). The right-angled triangle as shown in the diagram can be formed where $x = 72 \div 2 = 36°$ and its base length, y, is half the side d of the pentagon. Hence $y = 8 \sin 36°$ and so:

$$d = 2 \times 8 \times \sin 36° = 9.4 \text{ cm}$$

Fig. 9.45

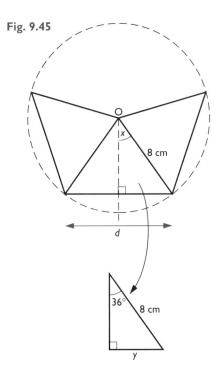

S5 See Fig. 9.46.

Fig. 9.46

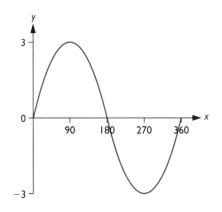

Fig. 9.47

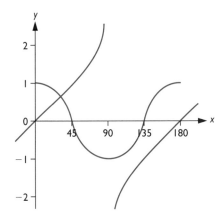

S6   See Fig. 9.47. The intersection will be the solution of $x \simeq 29°$.

S7 $\tan x = 2$; $x = 63.4°$ and $180 + 63.4 = 243.4°$.
(In any question like this you can always test your answers by finding their tangents on the calculator and checking that indeed they are equal to what you started with.)

S8   Since the information given (see Fig. 9.48) is an angle and its opposite side, and we do not have a right angle or know another side, then first find angle C. Here I use the sine rule as:

Fig. 9.48

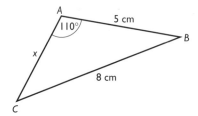

$\dfrac{\sin C}{5} = \dfrac{\sin 110°}{8} \Rightarrow \sin C = \dfrac{5 \sin 110°}{8} = 0.5873$

$\Rightarrow C = 36°$

Then angle $B = 180 - (110 + 36) = 34°$.

Use sine rule again to give $\dfrac{x}{\sin B} = \dfrac{8}{\sin 110°}$

$\Rightarrow x = \dfrac{8 \sin 34°}{\sin 110°} = 4.8 \text{ cm}$

S9   Area $= \frac{1}{2} \times 7 \times 15 \times \sin 41° = 34.4 \text{ cm}^2$

S10   Use cosine rule to give $x = \sqrt{(11^2 + 7^2 - 2 \times 11 \times 7 \times \cos 130°)}$
$= \sqrt{(121 + 49 + 99)} = \sqrt{269}$
$x = 16.4 \text{ cm}$

(The most common mistake is to forget to square root, but if you are in the commendable habit of checking that your answers are sensible then you will spot that error.)

S11   The smallest angle is always opposite the smallest length and, similarly, the largest angle is opposite the largest length. Hence smallest angle is opposite the smallest side of 9, hence C. This is found by the cosine rule as:

$\cos C = \dfrac{a^2 + b^2 - c^2}{2ab} \Rightarrow \cos C = \dfrac{10^2 + 11^2 - 9^2}{2 \times 10 \times 11} = 0.6364$

$\Rightarrow C = 50.5°$

The largest angle is opposite 11, the largest side, hence B. This also is found by the cosine rule to give $B = 70.5°$.

▶ EXAMINATION QUESTIONS

▶ **Question 1**   Find the value of x such that $90 < x < 180$ and $\sin x° = 0.4567$.   (NEAB)

▶ **Question 2**   Figure 9.49 shows a metal plate with four quadrants of a circle cut away at the corners. Calculate:

'Always round off your answers to a suitable degree of accuracy. If in doubt, round off to one more significant figure than the numbers given in the problem'

(a)   the radius of the circle of which the quadrants are a part,
(b)   the total area cut away.

Fig. 9.49

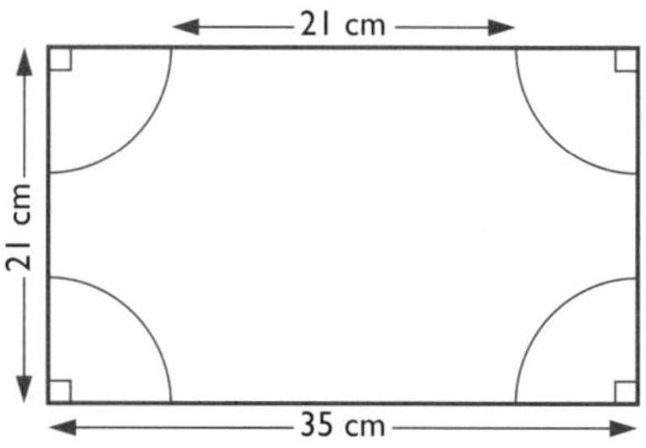

21 cm

21 cm

35 cm

(NICCEA)

▶ **Question 3**   Figure 9.50 shows that airport *A* is 400 km from airport *B* on a bearing of 120°. An aircraft leaves *A* at 21.55 hours to fly to *B*. Its speed over the ground is 320 km/h.

Fig. 9.50

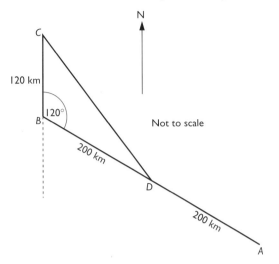

120 km

120°

Not to scale

200 km

200 km

(a) Calculate the time at which the aircraft is expected to arrive at *B*.
(b) When the aircraft is at *D*, halfway between *A* and *B*, it is diverted to airport *C* because of fog at airport *B*. Airport *C* is 120 km due north of *B*.
  (i) Calculate the distance from *D* to *C*.
  (ii) Calculate the bearing of *C* from *D*.
  (iii) The point on the aircraft's path nearest to *B* is X. Calculate the distance of X from *B*.   (MEG)

▶ **Question 4**   (In this question, give all distances to the nearest 0.01 km and all angles to the nearest one-tenth of a degree.)

Figure 9.51 represents three villages *A*, *B* and *C* on a hillside. *A*, *C* and *N* are the same height above sea level and *N* is vertically below *B*. Angle *CAB* is 90° and angle *BAN* is 2.5°. The villages are linked by three straight roads *AB*, *AC* and *CB*, where *AB* = 8 km and *AC* = 12 km.

Fig. 9.51

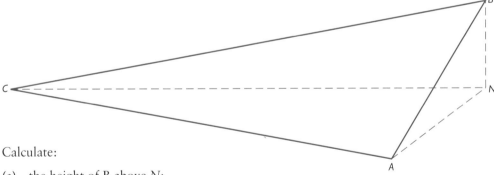

Calculate:

(a) the height of B above *N*;
(b) the horizontal distance *AN*;
(c) the horizontal distance *CN*;
(d) the angle of elevation *B* from *C*.   (London)

▶ **Question 5**   A field 100 metres square is divided into two trapeziums and a triangle, as shown in Fig. 9.52. *BD* is *x* metres long.

(a) What is the perpendicular distance from *B* to *AC* in terms of *x*?
(b) What is the area of triangle *ABC* in terms of *x*?
(c) What is the area of trapezium *CBDE* in terms of *x*?
(d) Each of the three parts of the field has the same area. What is the length of *BD*?

Fig. 9.52

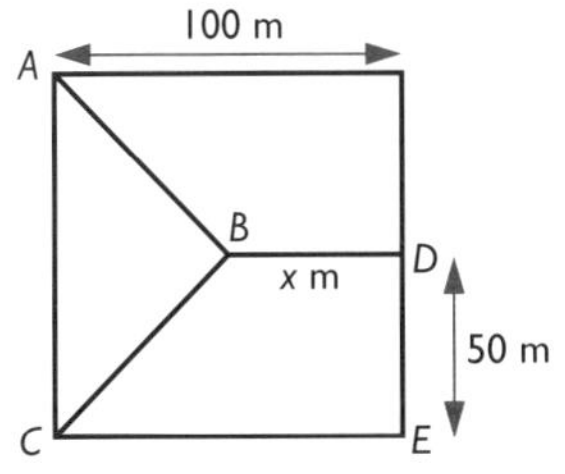

100 m

A

B

x m

D

50 m

C

E

(WJEC)

▶ **Question 6**

Fig. 9.53

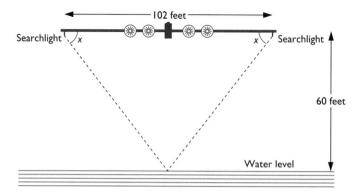

In 1943 the Royal Air Force had to fly an aeroplane at exactly 60 feet above the water level. To do this two searchlights were fitted, one at the end of each wing, so that they were 102 feet apart.

The rays shone down onto the water below. When the rays coincided on the surface of the water the pilot knew that he was flying at 60 feet above the water level.

Calculate the angle (marked x in Fig. 9.53) at which the searchlights had to be fitted to the aeroplane's wings.   (NEAB)

▶ **Question 7**   To estimate the volume of timber in the trunk of the conifer in Fig. 9.54, a pupil considered the trunk to be a cone and measured the circumference of the base to be 68 cm. To find the height she walked back 30 m from the base of the tree and took a sighting of the top of the tree. From her eye level (1.2 m above the ground) the angle of the elevation of the top of the tree was 26°.

Fig. 9.54

(a)   Calculate the height of the tree.
(b)   Calculate the volume of timber (in m³) in the trunk of the tree.   (NEAB)

▶ **Question 8**   A flat metal component is to be made in the shape shown in Fig. 9.55. The curves AB and DC are both arcs of circles with centre O. The radius of the arc AB is r, the radius of the arc DC is R. The angle $AOB = 60°$.

Fig. 9.55

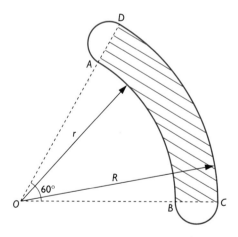

(a)   (i)   Write down a formula for the area of sector ODC in terms of R.
       (ii) Show that the area of the shaded region $ABCD$ is $\frac{1}{6}\pi(R^2 - r^2)$.

The unshaded ends of the shape are both semi-circles.

(b)   (i)   Write down the length of the diameter BC in terms of R and r.
       (ii) Find the total area of the two semi-circles in terms of R and r.
(c)   Find the area, in mm², to the nearest mm², of metal sheet required to make the component when $OD = 39$ mm and $OA = 27$ mm.   (London)

▶ **Question 9**   The box for a chocolate mint is a square-based pyramid with its point vertically above the middle of the base, as in Fig. 9.56. The sides of the base of the box are 6 cm long and the box is 6 cm tall.

Fig. 9.56

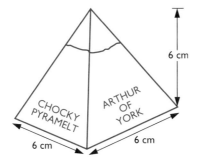

(a)   (i)   Calculate the diagonal distance across the base.
     (ii) Calculate the length of a sloping edge.
(b)   Sketch a net for the box, indicating the lengths of the sides.   (WJEC)

▶ **Question 10**   Figure 9.57 shows a shallow glass dish of uniform cross-section. The dimensions of the cross-section *ABCD* are as shown in the diagram.

Fig. 9.57

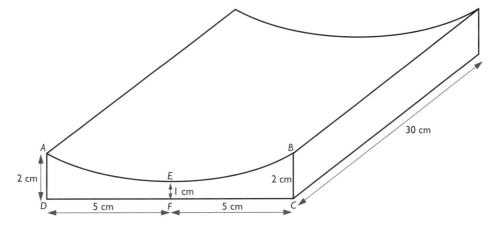

(a)   The curve *AEB* is the arc of a circle. Find the radius of the circle.
(b)   Given that the length of the dish is 30 cm and that the mass of 1 cm³ of glass is 2.45 g, find the mass of the dish.   (WJEC)

▶ **Question 11**   A hillside slopes up at a steady 10° to the horizontal, as shown in Fig. 9.58.

Fig. 9.58

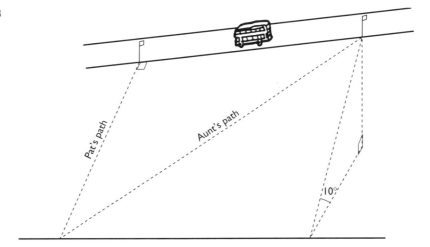

A horizontal road runs along the ridge at the top of the hill. Pat and her aunt want to walk up the hill to catch a bus which runs along the road. Pat takes the path which goes straight up the hill and meets the road at right angles; but her aunt prefers a gentler path which climbs at only 5° to the horizontal. Pat's path is 100 metres long. Calculate:

(a)   the height of the hill;
(b)   the length of her aunt's path;
(c)   the angle between their paths;
(d)   how far apart they are when they reach the road.   (OCSEB)

▶ **Question 12**   (a)   Figure 9.59(a) shows a circle touching the sides of a square and a square drawn inside the circle with its vertices touching the circle at the midpoints of the sides of the outside square. Given that the radius of the circle is 1 cm, find the perimeters of the two squares.

Fig. 9.59

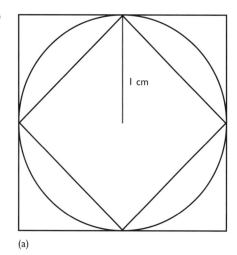

(a)

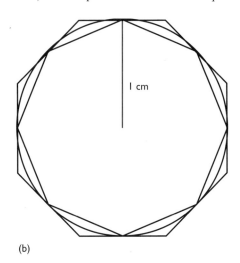

(b)

(b)   (i)   Figure 9.59(b) is like Fig. 9.59(a), but regular octagons are drawn instead of squares. Find the perimeter of the two octagons.
(ii)   What can you deduce from your results about the numerical value of π? (WJEC)

▶ **Question 13**   (a)   In Fig. 9.60, AB is an arc of a circle, whose centre is at O. The radius is r, and the angle AOB is $x°$. Show that the length of the arc AB is given by the formula:

$$\text{arc length} = \frac{\pi}{180}\,xr$$

Fig. 9.60

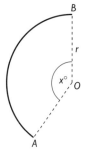

Fig. 9.61

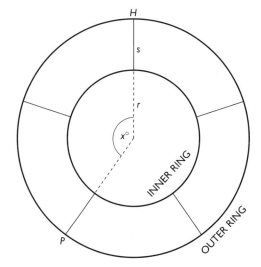

(b)   A housing estate has two circular roads with the same centre (the inner ring and the outer ring), with several radial roads joining them, as shown in Fig. 9.61. The inner ring has radius r metres, and the radial roads have length s metres, so that the outer

ring has radius ($r + s$) metres. My house H and the post office P are both on the outer ring, at the ends of radial roads. The angle between the radial roads leading to H and P is $x°$. Use the result in (a) to write down formulae for the distance from H to P:
  (i) if I go by the two radial roads and the inner ring;
  (ii) if I go by the outer ring.
(c) If $x = 120°$, which of the distances is greater? By how much? (The answer may involve r or s, or both.)
(d) Write down an equation if the two distances (i) and (ii) in (b) are equal. Solve it to find x to the nearest whole number of degrees. What is surprising about the answer?

(OCSEB)

▶ **Question 14**   Figure 9.62 shows a cone with circular base of radius 5 cm. The slant height of the cone is 20 cm. AB is a diameter of the base and V is the vertex of the cone. P is a point on VP such that $VP : PB = 1 : 3$. Find the shortest distance from A to P along the surface of the cone.

Fig. 9.62

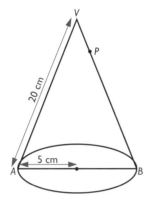

(WJEC)

▶ **EXAMINATION ANSWERS**

A1 $\sin^{-1} 0.4567 = 27.2°$, since $90 < x < 180$, then $x = 180 − 27.2 = 152.8°$.
(If you check this answer by finding $\sin 152.8°$, you will not get exactly 0.4567 since it is a rounded off answer.)

A2   (a) Radius is $(35 − 21) \div 2 = 7$ cm.
(b) Total area is a complete circle of radius 7 cm, which is 153.9 cm².

A3   (a) Time = distance ÷ speed, hence the time of the journey is 400 km divided by 320 km/h to give 1.25 hours, that is 1 hour 15 minutes. So from 2 1.55, add on 1 hour 15 minutes to get to 2 3.10, which is ten past eleven.

Fig. 9.63

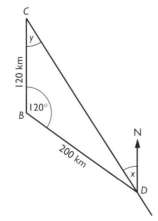

Fig. 9.64

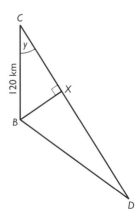

(b) (i) Since we have two sides and an included angle, we use the cosine rule to give

$$CD = \sqrt{(120^2 + 200^2 - 2 \times 120 \times 200 \times \cos 120)} = 280 \, \text{km}$$

(ii) Bearing $= 360° - x°$ (see Fig. 9.63).
$x° = y°$ (alternate angles), hence find y and use the sine rule:

$$\frac{\sin y}{200} = \frac{\sin 120°}{280} \quad \Rightarrow \quad \sin y = \frac{200 \sin 120°}{280}$$

$$\Rightarrow y = 38.2°$$

So the bearing of C from D is 322°.

(iii) The nearest distance will be the perpendicular from B to CD as shown in Fig. 9.64.

$$\text{Hence } \frac{BX}{120} = \sin 38.2°$$

$$BX = 120 \sin 38.2° = 74.2 \, \text{km}$$

A4 (a) $BN = 8 \sin 2.5° = 0.35 \, \text{km}$
(b) $AN = 8 \cos 2.5° = 7.99 \, \text{km}$
(c) By Pythagoras, $CN^2 = AC^2 + AN^2 = 12^2 + 7.99^2$,
hence $CN = 14.42 \, \text{km}$
(d) $\tan (BCN) = \dfrac{BN}{CN} = \dfrac{0.35}{14.42} = 0.0242$,

so the angle of elevation is 1.4°.

A5 (a) $100 - x$
(b) $\frac{1}{2} \times 100 \times (100 - x) = 50(100 - x) = 5\,000 - 50x$

(c) $\dfrac{50}{2}(x + 100) = 25x + 2\,500$

(d) If area of trapezium = area of triangle then:
$$25x + 2\,500 = 5\,000 - 50x$$
$$\Rightarrow 25x + 50x = 5\,000 - 2\,500$$
$$\Rightarrow 75x = 2\,500$$
$$x = \frac{2\,500}{75} = 33\tfrac{1}{3} \, \text{m}$$

A6 All that is needed is to consider one side of the diagram, a right-angled triangle and
$$\tan x = \frac{60}{51} \quad \longrightarrow \quad x = 49.6°.$$

A7 (a) You should have sketched a shape like that in Fig. 9.65. (You could perhaps make the horizontal distances more accurate by calculating the radius of the tree to be $68 \div 2\pi = 10.8 \, \text{cm} = 0.108 \, \text{m}$. Marks would not be lost whichever way you did it.)
Hence $x = 30 \tan 26 = 14.6 \, \text{m}$ (14.7 if the more accurate result were used) so height of tree $= 14.6 + 1.2 = 15.8 \, \text{m}$ (or 15.9 m).

Fig. 9.65

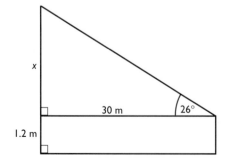

(b) Use the formula for the volume of a cone:

$$V = \tfrac{1}{3}\pi r^2 h = \tfrac{1}{3} \times \pi \times (0.108)^2 \times 15.8 = 0.193 \text{ m}^3 \text{ (or } 0.194 \text{ m}^3\text{)}$$

This is one of those GCSE questions that allows you to estimate in your own way, and hence gives you the choice of actual method and accuracy at the end. There is, of course, no single *correct* answer to this question, only acceptable ones.

A8 (a) (i) $\dfrac{60}{360} \times \pi \times R^2 = \dfrac{1}{6}\pi R^2 = $ area of sector ODC

(ii) Area of sector $OAB = \dfrac{1}{6}\pi r^2$

So, area of $ABCD = \dfrac{1}{6}\pi R^2 - \dfrac{1}{6}\pi r^2 = \dfrac{1}{6}\pi(R^2 - r^2)$.

(b) (i) $R - r$

(ii) $\pi\left(\dfrac{R-r}{2}\right)^2$ or $\dfrac{\pi}{4}(R-r)^2$

(c) Total area of the shape is given by $\dfrac{1}{6}\pi(R^2 - r^2) + \dfrac{\pi}{4}(R-r)^2$.

When $R = 39$ mm and $r = 27$ mm then total area is:

$$\dfrac{1}{6} \times \pi \times 792 + \dfrac{\pi}{4} \times 144 = 528 \text{ mm}^2$$

A9 (a) (i) Use Pythagoras' theorem to give diagonal $= \sqrt{(6^2 + 6^2)} = 8.5$ cm.
    (ii) Form a diagram as shown in Fig. 9.66, showing the right-angled triangle formed with the perpendicular from the vertex to the centre of the base and the sloping edge. Using Pythagoras again to give:

$$\text{slope} = \sqrt{(6^2 + 4.25^2)} \quad (4.25 \text{ being half of the diagonal})$$
$$= 7.3 \text{ cm}$$

Fig. 9.66

Fig. 9.67

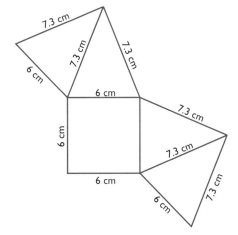

(b) A net is shown in Fig. 9.67, although this is not the only possible net for the pyramid.

A10 (a) (i) A diagram here (see Fig. 9.68) will help see us through the problem, where O is the centre of the circle having the arc *AEB*, angle *OEB* is found by tan $E = 5$.
      Hence $OEB = 78.7°$
      and $OBE = 78.7°$ (since *OEB* is isosceles).
      Hence $BOE = 180 - 2 \times 78.7 = 22.6°$.

So radius OB is found by $\dfrac{5}{r} = \sin 22.6$

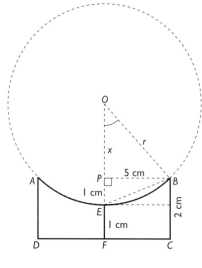

Fig. 9.68

$$\Rightarrow r = \frac{5}{\sin 22.6} = 13 \text{ cm}$$

(It is helpful, and most accurate, to keep the angles found as accurately as you can in your calculator, and only write down the rounded off value as we did here.)

(b) The area of the cross-section of the dish *EBCF* is made up of a rectangle 5 cm², plus a triangle 2.5 cm² and minus the segment *EB* of the circle.

Area of segment *EB* = Area of sector *OEB* − Area of triangle *OEB*

Area of sector $OEB = \frac{22.6}{360} \times \pi \times 13^2 = 33.36$

Area of triangle $OEB = \frac{1}{2} \times 13 \times 5 = 32.5$

Hence area of segment *EB* = 33.36 − 32.5 = 0.86 cm²
Hence area of cross-section *EFCB* = (5 + 2.5 − 0.86) cm² = 6.64 cm²
Hence area of cross-section *ADFCBE* = 2 × 6.64 = 13.28 cm²
Hence volume of dish = 13.28 × 30 = 398.4 cm³
Hence mass of dish = 398.4 × 2.45 g = 976 g

A11 Draw a diagram and fully label it as shown in Fig. 9.69 to help you see the triangles involved.

Fig. 9.69

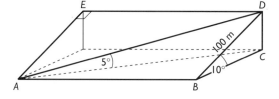

(a) Height *DC* given by *DC* = 100 sin 10° = 17.4 m

(b) Length *AD* given by $\frac{DC}{AD} = \sin 5°$

Hence $AD = \frac{DC}{\sin 5°} = \frac{17.4}{\sin 5°} = 199$ m

(c) Angle *EAD* found by $\cos A = \frac{AE}{AD} = \frac{100}{199} = 0.5019$

Hence angle = 60°

(d) Length *ED* given by *AD* sin *A* = 199 sin 60 = 172 m

A12 (a) Perimeter of large square = 4 × 2 cm = 8 cm. The length of the side of the smaller square is found by Pythagoras, see Fig. 9.70: if *x* is half the length, then $x^2 + x^2 = 1^2 \rightarrow 2x^2 = 1 \rightarrow x = \sqrt{0.5} = 0.71$ cm. (Keep the accurate value in the calculator.) So the perimeter of the small square = 4 × 2 × 0.71 = 5.66 cm.

Fig. 9.70

Fig. 9.71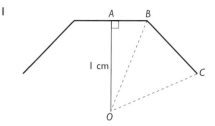

(b) (i) Large octagon:
A simple sketch of part of the octagon is drawn, where O is the centre of the circle (see Fig. 9.71).
Angle $BOC = 360 \div 8 = 45°$
Hence angle $AOB = 45 \div 2 = 22.5°$

Hence AB is found by $\dfrac{AB}{1} = \tan 22.5°$

So $AB = 0.4142$ and the total perimeter of the large octagon $= AB \times 2 \times 8$ $= 6.627$ cm.

Small octagon:
A similar sketch (see Fig. 9.72), but this time $OB = 1$ cm; angle AOB is still 22.5°. Hence $AB = 1 \times \sin 22.5° = 0.3827$.
Hence the total perimeter of the small octagon $= AB \times 2 \times 8 = 6.123$ cm.

Fig. 9.72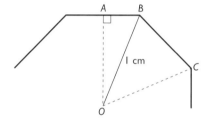

(ii) Since the value of the circumference of the circle lies between the perimeters of the octagons, then $6.123 <$ circumference < 6.627. The circumference of the circle is given by πD, so where $D = 2$ cm, circumference $= 2\pi$. So in this situation we have:

$$6.123 < 2\pi < 6.627$$
$$\rightarrow 3.062 < \pi < 3.314$$

A13 (a) The arc length AB is directly proportional to the angle x, hence arc length $= Kx$ (K being a constant.)
When $x = 360$, arc length $=$ circumference $= 2\pi r$, hence $2\pi r = K360$, i.e.:

$$\frac{2\pi r}{360} = K = \frac{\pi r}{180}$$

So arc length $= \dfrac{\pi r}{180} \times x = \dfrac{\pi}{180} xr$

(b) (i) $s + \dfrac{\pi}{180} xr + s = 2s + \dfrac{\pi}{180} xr$

(ii) $\dfrac{\pi}{180} x(r + s)$

(c) When $x = 120$ then: (i) $= 2s + \dfrac{\pi \times 120 \times r}{180} = 2s + \tfrac{2}{3} \pi r$

(ii) $= \tfrac{2}{3}\pi(r + s) = \tfrac{2}{3}\pi s + \tfrac{2}{3}\pi r$

Since $\frac{2\pi}{3} > 2$ then (ii) is the largest, and by $(\frac{2\pi}{3} - 2)s = 0.09s$

(d) The two distances are equal when $2s + \dfrac{\pi x r}{180} = \dfrac{\pi x r}{180} + \dfrac{\pi x s}{180} \quad \rightarrow \quad 2s = \dfrac{\pi x s}{180}$

$\Rightarrow 360s = \pi x s$
$\Rightarrow 360 = \pi x$
$\Rightarrow x = \dfrac{360}{\pi} = 115°$

What is surprising is that this answer is totally independent of the lengths of r and s.

A14 Sketch a net of the cone to give a sector as in Fig. 9.73, with the dotted line AP being the shortest distance.
We need to find angle AVP, call it x.
Arc distance AB is half the circumference of the base of the cone, i.e. $\pi \times 5 = 5\pi$.

Fig. 9.73

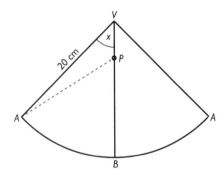

But from the circle with radius 20 cm,

$$\text{arc length } AB = \dfrac{x}{360} \times \pi \times 2 \times 20 = \dfrac{40\pi x}{360}$$

$$\text{hence } \dfrac{40\pi}{360}x = 5\pi \rightarrow x = \dfrac{5\pi \times 360}{40\pi} = 45$$

Since $VP : PB = 1 : 3$, then $VP = \frac{1}{4} \times 20 = 5$ cm
Hence we can use the cosine rule to give

$$AP = \sqrt{(20^2 + 5^2 - 20 \times 5 \times \cos 45°)} = \sqrt{354.3}$$
$$AP = 18.8 \text{ cm}$$

Grade checklist

For grade	You should be able to do the following:
B	Calculate areas and volumes.
	Use trigonometry in right-angled triangles.
	Use Pythagoras' theorem.
A	Calculate angles and distances in solids.
	Calculate arc lengths.
	Calculate sector areas.
	Calculate the surface area of cylinders.
	Calculate the volumes of cones and spheres.
	Find the sine, cosine or tangent of angles of any size.
	Sketch the graphs of trigonometrical functions.
A*	Understand the sine rule.
	Understand the cosine rule.

SUMMARY

▷ **Circumference of a circle** $= \pi D$ or $2 \times \pi \times r$

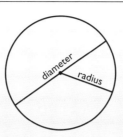

▷ **Area**   rectangle = length × breadth   triangle $= \frac{1}{2} \times$ base × height

parallelogram = base × height   circle $= \pi r^2$

trapezium $= \dfrac{h(a+b)}{2}$

▷ **Surface area of a sphere** $= 4\pi r^2$

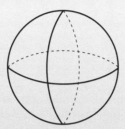

▷ **Volume**   cuboid = length × breadth × height   prism = end area × length

sphere $= \frac{4}{3}\pi r^2$ pyramid $= \frac{1}{3} \times$ base area × height

▷ **Sectors**   arc length $= \dfrac{\theta \times \pi D}{360}$ area $= \dfrac{\theta \times \pi r^2}{360}$

▷ **Pythagoras** $a^2 + b^2 = c^2$

▷ **Trigonometry**   sine $\theta = \dfrac{\text{opposite}}{\text{hypotenuse}}$ cosine $\theta = \dfrac{\text{adjacent}}{\text{hypotenuse}}$

tangent $\theta = \dfrac{\text{opposite}}{\text{adjacent}}$

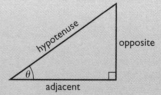

Sine rule: $\dfrac{a}{\text{sine } A} = \dfrac{b}{\text{sine } B} = \dfrac{c}{\text{sine } C}$

When you know two sides and the included angle, use the cosine rule as below to find the other side.

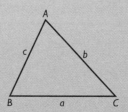

Cosine rule: $a^2 = b^2 + c^2 - 2bc \cos A$

When you know all three sides and you want to find an angle, use the cosine rule as below:

$\cos A = \dfrac{b^2 + c^2 - a^2}{2bc}$

Chapter

10

Transformation geometry

 GETTING STARTED

It will be assumed in this chapter that you are familiar with the ideas of reflection, rotation, enlargement and translation, as the emphasis at this level will be on more complex transformations as well as vector work. At Higher level, questions are often set on transformation geometry.

▶ **Useful definitions**

Co-linear	In the same straight line.
Enlargement	A change in size to a mathematically similar shape (could be smaller).
Invariant	Does not alter under a transformation.
Invariant line	The line of points that will not alter under transformation.
Invariant point	The point that will not alter under a transformation.
Reflection	A mirror image through a particular line.
Rotation	A turn around some particular point.
Shear	A 'pushing' over of a shape; involves a scale factor and an invariant line.
Stretch	A 'pull' on a shape; involves a scale factor and an invariant line.
Transformation	A change of position of a given shape.
Translation	A slide with no turning.
Vector	A movement of a specific magnitude and direction.

▶ **Topic chart** The following topic chart can be completed for each of the topics in 'Transformation geometry'. Tick the appropriate box when you have first studied that topic. You can also keep a record of when you have revised that topic for the first and second time, etc.

London	MEG	NEAB	NICCEA	SEG	WJEC	IGCSE	TOPIC	STUDY	REVISION I	REVISION 2
✓	✓	✓	✓	✓	✓	✓	Vectors			
✓	✓	✓	✓	✓	✓	✓	Some transformations			
✓	✓	✓	✓	✓	✓	✓	Inverse transformations			

 WHAT YOU NEED TO KNOW

▶ **Vectors** *What is a vector?*

A *vector* has magnitude (size) and direction, and can be represented by a straight line. Some examples of vectors are:

velocity	e.g. 16 kph	due west
acceleration	e.g. 10 km/s^2	due north west
displacement	e.g. 8 km	due south

Each of these could be represented by a suitable straight line drawn on a grid.

The mathematics of all these types of vector is the same, but it is easiest to study the type of vector involving displacement, hence that is why most of our vector work is based on displacement.

Representation of a vector

If we use a grid then the line representing a vector can be described by using the *displacements* parallel to the *x* and *y* axes.

Fig. 10.1
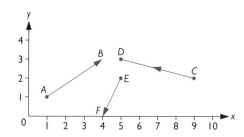

'In a printed book the bold **a** would be used – you will write <u>a</u> underlined'

The vector can be named in three different ways:

▶ by using the end letters, e.g. $\overrightarrow{AB}$, $\overrightarrow{CD}$, $\overrightarrow{EF}$
▶ by giving it a letter printed bold or underlined, e.g. **a** or <u>a</u>, **c** or <u>c</u>, **f** or <u>f</u>
▶ by using the horizontal and vertical displacement written as a column vector.

e.g. $\begin{pmatrix} 3 \\ 2 \end{pmatrix}$, $\begin{pmatrix} -4 \\ 1 \end{pmatrix}$, $\begin{pmatrix} -1 \\ -2 \end{pmatrix}$.

Notes 1. When using the column form for a vector:
   • the *top number* is the displacement parallel to the *x*-axis
   $\begin{pmatrix} +\text{ve when displacing from left to right} \\ -\text{ve when displacing from right to left} \end{pmatrix}$
   • the *bottom number* is the displacement parallel to the *y*-axis
   $\begin{pmatrix} +\text{ve when moving up} \\ -\text{ve when moving down} \end{pmatrix}$

2. Each vector must use an arrowhead to show its direction.

Equal and parallel vectors

Fig. 10.2
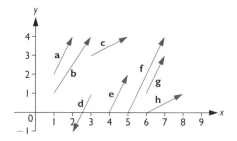

From Fig. 10.2:

$\mathbf{a} = \begin{pmatrix} 1 \\ 2 \end{pmatrix}$ and $\mathbf{e} = \begin{pmatrix} 1 \\ 2 \end{pmatrix}$ so we can say that $\mathbf{a} = \mathbf{e}$.

▶ The lines representing **a** and **e** are parallel and equal in length.

▶ $\mathbf{f} = \begin{pmatrix} 2 \\ 4 \end{pmatrix}$ and $\mathbf{g} = \begin{pmatrix} 1 \\ 2 \end{pmatrix}$ so $\mathbf{f} = 2\mathbf{g}$.

▶ The lines representing **f** and **g** are of different lengths but are parallel to each other.

▶ $\mathbf{a} = \begin{pmatrix} 1 \\ 2 \end{pmatrix}$ and $\mathbf{d} = \begin{pmatrix} -1 \\ -2 \end{pmatrix}$ so $\mathbf{a} = -\mathbf{d}$.

i.e. **a** and **d** are parallel and the same size, but they are in opposite directions.

▶ $\mathbf{a} = \begin{pmatrix} 1 \\ 2 \end{pmatrix}$ and $\mathbf{c} = \begin{pmatrix} 2 \\ 1 \end{pmatrix}$.

'Two important points'

Although **a** and **c** are the same length, they are not parallel and so $\mathbf{a} \neq \mathbf{c}$.

▶ Parallel vectors are multiples of each other.
▶ Equal vectors are parallel and of the same size (order).

Exercise 1

Fig. 10.3

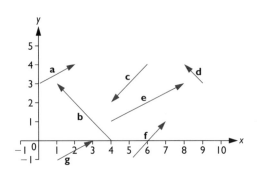

(a)   Write down each vector in Fig. 10.3 in the form $\begin{pmatrix} x \\ y \end{pmatrix}$.

(b)   Find the relationships between as many pairs of vectors as possible, giving them in the form $\mathbf{p} = K\mathbf{q}$.

Magnitude of a vector

The *magnitude* of a vector that is represented by a line is the length of that line.

For example, where $\mathbf{a} = \begin{pmatrix} 5 \\ 3 \end{pmatrix}$ then the magnitude of the vector, written as $|\mathbf{a}|$ will be found by Pythagoras (see Fig. 10.4):

$$|\mathbf{a}| = \sqrt{(5^2 + 3^2)}$$
$$= \sqrt{(25 + 9)} = \sqrt{34}$$
$$|\mathbf{a}| = 5.83 \text{ (3 s.f.)}$$

Fig. 10.4

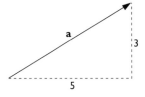

Exercise 2

(a) $\overrightarrow{AB} = \begin{pmatrix} 5 \\ -1 \end{pmatrix}$, calculate $|\overrightarrow{AB}|$.

(b)   A shape is translated with the vector $\begin{pmatrix} -4 \\ 3 \end{pmatrix}$. How far has it actually moved?

Addition of vectors

Did you know that aeroplanes often don't fly in the direction they are pointing? Or have you noticed that if you try to swim or row across a river, you do not always go in the direction in which you are pointing?

This is because forces are acting together and this gives a *resultant* force acting in a completely different direction and of a different magnitude.

We can see examples of this if we look at column vectors and their displacement.

For example, when $\mathbf{a} = \begin{pmatrix} 3 \\ 2 \end{pmatrix}$ and $\mathbf{b} = \begin{pmatrix} 2 \\ -1 \end{pmatrix}$ then $\mathbf{a} + \mathbf{b}$ can be defined as a move, first with $\mathbf{a}$ then with $\mathbf{b}$. What single vector would have the same effect?

Let's draw a diagram (Fig. 10.5).

Fig. 10.5

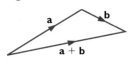

$$\mathbf{a} + \mathbf{b} = \begin{pmatrix} 5 \\ 1 \end{pmatrix}, \text{ notice } \begin{pmatrix} 3 \\ 2 \end{pmatrix} + \begin{pmatrix} 2 \\ -1 \end{pmatrix} = \begin{pmatrix} 5 \\ 1 \end{pmatrix}.$$

Subtraction of vectors

Remember that if $\vec{AB} = \mathbf{a}$ then $\vec{BA} = -\mathbf{a}$. So we see that $-\mathbf{a}$ is the vector $\mathbf{a}$ in the opposite direction.

So if $\mathbf{a} = \begin{pmatrix} 4 \\ 2 \end{pmatrix}$ then $-\mathbf{a} = -\begin{pmatrix} 4 \\ 2 \end{pmatrix} = \begin{pmatrix} -4 \\ -2 \end{pmatrix}$

and if $\mathbf{b} = \begin{pmatrix} 3 \\ -2 \end{pmatrix}$ then $-\mathbf{b} = \begin{pmatrix} -3 \\ 2 \end{pmatrix}$.

It will help us to see $\mathbf{x} - \mathbf{y}$ as $\mathbf{x} + (-\mathbf{y})$.

For example, when $\mathbf{a} = \begin{pmatrix} 4 \\ 2 \end{pmatrix}$ and $\mathbf{b} = \begin{pmatrix} 3 \\ -1 \end{pmatrix}$

then $\mathbf{a} - \mathbf{b} = \begin{pmatrix} 4 \\ 2 \end{pmatrix} + -\begin{pmatrix} 3 \\ -1 \end{pmatrix} = \begin{pmatrix} 4 \\ 2 \end{pmatrix} + \begin{pmatrix} -3 \\ 1 \end{pmatrix}$

$= \begin{pmatrix} 4 \\ 2 \end{pmatrix} - \begin{pmatrix} 3 \\ -1 \end{pmatrix} = \begin{pmatrix} 1 \\ 3 \end{pmatrix}$

Exercise 3

Let $\mathbf{a} = \begin{pmatrix} 4 \\ 3 \end{pmatrix}$, $\mathbf{b} = \begin{pmatrix} -2 \\ 4 \end{pmatrix}$, $\mathbf{c} = \begin{pmatrix} -1 \\ -2 \end{pmatrix}$

Draw diagrams to represent the following vectors and check that the calculated values agree with the diagram:

(a) $\mathbf{a} + \mathbf{b}$;   (b) $\mathbf{a} - \mathbf{c}$;   (c) $\mathbf{c} + \mathbf{b}$;   (d) $(\mathbf{a} + \mathbf{b}) - \mathbf{c}$

Vectors and geometry

As you have seen already in this chapter, every vector can be represented by a straight line of some length and direction. We can put them together to form triangles and other plane figures. For example, in Fig. 10.6 we have $\vec{AB} + \vec{BC} = \vec{AC}$.

Fig. 10.6

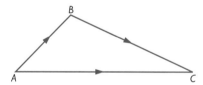

Many vector problems come in the form of plane diagrams as you will see as you work through the following worked examples.

WORKED EXAMPLE 1   In Fig. 10.7, $\vec{PQ} = \mathbf{p}$, $\vec{PR} = \mathbf{r}$. M and N are the midpoints of PQ and PR respectively.

Fig. 10.7

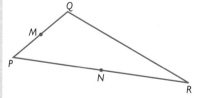

(a)   Write in terms of $\mathbf{p}$ and $\mathbf{r}$: (i) $\vec{QR}$;   (ii) $\vec{PM}$;   (iii) $\vec{PN}$;   (iv) $\vec{MN}$
(b)   Show that MN is parallel to QR.
(c)   What can be said about the lengths of MN and QR?

(a)   (i) $\vec{QR} = \vec{QP} + \vec{PR} = -\mathbf{p} + \mathbf{r} = \mathbf{r} - \mathbf{p}$

   (ii) $\vec{PM} = \frac{1}{2}\vec{PQ} = \frac{1}{2}\mathbf{p}$

   (iii) $\vec{PN} = \frac{1}{2}\vec{PR} = \frac{1}{2}\mathbf{r}$

   (iv) $\vec{MN} = \vec{MP} + \vec{PN} = -\frac{1}{2}\mathbf{p} + \frac{1}{2}\mathbf{r} = \frac{1}{2}\mathbf{r} - \frac{1}{2}\mathbf{p} = \frac{1}{2}(\mathbf{r} - \mathbf{p})$

(b) $\overrightarrow{MN} = \frac{1}{2}(\mathbf{r} - \mathbf{p})$, $\overrightarrow{QR} = \mathbf{r} - \mathbf{p}$

Hence $\overrightarrow{MN} = \frac{1}{2}\overrightarrow{QR}$

Hence MN and QR are parallel.

(c) Since $\overrightarrow{MN} = \frac{1}{2}\overrightarrow{QR}$, the length of QR is twice that of MN.

WORKED EXAMPLE 2   In Fig. 10.8, $\overrightarrow{AB} = \mathbf{b}$; $\overrightarrow{AE} = \overrightarrow{BC} = \mathbf{a}$; $\overrightarrow{CD} = \mathbf{a} - \mathbf{b}$.

Fig. 10.8

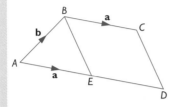

(a) Find $\overrightarrow{BE}$ and $\overrightarrow{AD}$ in terms of $\mathbf{a}$ and $\mathbf{b}$.

(b) What type of quadrilateral is $BCDE$?

(c) What can be said about points A, E and D?

(a) $\overrightarrow{BE} = \overrightarrow{BA} + \overrightarrow{AE} = -\mathbf{b} + \mathbf{a} = \mathbf{a} - \mathbf{b}$.

$\overrightarrow{AD} = \overrightarrow{AB} + \overrightarrow{BC} + \overrightarrow{CD} = \mathbf{b} + \mathbf{a} + (\mathbf{a} - \mathbf{b}) = \mathbf{b} + \mathbf{a} + \mathbf{a} - \mathbf{b} = 2\mathbf{a}$.

(b) Since $\overrightarrow{AD} = 2\mathbf{a}$, then $\overrightarrow{ED} = \mathbf{a} = \overrightarrow{BC}$, and $\overrightarrow{BE} = \overrightarrow{CD}$

Hence BC is parallel to ED, and BE is parallel to CD

Hence $BCDE$ is a parallelogram.

(c) Since $\overrightarrow{AD} = 2\mathbf{a}$, then AD is parallel to AE and $AE = ED$, hence A, E and D are co-linear (on the same straight line) and E is the midpoint of AD.

Exercise 4

In Fig. 10.9, P, Q, R and S are the midpoints of OA, AB, BC and OC respectively.

$\overrightarrow{OA} = \mathbf{a}$, $\overrightarrow{OB} = \mathbf{b}$, and $\overrightarrow{OC} = \mathbf{c}$.

Fig. 10.9

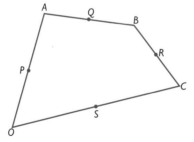

State in terms of $\mathbf{a}$, $\mathbf{b}$ and $\mathbf{c}$:

(a) $\overrightarrow{OP}$ (b) $\overrightarrow{AB}$ (c) $\overrightarrow{AQ}$ (d) $\overrightarrow{PQ}$ (e) $\overrightarrow{SR}$

(f) Show that PQ is parallel to SR

(g) Show that PS is parallel to QR

(h) What type of quadrilateral is $PQRS$?

Harder vector problems as applied to geometry

WORKED EXAMPLE 3 $OACB$ is a parallelogram (Fig. 10.10).

Fig. 10.10

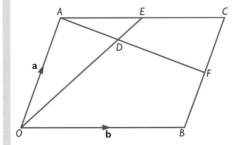

E and F are midpoints of the sides AC and CB respectively.

Find the ratios $\dfrac{AD}{DF}$ and $\dfrac{OD}{DE}$.

We have given our diagram (Fig. 10.10) the two basic vectors $\mathbf{a}$ and $\mathbf{b}$, which will define the parallelogram $OACB$.

We can now write the other lines on the diagram in terms of **a** and **b**, i.e. $\overrightarrow{AC} = \mathbf{b}$, and $\overrightarrow{AE} = \frac{1}{2}\mathbf{b}$.

Hence $\overrightarrow{OE} = \overrightarrow{OA} + \overrightarrow{AE} = \mathbf{a} + \frac{1}{2}\mathbf{b}$

and as $\overrightarrow{BC} = \mathbf{a}$, $\overrightarrow{CB} = -\mathbf{a}$, $\overrightarrow{CF} = -\frac{1}{2}\mathbf{a}$

Then $\overrightarrow{AF} = \overrightarrow{AC} + \overrightarrow{CF} = \mathbf{b} + (-\frac{1}{2}\mathbf{a}) = \mathbf{b} - \frac{1}{2}\mathbf{a}$

So far, then,

$$\overrightarrow{OA} = \mathbf{a}, \quad \overrightarrow{BC} = \mathbf{a}, \quad \overrightarrow{OB} = \mathbf{b}, \quad \overrightarrow{AC} = \mathbf{b}, \quad \overrightarrow{OE} = \mathbf{a} + \frac{1}{2}\mathbf{b}, \quad \overrightarrow{AF} = \mathbf{b} - \frac{1}{2}\mathbf{a}$$

Now, $\overrightarrow{OD}$ is in the same direction as $\overrightarrow{OE}$, hence $\overrightarrow{OD} = h\overrightarrow{OE}$, and hence $\overrightarrow{OD} = h(\mathbf{a} + \frac{1}{2}\mathbf{b})$.

Similarly $\overrightarrow{AD} = k\overrightarrow{AF}$, that is $\overrightarrow{AD} = k(\mathbf{b} - \frac{1}{2}\mathbf{a})$

We need to link $\overrightarrow{OD}$ and $\overrightarrow{AD}$ in some way. Look at the diagram and we see

$$\overrightarrow{OD} = \overrightarrow{OA} + \overrightarrow{AD}$$
$$\overrightarrow{OD} = \mathbf{a} + k(\mathbf{b} - \frac{1}{2}\mathbf{a})$$

but $\overrightarrow{OD}$ also equals $h(\mathbf{a} + \frac{1}{2}\mathbf{b})$. Hence:

$$h(\mathbf{a} + \frac{1}{2}\mathbf{b}) = \mathbf{a} + k(\mathbf{b} - \frac{1}{2}\mathbf{a})$$

$$h\mathbf{a} + \frac{h}{2}\mathbf{b} = \mathbf{a} + k\mathbf{b} - \frac{k}{2}\mathbf{a}$$

$$h\mathbf{a} - \mathbf{a} + \frac{k}{2}\mathbf{a} = k\mathbf{b} - \frac{h}{2}\mathbf{b}$$

$$\left(h - 1 + \frac{k}{2}\right)\mathbf{a} = \left(k - \frac{h}{2}\right)\mathbf{b}$$

but since **a** and **b** are *not* parallel this can only happen when

$$h - 1 + \frac{k}{2} = k - \frac{h}{2} = 0$$

This gives us two simultaneous equations:

$$h - 1 + \frac{k}{2} = 0$$

$$k - \frac{1}{2}h = 0$$

The simultaneous equations are solved to give the solution $h = \frac{4}{5}$ and $k = \frac{2}{5}$. Hence $\overrightarrow{OD} = \frac{4}{5}\overrightarrow{OE}$ and $\overrightarrow{AD} = \frac{2}{5}\overrightarrow{AF}$.

Hence D divides OE in the ratio 4 : 1 $\dfrac{OD}{DE} = \dfrac{4}{1}$

and   D divides AF in the ratio 2 : 3 $\dfrac{AD}{DF} = \dfrac{2}{3}$

Exercise 5

OABC is a trapezium (Fig. 10.11)
where AB and OC are parallel
and $\overrightarrow{AB} = 2\overrightarrow{OC}$.
AC intersects with OB at D.

Find the ratios $\dfrac{OD}{DB}$ and $\dfrac{AD}{DC}$.

Fig. 10.11

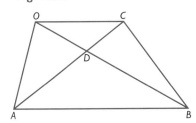

▶ **Some transformations**

'A stretch has a scale factor and an invariant line'

The stretch

A *stretch* is often called one-way stretch, as it is usually in one direction only (usually in the direction of one of the axes). A stretch is like a pull on a shape from one particular line, usually an axis.

A stretch has a *scale factor, n*, which will move every point on the shape a distance of *n* times its current distance from a given line. This line is called the *invariant* line, because points on it will not move.

Examples

Fig. 10.12

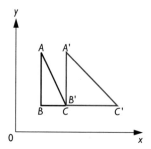

Triangle *ABC* (Fig. 10.12) has been stretched parallel to the *x*-axis with a scale factor 2, with the *y*-axis being the invariant line.

Fig. 10.13

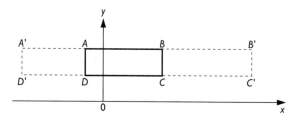

The rectangle *ABCD* (Fig. 10.13) has been stretched parallel to the *x*-axis with a scale factor 3, with the *y*-axis being the invariant line.

Fig. 10.14

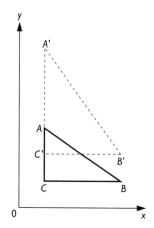

The triangle *ABC* (Fig. 10.14) has been stretched parallel to the *y*-axis with a scale factor of 2, with the *x*-axis being the invariant line.

Exercise 6

(a) Draw the triangle with vertices *A*(1, 1), *B*(3, 2), *C*(2, 2).
(b) Draw the image of *ABC* after a stretch parallel to the *x*-axis, scale factor 3, with the *y*-axis invariant.

The shear

'A shear has a scale factor and an invariant line'

A *shear* can be thought of as 'pushing a shape over' (see Fig. 10.15).

▶   A shear will have an *invariant line* where points do not move.
▶   A shear will have a *scale factor*, say *n*.

Fig. 10.15

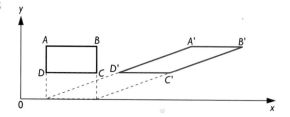

Each point on the shape will be moved parallel to the invariant line a distance equal to:
n × the distance from the invariant line.

The example in Fig. 10.15 is a shear, scale factor 3, with the *x*-axis invariant.

Examples

Fig. 10.16

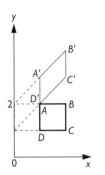

The square *ABCD* (Fig. 10.16) has been sheared with a scale factor of 1, and with the *y*-axis invariant.
Note: each point moves up a distance of (1 × its distance from the *y*-axis).

Fig. 10.17

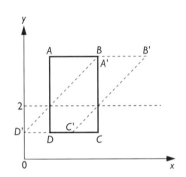

The rectangle *ABCD* (Fig. 10.17) has been sheared with a scale factor of 2 and with the line $y = 2$ invariant, to give the image *A′B′C′D′*.
Note: each point moves 'clockwise' a distance of (2 × its distance from the line $y = 2$).

Negative enlargement

'This is the most difficult one, and is often done badly. So go carefully'

You have seen how to transform a shape with a positive enlargement. However, you could be given a *negative* scale factor. In this case we draw the lines back through the centre of the enlargement and then enlarge as shown in Fig. 10.18 in an enlargement of the small triangle through * with an enlargement of −2. Notice how, with a negative scale factor, the enlarged shape has ended up *upside down* but still has a similar shape.

Fig. 10.18

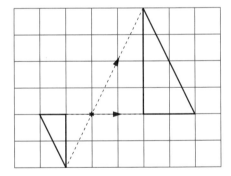

Exercise 7
(a)   Draw the triangle with the vertices *F*(1, 1), *G*(3, 1), *H*(1, 2).
(b)   Draw the image of *FGH* after a shear with scale factor 2, *y*-axis invariant.

▶ Inverse transformations

The *inverse* of a transformation is that transformation which moves a shape back to where it started.

For example: the inverse of rotation of 90° clockwise around the origin is a rotation of 90° *anticlockwise* around the origin. Or, the inverse of an enlargement of scale factor 3, centre of enlargement (0, 0), is an enlargement of scale factor $\frac{1}{3}$, centre of enlargement (0, 0).

Self-inverses are those that are the inverses of themselves; all reflections are self-inverses.

For example, the inverse of a reflection in the *x*-axis is a reflection in the *x*-axis.

Invariance

Most transformations have a point or a line of points that do not alter under the transformation. These are called *invariant points* or the *invariant line*. For example, in the transformation 'rotation of 90° clockwise about (0, 0)', the point (0, 0) is the invariant point (see Fig. 10.19).

Fig. 10.19

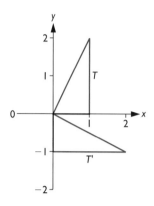

Note: the centre of rotation will always be the point of invariance of a rotation. As in any reflection, the line of reflection is the invariant line.

Most transformations have some invariant points, i.e. points that will not change under the transformation.

Reflections	have the mirror line as invariant
Rotations	have the centre of rotation as an invariant point
Enlargements	have the centre of enlargement as an invariant point
Stretches	have any given line as invariant
Shears	have any given line as invariant
Translations	have no invariant points

▶ SOLUTIONS TO EXERCISES

S1 (a) $\mathbf{a} = \begin{pmatrix} 2 \\ 1 \end{pmatrix}$; $\mathbf{b} = \begin{pmatrix} -3 \\ 3 \end{pmatrix}$; $\mathbf{c} = \begin{pmatrix} -2 \\ -2 \end{pmatrix}$; $\mathbf{d} = \begin{pmatrix} -1 \\ 1 \end{pmatrix}$; $\mathbf{e} = \begin{pmatrix} 4 \\ 2 \end{pmatrix}$; $\mathbf{f} = \begin{pmatrix} 2 \\ 2 \end{pmatrix}$; $\mathbf{g} = \begin{pmatrix} 2 \\ 1 \end{pmatrix}$

  (b) $\mathbf{e} = 2\mathbf{a}$; $\mathbf{a} = \mathbf{g}$; $\mathbf{b} = 3\mathbf{d}$; $\mathbf{c} = -\mathbf{f}$

S2 (a) $|\overrightarrow{AB}| = \sqrt{(5^2 + (-1)^2)} = \sqrt{(25 + 1)} = \sqrt{26} = 5.1$

  (b) It has moved the length of the vector $\begin{pmatrix} -4 \\ 3 \end{pmatrix}$

  $= \sqrt{(-4^2 + 3^2)} = \sqrt{(16 + 9)} = \sqrt{25} = 5$

S3 (a) $\mathbf{a} + \mathbf{b} = \begin{pmatrix} 2 \\ 7 \end{pmatrix}$; (b) $\mathbf{a} - \mathbf{c} = \begin{pmatrix} 5 \\ 5 \end{pmatrix}$; (c) $\mathbf{c} + \mathbf{b} = \begin{pmatrix} -3 \\ 2 \end{pmatrix}$; (d) $(\mathbf{a} + \mathbf{b}) - \mathbf{c} = \begin{pmatrix} 3 \\ 9 \end{pmatrix}$

S4 (a) $\overrightarrow{OP} = \tfrac{1}{2}\mathbf{a}$; (b) $\overrightarrow{AB} = \mathbf{b} - \mathbf{a}$; (c) $\overrightarrow{AQ} = \tfrac{1}{2}(\mathbf{b} - \mathbf{a})$
  (d) $\overrightarrow{PQ} = \overrightarrow{PA} + \overrightarrow{AQ} = \tfrac{1}{2}\mathbf{a} + \tfrac{1}{2}(\mathbf{b} - \mathbf{a}) = \tfrac{1}{2}\mathbf{b}$
  (e) $\overrightarrow{SR} = \overrightarrow{SC} + \overrightarrow{CR} = \tfrac{1}{2}\mathbf{c} + \tfrac{1}{2}(\mathbf{b} - \mathbf{c}) = \tfrac{1}{2}\mathbf{b}$
  (f) $\overrightarrow{PQ} = \tfrac{1}{2}\mathbf{b}$ and $\overrightarrow{SR} = \tfrac{1}{2}\mathbf{b}$ hence $\overrightarrow{PQ} = \overrightarrow{SR}$, parallel and equal
  (g) $\overrightarrow{PS} = \tfrac{1}{2}\mathbf{c} - \tfrac{1}{2}\mathbf{a} = \tfrac{1}{2}(\mathbf{c} - \mathbf{a})$
    $\overrightarrow{QR} = \overrightarrow{QB} + \overrightarrow{BR} = \tfrac{1}{2}(\mathbf{b} - \mathbf{a}) + \tfrac{1}{2}(\mathbf{c} - \mathbf{b}) = \tfrac{1}{2}\mathbf{b} - \tfrac{1}{2}\mathbf{a} + \tfrac{1}{2}\mathbf{c} - \tfrac{1}{2}\mathbf{b} = \tfrac{1}{2}(\mathbf{c} - \mathbf{a})$
    Hence $\overrightarrow{PS} = \overrightarrow{QR}$, parallel and equal

  (h) The quadrilateral *PQRS* is a parallelogram

S5   We need to define a minimum number of vectors.

Let $\vec{OC} = \mathbf{c}$, then $\vec{AB} = 2\mathbf{c}$ and $\vec{OA} = \mathbf{a}$

It follows that

$$\vec{OB} = \mathbf{a} + 2\mathbf{c}$$
$$\vec{AC} = -\mathbf{a} + \mathbf{c} = \mathbf{c} - \mathbf{a}$$

To define D

$$\vec{OD} = h\vec{OB} \qquad\qquad \vec{AD} = k\vec{AC}$$
$$= h(\mathbf{a} + 2\mathbf{c}) \qquad\qquad = k(\mathbf{c} - \mathbf{a})$$

Express $\vec{OD}$ in two different ways:

$$\vec{OD} = h(\mathbf{a} + 2\mathbf{c}) \quad \text{and} \quad \vec{OD} = \vec{OA} + \vec{AD}$$
$$= \mathbf{a} + k(\mathbf{c} - \mathbf{a})$$

Hence $h(\mathbf{a} + 2\mathbf{c}) = \mathbf{a} + k(\mathbf{c} - \mathbf{a})$
$$h\mathbf{a} + 2h\mathbf{c} = \mathbf{a} + k\mathbf{c} - k\mathbf{a}$$
$$h\mathbf{a} - \mathbf{a} + k\mathbf{a} = k\mathbf{c} - 2h\mathbf{c}$$
$$(h - 1 + k)\mathbf{a} = (k - 2h)\mathbf{c}$$

Since $\mathbf{a}$ and $\mathbf{c}$ are *not* parallel then $(h - 1 + k) = (k - 2h) = 0$. This forms two simultaneous equations which solve to give:

$$h = \tfrac{1}{3} \text{ and } k = \tfrac{2}{3}$$

Hence $\vec{OD} = \tfrac{1}{3}\vec{OB}$ and $\vec{AD} = \tfrac{2}{3}\vec{AC}$

Hence D divides OB in the ratio $1:2$ $\quad \dfrac{OD}{DB} = \dfrac{1}{2}$

D divides AC in the ratio $2:1$ $\quad \dfrac{AD}{DC} = \dfrac{2}{1}$

S6   See Fig. 10.20.

Fig. 10.20

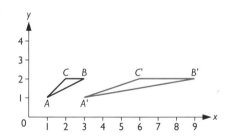

S7   See Fig. 10.21.

Fig. 10.21

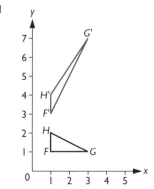

EXAMINATION QUESTIONS

▶ **Question 1**

In the video game in Fig. 10.22, the screen is 100 units by 100 units. The player has to enter a vector to give the direction the ball will travel. The ball starts at $O(0, 0)$.

Fig. 10.22

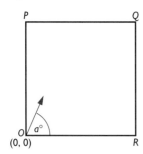

John enters the vector $\begin{pmatrix} 1 \\ 2 \end{pmatrix}$ and the ball moves, making an angle a° with OR.

(a) What is the value of a?
(b) The position of the ball as it moves to the top of the screen, PQ, can be written as $K\begin{pmatrix} 1 \\ 2 \end{pmatrix}$. What is the value of K when the ball reaches PQ?
(c) What are the coordinates of the point where the ball hits PQ?
(d) When the ball hits PQ it rebounds so that the 'new' path is 90° to the 'old' path. Which vector describes the ball's direction after it rebounds from PQ?
(e) What are the coordinates of the point where the ball hits QR?   (WJEC)

▶ **Question 2**

On the isometric grid in Fig. 10.23, $\overrightarrow{OA}$ and $\overrightarrow{OB}$ represent **a** and **b** respectively.

Fig. 10.23

'Remember, underlined letters (as in diagram) or bold letters indicate vectors'

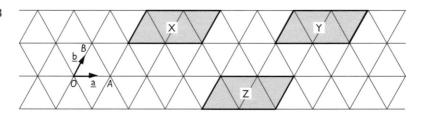

Express, in terms of a and b, the translation which maps:
(a) shape X onto shape Y.
(b) shape X onto shape Z.   (NEAB)

▶ **Question 3**

Transformation A is 'reflect in the line $y = x$', followed by the translation $\begin{pmatrix} -1 \\ 1 \end{pmatrix}$.
Transformation B is 'reflect in the line $x + y = 0$'.

(a) On graph paper, using a scale of 2 cm to 1 unit on each axis,
   (i) draw the triangle, T, with corners at (0, 0), (2, 0) and (2, 1),
   (ii) draw the image of T under A. Label it T'.
(b) Draw the image of T' under B. Label it T".
(c) T may be mapped directly onto T" by the transformation C:

   half-turn about point W, followed by a translation $\begin{pmatrix} p \\ q \end{pmatrix}$.

   Find the coordinates of W and the vector $\begin{pmatrix} p \\ q \end{pmatrix}$.   (London)

▶ **Question 4**

$OPQR$ is a parallelogram. The vectors **x** and **y** are such that

$$\overrightarrow{OP} = \mathbf{x} + \mathbf{y} \quad \text{and} \quad \overrightarrow{OR} = \mathbf{x} - \mathbf{y}.$$

(a) Express. as simply as possible, in terms of **x** and/or **y**: (i) $\overrightarrow{OQ}$; (ii) $\overrightarrow{RP}$
(b) What special type of parallelogram is $OPQR$,
   (i) when $|\mathbf{x} + \mathbf{y}| = |\mathbf{x} - \mathbf{y}|$?
   (ii) when $|\mathbf{x}| = |\mathbf{y}|$?   (MEG)

▶ **Question 5**

Fig. 10.24

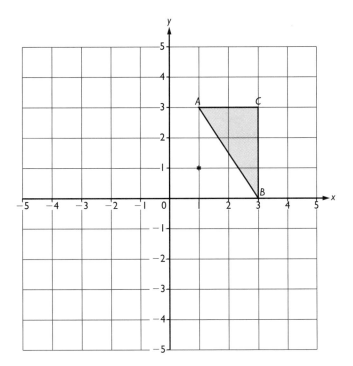

(a) Enlarge the shaded shape in Fig. 10.24 with a scale factor of 1.5 from centre of enlargement (1, 1), label this shape A.
(b) Enlarge the shaded shape with a scale factor of −2 from the centre of enlargement (1, 1), label this shape B.
(c) State fully the single transformation that will transform shape B to shape A.

▶ **Question 6**

Fig. 10.25

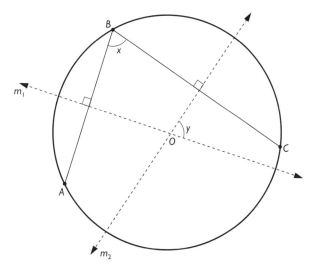

In Fig. 10.25, A, B and C are three points on the circumference of a circle with centre O. The diameters at right angles to AB and BC are m_1 and m_2 respectively. M_1 and M_2 are the transformations 'reflect in m_1' and 'reflect in m_2' respectively.
(a) Identify $M_1(A)$, the image of A under the transformation M_1.
(b) Identify: (i) $M_2(B)$; (ii) $M_2M_1(A)$.
(c) Explain why, in the figure, the angles marked x and y are equal.
(d) Describe fully the single transformation equivalent to M_2M_1 and hence express angle AOC in terms of y.
(e) Comment on the relationship between the angles AOC and ABC.   (MEG)

▶ **Question 7**   Look at Fig. 10.26.

Fig. 10.26

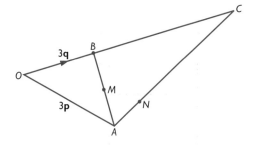

(a)   Express $\overrightarrow{AC}$ in terms of $\overrightarrow{AB}$ and $\overrightarrow{BC}$.

(b)   Given that $\overrightarrow{OA} = 3\mathbf{p}$, $\overrightarrow{OB} = 3\mathbf{q}$ and $\overrightarrow{OC} = 4\overrightarrow{OB}$, show that $\overrightarrow{AC} = 12\mathbf{q} - 3\mathbf{p}$.

(c)   Given that $\overrightarrow{AM} = \frac{2}{3}\overrightarrow{AB}$ and $\overrightarrow{AN} = \frac{1}{3}\overrightarrow{AC}$

   (i)   show that $\overrightarrow{OM} = \mathbf{p} + 2\mathbf{q}$;

   (ii)   express $\overrightarrow{ON}$ in terms of $\mathbf{p}$ and $\mathbf{q}$.

(d)   What can you say about the points O, M and N?   (NEAB)

▶ **Question 8**   Table 10.1 shows the values of y for $-3 \leqslant x \leqslant 4$ where $y = (x - 2)^2 + 4$.

Table 10.1

x	-3	-2	-1	0	1	2	3	4
y	29	20	13	8	5	4	5	8

(a)   Draw the graph of $y = (x - 2)^2 + 4$.

(b)   On the same axes draw the graph of $y = x^2$.

(c)   Describe how the graph of $y = (x - 2)^2 + 4$ can be obtained from the graph of $y = x^2$ by a transformation. State clearly what this transformation is.   (NEAB)

▶ **Question 9**   In Fig. 10.27, $OABC$ is a plane quadrilateral with $\overrightarrow{OA} = 4\mathbf{a}$, $\overrightarrow{OB} = 2\mathbf{a} + 2\mathbf{c}$, $\overrightarrow{OC} = 3\mathbf{c}$.

Fig. 10.27

'Again, remember you can underline a letter or (as in the diagram) show the letter as bold to indicate a vector'

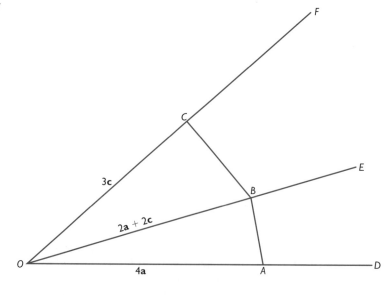

(a)   Express the vectors $\overrightarrow{CO}$, $\overrightarrow{CB}$ and $\overrightarrow{AB}$ in terms of $\mathbf{a}$ or $\mathbf{c}$ or $\mathbf{a}$ and $\mathbf{c}$.

(b)   The lines OA, OB and OC are produced to D, E and F respectively, where $OC = CF$ and $OB : BE = OA : AD = 2 : 1$. Find $\overrightarrow{FC}$, $\overrightarrow{FE}$ and $\overrightarrow{DE}$ in terms of $\mathbf{a}$ or $\mathbf{c}$ or $\mathbf{a}$ and $\mathbf{c}$.

(c)   Write down two geometrical facts about the points D, E and F.   (London)

▶ **Question 10**   In the triangle OAB shown in Fig. 10.28, T is the midpoint of AB, and M is the midpoint of AT.

Fig. 10.28

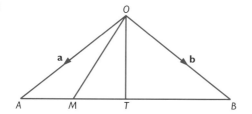

(a) Given that $\overrightarrow{OA} = \mathbf{a}$ and $\overrightarrow{OB} = \mathbf{b}$, express as simply as possible in terms of $\mathbf{a}$ and/or $\mathbf{b}$:
(i) $\overrightarrow{AM}$;   (ii) $\overrightarrow{OM}$.

(b) Given that $\mathbf{a} = \begin{pmatrix} 5 \\ 3 \end{pmatrix}$ and $\overrightarrow{AB} = \begin{pmatrix} -2 \\ 1 \end{pmatrix}$ find: (i) the coordinates of B; (ii) $|\overrightarrow{AB}|$;

(iii) the coordinates of a point R such that $\overrightarrow{OR} = \overrightarrow{BA}$.

(c) Given that $\mathbf{s} = \begin{pmatrix} 1 \\ 1 \end{pmatrix}$ and $\mathbf{u} = \begin{pmatrix} 8 \\ 2 \end{pmatrix}$ and that $k\mathbf{a} + l\mathbf{s} = \mathbf{u}$ then find the values of k and l.

▶ **Question 11**   Write down the inverse of:

(a) a translation of $\begin{pmatrix} 2 \\ -1 \end{pmatrix}$;

(b) a reflection in the line $y = x$.

▶ **Question 12**   (a) A translation, T, maps the point $(5, 7)$ to the point $(-2, 6)$.

Express this translation in the form $\begin{pmatrix} x' \\ y' \end{pmatrix} = \begin{pmatrix} x \\ y \end{pmatrix} + \begin{pmatrix} a \\ b \end{pmatrix}$, stating the values of a and b.

(b) State the inverse of the translation T.

(c) Give the coordinates of the point that would be translated to $(4, -1)$, under the translation T.

▶ **EXAMINATION ANSWERS**

Fig. 10.29

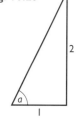

A1   (a) $a = \tan^{-1} \frac{2}{1}$, giving $a = 63.4°$. See Fig. 10.29.

(b) At the top of the screen, the y ordinate will be 100, hence K will be 50 as $2 \times 50 = 100$.

(c) $50 \begin{pmatrix} 1 \\ 2 \end{pmatrix} = \begin{pmatrix} 50 \\ 100 \end{pmatrix}$, hence coordinate is $(50, 100)$.

(d) As in Fig. 10.30, the vector perpendicular to $\begin{pmatrix} 1 \\ 2 \end{pmatrix}$ will be $\begin{pmatrix} 2 \\ -1 \end{pmatrix}$.

(e) The ball needs to go 50 units to the right, hence the ball will move $25 \begin{pmatrix} 2 \\ -1 \end{pmatrix} = \begin{pmatrix} 50 \\ -25 \end{pmatrix}$.

25 units down from the top is 75 on the y-axis, and QR is $x = 100$, so the coordinate where QR is hit is $(100, 75)$.

Fig. 10.30

A2   (a)   Count how many moves equivalent to **a** *each* point takes, and this is 4, hence the translation is given by **4a**.

(b) $3\mathbf{a} - 2\mathbf{b}$. Notice how in order to move down the grid you need to use $-\mathbf{b}$.

A3   (a), (b)   Your solution should be as in Fig. 10.31.

Fig. 10.31

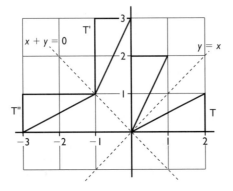

(c)   There are many different possible answers here, some of which are:

half turn about $(0, 0)$ followed by $\begin{pmatrix} -1 \\ 1 \end{pmatrix}$, or

half turn about $(2, 1)$ followed by $\begin{pmatrix} -5 \\ -1 \end{pmatrix}$, or

half turn about $(-\frac{1}{2}, \frac{1}{2})$ followed by $\begin{pmatrix} 0 \\ 0 \end{pmatrix}$.

A4   (a)   Find your parallelogram from the vectors **x** and **y**, as in Fig. 10.32:

Fig. 10.32

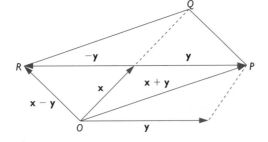

Then it can clearly be seen that:

(i) $\overrightarrow{OQ} = \mathbf{x} + \mathbf{y} + (\mathbf{x} - \mathbf{y}) = 2\mathbf{x}$

(ii) $\overrightarrow{RP} = (\mathbf{x} + \mathbf{y}) - (\mathbf{x} - \mathbf{y}) = 2\mathbf{y}$

(b)   (i)   When $|\mathbf{x} + \mathbf{y}| = |\mathbf{x} - \mathbf{y}|$ then the sides of the parallelogram $OPQR$ are equal, hence it is a rhombus.

(ii)   When $|\mathbf{x}| = |\mathbf{y}|$, then the diagonals RP and OQ, given by $2\mathbf{x}$ and $2\mathbf{y}$ respectively, will be the same length, hence it will be a rectangle.

A5   (a)   You will have drawn the shape with coordinates $A'(1, 4)$, $B'(4, 0)$ and $C'(4, 4)$.

(b)   You will have drawn the shape with coordinates $A''(1, -3)$, $B''(-3, 2)$, $C''(-3, -3)$.

(c)   An enlargement of scale factor $-\frac{3}{4}$ from centre of enlargement $(1, 1)$.

A6 (a) $M_1(A)$ will be point B.

(b) (i) $M_2(B)$ will be point C;   (ii) $M_2M_1(A)$ will be point C.

(c) Sketch the shape as in Fig. 10.33 and label the midpoints of AB and BC, P and Q respectively. Then since angles BPO and BQO are 90° each, $x + QOP = 180°$ and $y + QOP = 180°$. Hence $x = y$.

(d) The combination of two reflections always gives a rotation with centre of rotation the point of intersection of both lines of reflection, with the angle of rotation double the size of the angle both lines of reflection make.

Fig. 10.33

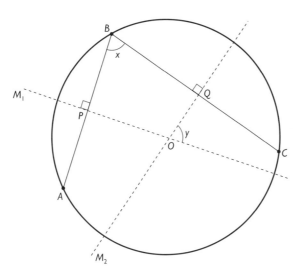

So here the transformation is a rotation, centre of rotation O, through an angle of $2y$. Hence $AOC = 2y$.

(e) AOC is double the size of ABC.

A7 (a) $\overrightarrow{AB} + \overrightarrow{BC}$

(b) $\overrightarrow{AC} = \overrightarrow{AO} + \overrightarrow{OC} = -3\mathbf{p} + 4 \times 3\mathbf{q} = -3\mathbf{p} + 12\mathbf{q}$

(c) (i) $\overrightarrow{OM} = \overrightarrow{OA} + \overrightarrow{AM} = 3\mathbf{p} + \frac{2}{3}\overrightarrow{AB} = 3\mathbf{p} + \frac{2}{3}(-3\mathbf{p} + 3\mathbf{q})$
$$= 3\mathbf{p} - 2\mathbf{p} + 2\mathbf{q} = \mathbf{p} + 2\mathbf{q}$$

(ii) $\overrightarrow{ON} = \overrightarrow{OA} + \overrightarrow{AN} = 3\mathbf{p} + \frac{1}{3}(12\mathbf{q} - 3\mathbf{p}) = 3\mathbf{p} + 4\mathbf{q} - \mathbf{p} = 2\mathbf{p} + 4\mathbf{q}$

(d) All points are co-linear, that is they all lie on the same straight line.

A8 (c) You should notice a translation of $\begin{pmatrix} 2 \\ 4 \end{pmatrix}$.

A9 (a) $\overrightarrow{CO} = -3\mathbf{c}$; $\overrightarrow{CB} = -3\mathbf{c} + (2\mathbf{a} + 2\mathbf{c}) = 2\mathbf{a} - \mathbf{c}$
$\overrightarrow{AB} = -4\mathbf{a} + 2\mathbf{a} + 2\mathbf{c} = 2\mathbf{c} - 2\mathbf{a}$

(b) $\overrightarrow{FC} = -3\mathbf{c}$; $\overrightarrow{BE} = \frac{1}{2}(2\mathbf{a} + 2\mathbf{c}) = \mathbf{a} + \mathbf{c}$
$\overrightarrow{FE} = -6\mathbf{c} + (3\mathbf{a} + 3\mathbf{c}) = 3\mathbf{a} - 3\mathbf{c}$; $\overrightarrow{DE} = -6\mathbf{a} + (3\mathbf{a} + 3\mathbf{c}) = 3\mathbf{c} - 3\mathbf{a}$

(c) $\overrightarrow{FE} = 3\mathbf{a} - 3\mathbf{c}$ and $\overrightarrow{DE} = -3\mathbf{a} + 3\mathbf{c} = -(3\mathbf{a} - 3\mathbf{c})$

Hence $\overrightarrow{FE} = -\overrightarrow{DE}$ or rather $\overrightarrow{FE} = \overrightarrow{ED}$. Hence we see that F, E and D are co-linear (all on the same straight line) and that E is exactly halfway between F and D.

A10 (a) (i) $\overrightarrow{AM} = \frac{1}{4}\overrightarrow{AB}$, and $\overrightarrow{AB} = \mathbf{b} - \mathbf{a}$, hence $\overrightarrow{AM} = \frac{1}{4}(\mathbf{b} - \mathbf{a})$.

(ii) $\overrightarrow{OM} = \mathbf{a} + \overrightarrow{AM} = \mathbf{a} + \frac{1}{4}(\mathbf{b} - \mathbf{a}) = \frac{3}{4}\mathbf{a} + \frac{1}{4}\mathbf{b} = \frac{1}{4}(3\mathbf{a} + \mathbf{b})$.

(b) (i) Position vector of B given by $\begin{pmatrix} 5 \\ 3 \end{pmatrix} + \begin{pmatrix} -2 \\ 1 \end{pmatrix} = \begin{pmatrix} 3 \\ 4 \end{pmatrix}$,

hence coordinate of B is (3, 4).

(ii) Modulus of $\overrightarrow{AB} = \sqrt{(2^2 + 1^2)} = \sqrt{5} = 2.24$

(iii) $\overrightarrow{AB} = \begin{pmatrix} -2 \\ 1 \end{pmatrix}$ then $\overrightarrow{BA} = \begin{pmatrix} 2 \\ -1 \end{pmatrix}$, hence $\overrightarrow{OR} = \begin{pmatrix} 2 \\ -1 \end{pmatrix}$, so coordinate of R will be (2, −1).

(c) $k\begin{pmatrix} 5 \\ 3 \end{pmatrix} + l\begin{pmatrix} 1 \\ 1 \end{pmatrix} = \begin{pmatrix} 8 \\ 2 \end{pmatrix} \rightarrow \begin{array}{l} 5k + l = 8 \\ 3k + l = 2 \end{array}$

Solve simultaneously to give $k = 3, l = -7$.

A11 (a) Translation of $\begin{pmatrix} -2 \\ 1 \end{pmatrix}$.

(b) A reflection in the line $y = x$.

A12 (a) $\begin{pmatrix} x' \\ y' \end{pmatrix} = \begin{pmatrix} x \\ y \end{pmatrix} + \begin{pmatrix} -7 \\ -1 \end{pmatrix}$

(b) $T^{-1} : \begin{pmatrix} x' \\ y' \end{pmatrix} = \begin{pmatrix} x \\ y \end{pmatrix} + \begin{pmatrix} 7 \\ 1 \end{pmatrix}$

(c) $\begin{pmatrix} 4 \\ -1 \end{pmatrix} + \begin{pmatrix} 7 \\ 1 \end{pmatrix} = \begin{pmatrix} 11 \\ 0 \end{pmatrix}$ answer (11, 0)

Grade checklist	
For grade	**You should be able to understand the following:**
B	Vector notation and its uses.
A	The laws of addition and subtraction of vectors.
A*	How transformations are related by combinations and inverses.

► **EXAMINATION QUESTION WITH STUDENT ANSWER**

Question

In the diagram, X is the midpoint of BC.

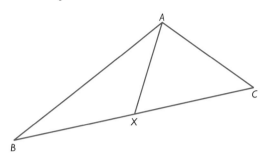

(a) Show that $\overrightarrow{AB} + \overrightarrow{AC} = 2\overrightarrow{AX}$

'A good answer, but should have used the → all through'

$\overrightarrow{AB} = \overrightarrow{AX} + \overrightarrow{XB}$

$\overrightarrow{AC} = \overrightarrow{AX} + \overrightarrow{XC}$

$AB + AC = AX + XB + AX + XC$

$\qquad = 2AX + XB + XC$

$but \quad XB = -XC, \text{ so } XB + XC = 0$

$so \quad AB + AC = 2AX$ (3)

(b)

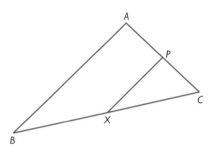

In the diagram, P is the midpoint of AC and X is the midpoint of BC.

(i) Show that $\overrightarrow{XP} = \frac{1}{2}\overrightarrow{BA}$.

$\overrightarrow{BA} = \overrightarrow{BC} + \overrightarrow{CA}$ $\qquad\qquad XP = \overrightarrow{XC} + \overrightarrow{CP} = \frac{1}{2}\overrightarrow{BC} + \frac{1}{2}\overrightarrow{CA}$

'Another good answer'

$\qquad\qquad\qquad\qquad\qquad\qquad = \frac{1}{2}(BC + CA) = \frac{1}{2}BA$

(2)

(ii) State one fact that this tells you about the lines BA and XP.

'Good, could also have said BA is double length PX'

Parallel

(1)

SUMMARY

▷ **Reflections**
The reflection of each point in a shape is exactly the same perpendicular distance from the mirror line as the original. The original shape and the reflection are both congruent.

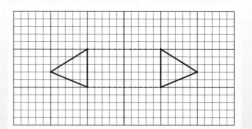

▷ **Rotations**
A shape will rotate about a centre of rotation, so that each point remains the same distance from the centre of rotation as the original. The original shape and the reflected shape are congruent.

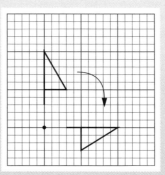

▷ **Enlargements**
After an enlargement each length has been enlarged by the same scale factor. The original and the enlarged shape are called 'similar shapes'. An enlargement can have a scale factor of less than 1, when it then becomes a reduction, and the scale factor can be negative, where the enlarged shape would be constructed backwards.

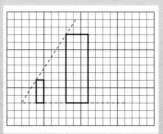

▷ **Translations**
A translation is a movement along the plane with no rotating, reflecting or enlarging. A translation is often described with a column vector.

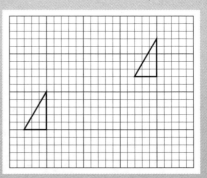

▷ **Vectors**
A vector is a given displacement or movement. Vectors can be added or subtracted.

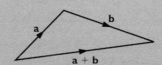
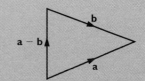

Chapter

11

Probability and statistics

GETTING STARTED

At the Higher level of GCSE mathematics, probability and statistics is an important topic area. You must be able to read and construct charts and graphs in order to find out information. You may well be asked to draw conclusions from the statistics that you are faced with.

▶ Useful definitions

Bar chart	A histogram with equal intervals, but may include a space between bars.
Continuous data	Data that can take on every possible value between two numbers and when measured is usually rounded off.
Cumulative	Increasing by successive additions.
Discrete data	Data that can be identified by a single number.
Frequency	The number of times some defined event occurs.
Histogram	A chart with rectangular bars whose area is proportional to the frequency. Often the width of the bars will be different.
Mean	The result of adding together n items of data, then dividing by n.
Median	The middle item of data once the data have been put into order.
Mode	The item of data which occurs most frequently.
Ogive	The line representing cumulative frequency on a graph.
Pictogram	A display of information using pictures to represent the frequency.
Pie chart	A circular picture divided in the ratio of the frequencies it is illustrating.

▶ Topic chart

The following topic chart can be completed for each of the topics in 'Probability and statistics'. Tick the appropriate box when you have first studied that topic. You can also keep a record of when you have revised that topic for the first and second time, etc.

London	MEG	NEAB	NICCEA	SEG	WJEC	IGCSE	TOPIC	STUDY	REVISION I	REVISION 2
✓	✓	✓	✓	✓	✓	✓	Averages			
✓	✓	✓	✓	✓	✓	✓	Illustrating data			
✓	✓	✓	✓	✓	✓	✓	Discrete or continuous data			
✓	✓	✓	✓	✓	✓	✓	Cumulative frequency			
✓	✓	✓	✓	✓	✓	✓	Dispersion: standard deviation			
✓	✓	✓	✓	✓	✓	✓	Probability and expectation			
✓	✓	✓	✓	✓	✓	✓	Surveys and sampling			

193

▶ **WHAT YOU NEED TO KNOW**

▶ **Averages** You need to know how to calculate the mode, median and mean from a *frequency distribution*. Now, from a given list of data this is usually no problem. It is when we have *grouped* frequency and need to estimate our averages that the fun begins!

Grouped frequency

Table 11.1

Score	Frequency
0–20	8
21–40	15
41–60	36
61–80	27
81–100	14

Suppose we are told the information in Table 11.1 about a maths exam, and the scores that the year 11 had obtained.

We can tell straight away that the *modal group* is 41–60. We have no way of estimating the modal individual score without drawing a bar chart.

Estimating the median

This can be done in a number of ways. One is by using a cumulative graph, and this will be fully explained in the later part of this chapter dealing with cumulative frequency. The other way is to do a *linear interpolation*, estimating where the median item of data is within its group. Here, we assume that items are spread evenly among any group (or class interval).

For the example given, the median item is the $(100 + 1)/2 = 50\frac{1}{2}$th item of data. We need to find a score corresponding to that item. Just evaluate the cumulative frequency here as 8, 23, 59, … until you get beyond the median ($50\frac{1}{2}$). Now we say that the median is:

$$\frac{50\frac{1}{2} - 23}{59 - 23} \times (60 - 41) + 41 = 55.51 \text{ or } 56$$

What we have done is to work out what *fraction of the way along the group* (41–60) the median is. Hence:

$$\frac{50\frac{1}{2} - 23}{59 - 23}$$

works out this fraction of (60 − 41), which is then added onto the *lowest value* of that group.

Note: be careful with *continuous data*, since the lowest value of the group is often found *halfway between* the bottom value of that group and the top of the previous group.

Estimating the mean

This can be done by assuming that each person scored the middle mark of the group that they are in, then calculating the total estimated scores and hence the mean. The table of values to do this will be as in Table 11.2.

Table 11.2

'Notice how the midway is found by adding each 'end score' and dividing by 2. Check it'

Score	Midway (m)	Frequency (f)	m × f
0–20	10	8	80
21–40	30.5	15	457.5
41–60	50.5	36	1 818
61–80	70.5	27	1 903.5
81–100	90.5	14	1 267
	Total	100	5526

So the estimated mean is $5\,526 \div 100$, which is 55.26 or 55.

▶ **Illustrating data** You need to be familiar with bar charts and pictograms, but it is unlikely that you will have questions involving these at this high level of GCSE mathematics.

Pie charts

You could well be asked to interpret information from, or construct, a *pie chart*. You should be familiar with this, but do follow through the two worked examples.

WORKED EXAMPLE 1

The 'average family' split their net income in the way indicated in the pie chart in Fig. 11.1. Malcolm had an average family who one month spent £56 on clothes. Calculate: (i) how much they spent on leisure that month; (ii) how much their net income was that month.

(i) $£\dfrac{56}{24} \times 136 = £317.33$

  (Notice we do it by simple proportions.)

(ii) $£\dfrac{56}{24} \times 360 = £840$

Fig. 11.1

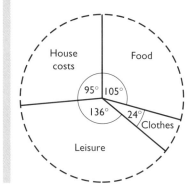

WORKED EXAMPLE 2

A simple survey was done of the supporters of Sheffield Wednesday FC and it was found to show the following age distribution of people present at one particular match:

Under 16   5 770
Over 60   9 800
The rest   16 450

Present this information on a pie chart. Build up a table to evaluate the angles of the chart, as in Table 11.3.

Table 11.3

Age	Frequency	Angle
Under 16	5 770	$\dfrac{5\,770}{32\,020} \times 360 = 65°$
Over 60	9 800	$\dfrac{9\,800}{32\,020} \times 360 = 110°$
The rest	16 450	$\dfrac{16\,450}{32\,020} \times 360 = 185°$
Total	32 020	360°

This now needs drawing, starting with the smallest angle first, as in Fig. 11.2.

Fig. 11.2

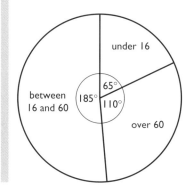

▶ **Discrete or continuous data**

Data are either *discrete* or *continuous*, they cannot be both.

Discrete data are data that can take on only a limited number of different values. For example: the number of children in a family; the number of cars in a car park; the price of sweets.

All these examples can only take on a limited number of values, and these are usually integers (whole numbers).

Continuous data are data that can take on an infinite number of different values. For example: your height; your age; the weight of a banana; the amount of petrol in a tank.

All these examples can take on any value and need not be integers. For example height could be 75 cm or 75.1 cm or 75.11 cm or 75.111 cm and so on.

Continuous data are often rounded off to a particular number of decimal places for practical purposes, but nevertheless there are still an infinite number of actual possible numbers.

Histograms

A *histogram* is quite similar to a bar graph, the three main differences being that in a histogram:

'Remember, frequency is the number of times the event has happened'

▶ there are no gaps between the bars;
▶ the horizontal axis will have a continuous scale;
▶ the areas of the bars represent the frequency of the distribution; hence the frequency scale will always start at 0.

Equal-width histograms
We first look at histograms in which the width of each bar is the same for all the bars in the histogram.

Table 11.4 is an example of a *grouped frequency table* showing the time that 165 different people had to wait to catch a train one morning. On each occasion, instead of being recorded separately, the piece of data was placed in a *group* showing the time to the nearest minute.

Table 11.4

Time (nearest minute)	0	1	2	3	4	5	6	7	8	9	10
Frequency	15	27	35	30	21	15	9	6	4	2	1

Figure 11.3 presents a visual picture of this data in the form of a histogram. It is important to draw a *boundary* for each bar in the histogram. This boundary tells us the value of the observation which separates one group in the frequency distribution from another group.

Fig. 11.3

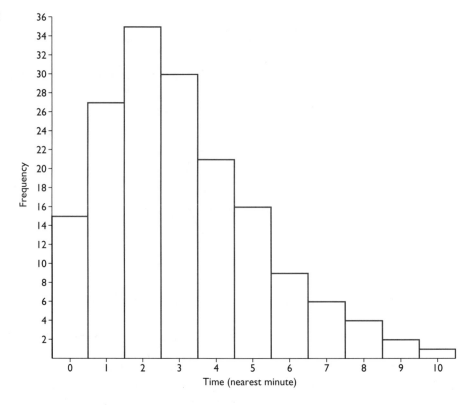

'The vertical axis on a histogram of equal widths is labelled frequency, while the vertical axis on a histogram of unequal widths is labelled frequency density'

Note that the boundary of each bar in Fig. 11.3 is halfway between the times. This is owing to the fact that 1 minute will be in the group $0.5 \leqslant$ time < 1.5 minutes, and so on (since we take the time to the nearest minute). (Note also that in this case we start the first group at -0.5 minutes to allow the bar for 0 minutes to be of an equal width to the others.)

When we use equal-width histograms we can write *frequency* on the vertical axis. As we shall see, we have to use a different term when we consider unequal-width histograms.

Unequal-width histograms

Sometimes the data will be such that we define our *groups* to be of different sizes. In the previous example each group was 1 minute in size. In this next example we have a frequency table (Table 11.5) in which the sizes of the groups vary between 1 minute and 2 minutes.

Table 11.5

Time (nearest minute)	0–1	2	3	4	5	6–7	8–9	10
Frequency	42	35	30	21	15	15	6	1

The histogram representing this frequency table is drawn in Fig. 11.4.

Remember that in a histogram it is the *area* of each bar that represents the frequency. So if we *double* the *width* of the bar, we *halve* the *height* of the bar. Instead of 'frequency' on the vertical axis we now have 'frequency density' (f.d.). This is because we need to multiply each vertical height by the group width in order to find the frequency.

Fig. 11.4

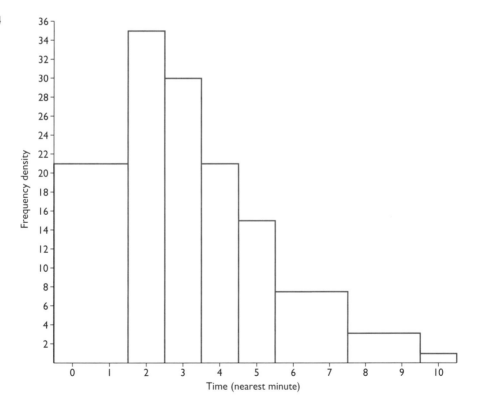

Hence a bar of half a unit width will have a *frequency* of its height multiplied by one-half; and a bar of three units width will have a *frequency* of the height multiplied by three.

Notice how the group 6–7 minutes in Fig. 11.4 is shown on the histogram as $5.5 \leqslant$ time < 7.5, a width of 2 units. Hence the *frequency* is found by 2×7.5 (the frequency density) to give 15, which is shown in our group frequency table. The same principles apply to the 0–1 and 8–9 minute groups.

WORKED EXAMPLE 3

The heights of a group of boys were measured to the nearest centimetre. The results were classified in groups, as shown in Table 11.6.

Table 11.6

Height (nearest cm)	162	163	164	165	166	167	168	169	170	171
Frequency	41	72	87	89	77	60	44	34	21	8

Make a histogram to illustrate the data. Use the groups of 162–163, 164, 165, 166–167, 168–170, 171.

Draw up a new grouped frequency table, as in Table 11.7.

Table 11.7

Height (nearest cm)	162–163	164	165	166–167	168–170	171
Frequency	113	87	89	137	99	8

The unit common to all the groups is 1 cm (or some multiple of 1 cm). We will therefore use 1 cm as our unit.

Each of the class intervals shown in the top row of our table will therefore be treated in the following way in our histogram.

162–163 will be 2 units wide
164 and 165 will each be 1 unit wide
166–167 will be 2 units wide
168–170 will be 3 units wide
171 will be 1 unit wide

The heights on the frequency density axis will be as shown in Table 11.8.

Table 11.8

Groups	Unit width	Frequency	Height on frequency density
161.5–163.5	2 units	113	$113 \div 2 = 56.5$
163.5–164.5	1 unit	87	87
164.5–165.5	1 unit	89	89
165.5–167.5	2 units	137	$137 \div 2 = 68.5$
167.5–170.5	3 units	99	$99 \div 3 = 33$
170.5–171.5	1 unit	8	8

So the unequal-width histogram for this table will be constructed as shown in Fig. 11.5.

Fig. 11.5

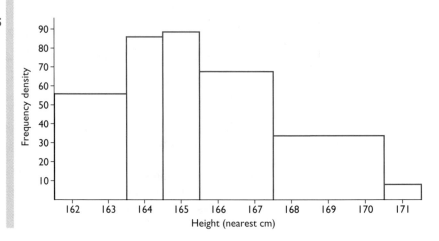

Exercise 1

(a) Draw a histogram for the grouped frequency distribution shown in Table 11.9.

Table 11.9

Age (nearest year)	12–15	16–17	18–19	20–21	22–25
Frequency	54	40	24	15	6

(b) Write down the grouped frequency table from which the histogram in Fig. 11.6 has been drawn.

Fig. 11.6

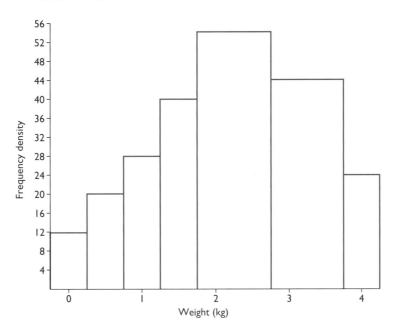

Frequency polygon

A *frequency polygon* is a straight-lined diagram often used to represent data, whether ungrouped (all data known) or grouped. However, the rules for drawing a frequency polygon depend on the type of data used.

Ungrouped data

In Table 11.10 we know *all* the data; here the number of families (frequency) having a particular number of children in the family.

Table 11.10

Children	0	1	2	3	4	5
Frequency	11	24	37	27	15	10

Figure 11.7 shows the frequency polygon for this ungrouped data. Notice how we simply plot the coordinate from each ordered pair (children : frequency) in the table, then join each point up with a straight line.

Grouped data

In Table 11.11 we only know the data in terms of *groups* (of five) rather than individual scores.

Table 11.11

Score	1–5	6–10	11–15	16–20	21–25	26–30
Frequency	4	13	25	32	17	9

Figure 11.8 shows the frequency polygon for this *grouped* data. Notice how:

▶ we use the midpoint of each group;
▶ we plot the ordered pairs of midpoints of the groups, together with their frequency, i.e. (3, 4), (8, 13), (13, 25), (18, 32), (23, 17), (28, 9);

Fig. 11.7
Ungrouped
data

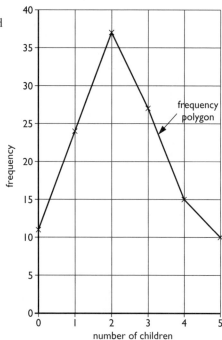

Fig. 11.8
Grouped
data

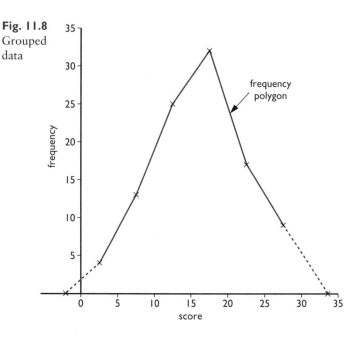

▶ we now start and finish the polygon by extending each side of the polygon to the horizontal axis (frequency 0). This is shown as a dashed line at each side of the polygon. The midpoints rise by 5 for each group; so we have a coordinate $(-2, 0)$ at the left and $(33, 0)$ at the right.

▶ **Cumulative frequency**

It is on your syllabus and there is a very good chance that you will find a question on *cumulative frequency*. It is usually used to create an *ogive*, which is the graph you get if you graph the cumulative frequency (c.f.). From this ogive you can estimate the median as well as quartiles and percentiles.

It is often called a running total, since that indeed is how the cumulative frequency is calculated. Follow through the example below to see how we draw the graph and how we find information from it.

Example
On 5 September 1996, all the pupils in Pope Pius X School were measured in height to the nearest centimetre; Fig. 11.9 illustrates the distribution.

Table 11.12

Heights (cm)	Frequency (f)	Cumulative frequency (c.f.)
115–120	6	6
121–130	30	36
131–140	85	121
141–150	160	281
151–160	180	461
161–170	41	502
171–175	2	504

Fig. 11.9

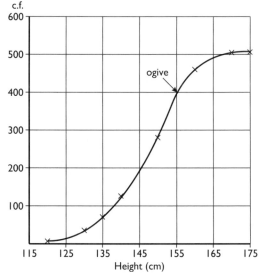

The cumulative frequency has been graphed against the height to give the ogive. Notice its distinctive shape and that the cumulative frequency is on the vertical axis, as it should always be.

We can estimate information such as, how many pupils are over 165 cm? We look at the c.f. for 165 cm by reading up, then along to 490, then we know that there are $504 - 490 = 14$, representing 14 pupils over 165 cm.

Estimating the median

From the c.f., find the middle item of data, where n is the total of the c.f., then the median is found by reading along, from $(n + 1)/2$ on the c.f., to the ogive and down.

When we have large numbers, as in our example of 504, then it is often just as good to use the $n/2$ on the c.f. Here, the estimated median can be found by reading along from 252 on the c.f. to the ogive and down, to give the estimated median as 148.5 cm.

Quartiles

Quartiles are found by dividing the c.f. into quarters and finding the 'quarter' marks. There are three divisions of the c.f. if we quarter it. The first one, the *lower quartile*, is found by reading along from $\frac{1}{4}(n + 1)$ on the c.f. The second one is the *median*, and the third is the *upper quartile*, found by reading along from $\frac{3}{4}(n + 1)$. Again, for large n you would round off to the nearest suitable integer to read on the c.f.

So, for our example above, we will have the quartiles shown in Fig. 11.10.

Fig. 11.10

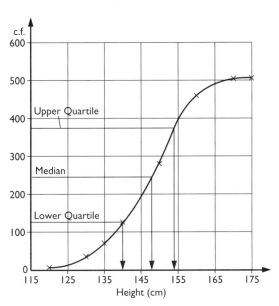

$\frac{1}{4}(504) \rightarrow 126$ on c.f. to give lower quartile of 140.5 cm.
$\frac{3}{4}(504) \rightarrow 378$ on c.f. to give upper quartile of 154.5 cm.

Interquartile range

This is the difference between the upper quartile and the lower quartile, and is expressed simply as this difference. Hence for our example above, the interquartile range is $154.5 - 140.5 = 14$ cm.

This range is useful to see how well the frequency is dispersed, as is the 'semi-interquartile range' which is simply half of the interquartile range.

Exercise 2
Find the semi-interquartile range and estimate the median for the distribution of the weights of boxes of chocolates that were supposed to be 200 g, shown in Table 11.13.

Table 11.13

Weight (g)	−196	−197	−198	−199	−200	−201	−202	−203	−204
Frequency	6	23	35	50	65	44	36	32	9

▶ **Dispersion: standard deviation**

Standard deviation

As well as having an idea of the 'average' of the data, it is useful to know how the data are distributed around the average. Do most observations occur near to the average or well away from the average? The interquartile range and the *standard deviation* are called *measures of dispersion* as they tell us something about how the data are dispersed (distributed) around the average.

We will illustrate the calculation of the standard deviation by comparing the homework marks of a group of ten students in maths and science. Table 11.14 shows the marks, with A, B, C, etc., being used as a code to represent the ten different students.

Table 11.14

Individual	Maths mark	Science mark
A	3	2
B	9	3
C	3	4
D	6	6
E	5	3
F	10	10
G	7	5
H	4	1
I	8	8
J	5	6

We will start with the maths marks. First, we calculate the *mean average* in the normal way, by adding all the marks together and then dividing by the number of marks. For our maths homework marks this gives:

$$\text{mean average} = \frac{60}{10} = 6$$

We now add a column to our table, showing the *deviation* (difference) of each mark from this mean value. Our table looks like Table 11.15.

Table 11.15

Individual	Maths mark	Deviation
A	3	−3
B	9	+3
C	3	−3
D	6	0
E	5	−1
F	10	+4
G	7	+1
H	4	−2
I	8	+2
J	5	−1
Total	60	0

Notice that the total of the deviations from the mean is zero, which is what we should expect for any distribution, because the mean is calculated as the arithmetical centre of the distribution of values.

A value that is zero for any distribution is useless for making comparisons between distributions so, to produce a value that differs from distribution to distribution, we now *square* the deviations. This has the effect of making all the quantities positive. Our table now looks like Table 11.16.

Table 11.16

Individual	Maths mark	Deviation	Squared deviation
A	3	−3	9
B	9	3	9
C	3	−3	9
D	6	0	0
E	5	−1	1
F	10	4	16
G	7	1	1
H	4	−2	4
I	8	2	4
J	5	−1	1
Total	60	0	54

So our 10 marks have a total squared deviation of 54 from the mean average. We now calculate the mean average of these squared deviations. This value is called the *variance* of a distribution. For our maths marks we have:

$$\text{variance} = \frac{54}{10} = 5.4$$

Finally, we calculate the *standard deviation*. This is defined as the *square root of the variance*. So, for our maths marks, standard deviation = $\sqrt{5.4}$ = 2.3 (to 1 d.p.). Here is a summary of the calculation in the example.

Standard deviation

The standard deviation is a **measure of dispersion**, that is to say, a measure of how widely the values in a distribution are spread. We calculate it by:

1   finding the mean average of the distribution (i.e. arithmetic mean);
2   finding the deviation (d), of each value from the mean average;
3   squaring the deviations (d^2) from the mean;
4   finding the total of the squared deviations (Σd^2);
5   dividing this total by the number of values in the distribution to find the variance $\left(\dfrac{\Sigma d^2}{n}\right)$;
6   square rooting the variance to find the standard deviation $\sqrt{\left(\dfrac{\Sigma d^2}{n}\right)}$.

It should be obvious that a distribution in which the values are widely spread will produce a high value for the standard deviation, and a distribution in which the values are closely grouped will produce a low value for the standard deviation. The standard deviation is a useful way to compare the spread of values in two or more distributions.

Using the data in Table 11.17, the required calculations to find the standard deviation of our science marks are given below.

Table 11.17

Individual	Science mark	Deviation	Squared deviation
A	2	−2.8	7.84
B	3	−1.8	3.24
C	4	−0.8	0.64
D	6	1.2	1.44
E	3	−1.8	3.24
F	10	5.2	27.04
G	5	0.2	0.04
H	1	−3.8	14.44
I	8	3.2	10.24
J	6	1.2	1.44
Totals	48	0	69.60

$$\text{Mean average} = \frac{48}{10} = 4.8$$

$$\text{Variance} = \frac{69.6}{10} = 6.96$$

Standard deviation $= \sqrt{6.96} = 2.6$ (to 1 d.p.)

So, for our mark distributions, we have:

Maths	mean = 6	standard deviation = 2.3
Science	mean = 4.8	standard deviation = 2.6

From these calculations we can compare the mark distributions and conclude that the maths marks tended to be higher and more tightly grouped than the science marks.

WORKED EXAMPLE 4   Calculate the arithmetic mean and standard deviation of the following distribution of heights of eight plants (in cm): 4, 6, 7, 9, 10, 13, 14, 17.

Table 11.18

Plant	Height (cm)	Deviation, d (cm)	Squared deviation, d^2 (cm²)
A	4	−6	36
B	6	−4	16
C	7	−3	9
D	9	−1	1
E	10	0	0
F	13	3	9
G	14	4	16
H	17	7	49
Total	80	0	$\Sigma d^2 = 136$

From the information in Table 11.18, we have:

$$\text{Mean average} = \frac{80}{8} = 10 \text{ cm}$$

$$\text{Variance} = \frac{136}{8} = 17 \text{ cm}^2$$

Standard deviation $= \sqrt{17} = 4.12 \text{ cm}$

So the arithmetic mean of the plant heights is 10 cm and the standard deviation is 4.12 cm (to 2 d.p.).

Exercise 3
Calculate the arithmetic mean and the standard deviation of the marks of six pupils: 11, 14, 18, 22, 27, 28.

▶ **Probability and expectation**

'You need to be able to work out fractions with probability; you'll score few marks if you can't'

Combined events

Combined events are where two or more events are being combined in some way. When this happens we need to be aware of whether the events are dependent or independent. We need to consider two main situations AND and OR.

AND
AND is the type of situation where two or more events happen at the same time. You need to *multiply together* each probability.

WORKED EXAMPLE 5   Find the probability of tossing a coin 10 times and getting a head each time.

The chance of tossing a head is $\frac{1}{2}$ each time, hence for ten heads in a row, calculate $\frac{1}{2} \times \frac{1}{2} \times \frac{1}{2} \dots$ (ten times) which is $(\frac{1}{2})^{10} = 9.8 \times 10^{-4}$.

Exercise 4
Calculate the probability of dealing four cards face up on the table and each one being an ace.

OR
OR is the type of situation when one event *or* the other *or* both occur. In this case we must *add together* the probabilities. This only makes sense, however, in a situation where all the possible combinations have been considered.

WORKED EXAMPLE 6
Find the probability of cutting a pack of cards and finding a king or a queen.

The probability of a king is $\frac{1}{13}$, of a queen is $\frac{1}{13}$ and they cannot both happen at the same time, hence the probability of cutting one or the other is $\frac{1}{13} + \frac{1}{13} = \frac{2}{13}$.

AND and OR
This is how many of your examination problems are going to come, in situations where you need a combination of AND and OR.

WORKED EXAMPLE 7
The probability of Paul getting to school on time is 0.95. The probability of Michael being late for school is 0.1. What is the probability on any one day that either Paul or Michael (or both) are late for school?

The events that we can have are:

    A: Paul late AND Michael not late
    B: Paul not late AND Michael late
    C: Paul late AND Michael late

As the probability of Paul not being late is 0.95, the probability that he is late is $(1 - 0.95) = 0.05$. As the probability of Michael being late is 0.1, the probability that he is not late is $(1 - 0.1) = 0.9$. Hence:

    $P(A) = 0.05 \times 0.9 = 0.045$
    $P(B) = 0.95 \times 0.1 = 0.095$
    $P(C) = 0.05 \times 0.1 = 0.005$

As we can have *A* OR *B* OR *C*, then add the probabilities to give:

    $P(A) + P(B) + P(C) = 0.145$

Note: This worked example illustrates the way in which AND and OR can be combined, but for this particular example there is a quicker way of getting to the final answer. That is to first find the probability of neither being late, i.e. Paul is on time AND Michael is on time. This is $0.95 \times 0.9 = 0.855$.

    The probability that one or the other is late = 1 − probability of both not being late = $1 - 0.855 = 0.145$.

    As you see, this way is much quicker – if you spot it.

Tree diagrams

Tree diagrams are useful to illustrate some situations, but are often misused, and in fact used quite unnecessarily in many questions. If you can see what parts you need to get through a probability question then only use a tree diagram if you are specifically told to.

WORKED EXAMPLE 8
When Brian goes to Wales for his holiday he reckons that the chances of a hold-up on the motorway are:

    on the M1 a probability of 0.4, and
    on the M50 a probability of 0.05

What are the chances of his being held up on the motorways on his way to Wales?

We can illustrate the chances on a tree diagram, as in Fig. 11.11.

Fig. 11.11

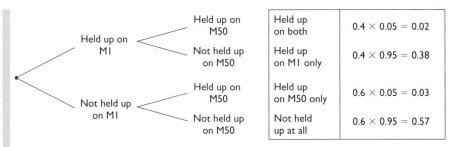

Note: In this situation we were not asked for any one or two probabilities, but for all of them. Hence the tree diagram was useful to do this. Note also that all the final probabilities add up to 1.

WORKED EXAMPLE 9   In a group of 12 men and 9 women, only 2 of them are known to be Welsh. What is the probability that these two are both of the same sex?

This problem, as far as we can tell, is about choosing, at random, two people, both of them being of the same sex. Here we either choose:

man then man: $\dfrac{12}{21} \times \dfrac{11}{20} = \dfrac{132}{420}$, or

woman then woman: $\dfrac{9}{21} \times \dfrac{8}{20} = \dfrac{72}{420}$

(Note how the second fraction is changed by the first one.)

Hence both the same sex has a chance of $\dfrac{132 + 72}{420} = \dfrac{204}{420}$.

Exercise 5
In a bag of sweets there are 10 chocolates, 5 jellies and 6 mints. Find the probability of taking out any two sweets and both of them being different.

Expectation

One of the main uses of probability is that of predicting some *expected* results. The expected number of times that event *A* will happen is found by multiplying the probability of *A* by the number of times that the event has the opportunity of happening.

WORKED EXAMPLE 10   The AA reckons that any car taken at random has a probability of 0.004 of breaking down. They estimate that on August Bank Holiday there are 300 000 cars using the motorway networks. If they tried to have one patrol car for every 25 breakdowns, how many patrol cars should they use on that day?

The expected number of breakdowns is $0.004 \times 300\,000$ which is 1 200. So the number of patrol cars will be $1\,200 \div 25 = 48$.

▶ **Surveys and sampling**   A *survey* is an organised way of asking a lot of people a few well-thought-out questions, or making a lot of observations in order to reach a conclusion about something.

We use surveys to ascertain people's opinions or to test a hypothesis (theory) that has been suggested. The survey can take the form of asking a few questions by use of a questionnaire. Alternatively, it may take the form of collecting data by using a simple data capture sheet in which we note our observations of a situation or the results of asking one simple question.

Questionnaire

A *questionnaire* is a data collection sheet with questions on it. The questions should neither be embarrassing nor actively encourage particular responses to be given by the way in which the question is presented (we call such questions 'leading questions'). Examples of questions to be avoided are:

What is your age?

This can be an embarrassing question, so don't use it. Use instead a question such as:

Which age range are you in: 0–20, 21–40, 41–60, etc.

This is a more acceptable way of asking people to identify their age range, unless, of course, you need more precise information for your study.

Experimenting on animals is a cruel, evil way to treat animals. Do you agree?

This leading question suggests to people that experimenting on animals *is* cruel and evil *before* they give a response.

Do you think experimenting on animals is cruel and evil?

This is a better way of asking the same question without it being a leading question.

Every question must be designed to give the information that you require, so avoid questions such as:

What type of toothpaste do you use?

This type of question will get all sorts of different answers. If, for example, you were interested in toothpaste with or without fluoride, then you would simply ask the question:

Do you use a toothpaste containing fluoride?

Every question must be able to be answered by the person interviewed. So avoid questions such as:

How many apples do you eat a week?   1, 2 or 3?

This question cannot be answered by people who eat none or more than three apples a week. It would be better to ask:

How many apples do you eat a week?   0, 1, 2, 3, or more than 3?

Data collection sheet

This is a sheet used to help you to collect data so that it can be processed later. It usually consists of a *tally sheet* that is filled in after asking one question or after making an observation.

Example
Which day do you want to have a school outing? Design a data capture sheet to collect information that can help you to decide which day is best.

Table 11.19 Which day do you want to have a school outing?

Day of the week	Tally	Frequency
Monday	Жʃ Жʃ ΙΙ	12
Tuesday	Жʃ ΙΙ	7
Wednesday	Жʃ Жʃ Жʃ ΙΙΙ	18
Thursday	Жʃ ΙΙΙ	8
Friday	Жʃ Жʃ ΙΙ	12
Saturday	Жʃ Жʃ	10
Sunday	ΙΙΙ	3
	Total	70

From the data captured in Table 11.19 a decision can be made.

▶   Notice how we made space for tally marks and note how we 'gate' (put a diagonal line through) the tallies in order to give groups of fives: this makes it easier to count up once the survey is completed.

▶ Notice also that since the original question asked 'which day of the week', we must use all seven days of the week on our data collection sheet. You would lose marks in the exam if you only listed selected days or if you asked the open question, 'Which day do you want to have a school outing?' and then just wrote down the answers such as:

Monday, Wednesday, Wednesday, Saturday, Thursday, Wednesday

Sampling

Statisticians often have to carry out surveys to investigate a hypothesis they might have about a large sample or a population. In this sense, 'population' is used to denote all the items in a particular set and not just the people occupying some designated geographical area. It is seldom possible to survey all the people or items in a population, and so we *sample* them. That is, we survey a small set of that population. This is both cheaper and less time-consuming than asking everybody or checking every item.

Before we take a sample we have to ask some important questions:

1. How is our sample going to fully represent the whole population?
2. How large should our sample be to give reliable results?

When thinking about the sample, you should bear in mind the different aspects or characteristics of the population. Suppose in this case we are considering a group of people, then the aspects we might take into account could include age, sex, race, intelligence and so on.

The size of your sample should also be carefully thought about. It is seldom a good idea to ask over half the population, since in that case you may as well ask them all and be certain about the results.

The size of the sample should usually be less than 20% of the population yet more than 5%. This is a very crude idea of the size of the sample as it should take into consideration the type of situation you are in.

Example

A survey was to be conducted as to the views of a crowd of 30 000 football supporters at a game.

You do not want to ask them all, so perhaps you will settle for about 20%, which will be 6 000.

1. Since there are approximately ten times as many men at the game as women, you will want to ask a proportion of each in the chosen ratio. Hence, ask:

$6\,000 \times 10/11 = 5\,454$ men   and $6\,000 \times 1/11 = 546$ women

rounded to 5 500 men and 500 women.

2. About 20% of the crowd are aged under 20 years, so similarly we should ask 4 800 (= 80% of 6 000) over 20s and 1 200 (= 20% of 6 000) under 20s.

3. We also ought to ask the people sitting in the different parts of the ground in similar proportions so as to get a balanced view. Assuming that this breaks down into four equal groups, the north, east, south and west stands, you will need to ask 1 500 from each stand.

If we now assume that one person can survey 40 people at the match, then this will break down into the following sampling strategy:

▶ Each stand will require 38 people to survey the 1 500 people in that stand.
▶ Each person surveying people in a particular stand will need to ask:

29 men over 20 and 7 men under 20;
3 women over 20 and 1 woman under 20.

This, then, has addressed some of the problems associated with taking a non-biased sample.

► **SOLUTIONS TO EXERCISES**

S1 (a) The class boundaries are 11.5–15.5, etc. Make sure the *vertical height* of each rectangle in the histogram is adjusted in proportion to the *base* of the rectangle. For example, the heights of the rectangles for the first and last class intervals should be *halved* as the bases of these rectangles are *double* those of the other class intervals.

Table 11.20 (b)

Weight	0	0.5	1	1.5	2–2.5	3–3.5	4
Frequency	6	10	14	20	54	44	12

S2 You need a cumulative frequency and graph, as in Table 11.21 and Fig. 11.12.

Table 11.21

Weight	f	c.f
−196	6	6
−197	23	29
−198	35	64
−199	50	114
−200	65	179
−201	44	223
−202	36	259
−203	32	291
−204	9	300

Fig. 11.12

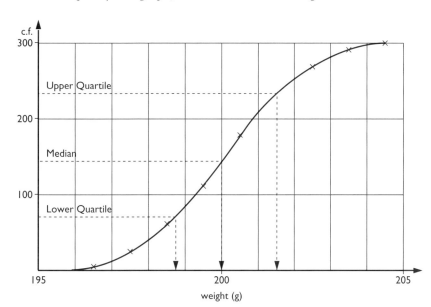

Note where we've plotted the points – using 196.5, 197.5, etc. on the horizontal axis as being the most accurate figure for the c.f. due to the giving of information to the nearest gram and rounding off. This is necessary where you can tell this difference easily on the graph.

Look on the $(301) \times \frac{1}{4}$ for the lower quartile, which is $75.25 \rightarrow 198.75$ g

Look on the $(301) \times \frac{3}{4}$ for the upper quartile, which is $225.75 \rightarrow 201.6$ g

Hence the semi-interquartile range is $(201.6 - 198.75) \div 2 = 1.425$ g

Look on the $(301)/2$ for the median, which is $150.5 \rightarrow 200$ g

S3 Arithmetic mean $= (11 + 14 + 18 + 22 + 27 + 28) \div 6 = 20$

$\sum d^2 = (9^2 + 6^2 + 2^2 + 2^2 + 7^2 + 8^2) = 238$

$\dfrac{\sum d^2}{n} = \dfrac{238}{6} = 39.667$

Standard deviation $= \sqrt{39.667} = 6.3$

S4 The probability of the first card being an ace is $\dfrac{4}{52}$

The probability of the second being an ace, given the first is an ace, is $\dfrac{3}{51}$

The probability of the third being an ace, given the first two are aces, is $\dfrac{2}{50}$

Hence of the fourth being an ace is $\dfrac{1}{49}$

Hence the probability that all 4 are aces is: $\dfrac{4}{52} \times \dfrac{3}{51} \times \dfrac{2}{50} \times \dfrac{1}{49} = 3.7 \times 10^{-6}$

S5   The probability is 1 − (both being the same)
The probability both being the same is given by:
P(both chocolate) + P(both jellies) + P(both mints),

$$\left(\frac{10}{21} \times \frac{9}{20}\right) + \left(\frac{5}{21} \times \frac{4}{20}\right) + \left(\frac{6}{21} \times \frac{5}{20}\right) = \frac{90 + 20 + 30}{21 \times 20}$$

$$= \frac{140}{420} = \frac{1}{3}$$

Hence the chance of both being different is $1 - \frac{1}{3} = \frac{2}{3}$.

▶ **EXAMINATION QUESTIONS**

▶ **Question 1**   The pie charts in Fig. 11.13 indicate the proportion of steel produced in the world by various economies in 1974 and 1985. Use these diagrams to answer the following questions.

Fig. 11.13

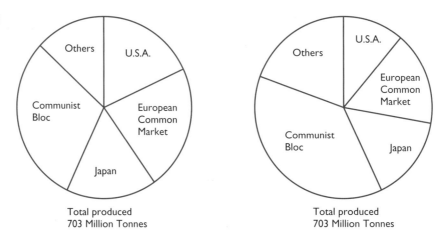

Total produced
703 Million Tonnes

Total produced
703 Million Tonnes

(a)   Which economies did not improve their world proportion from 1974 to 1985?
(b)   (i) Measure and state the angle of the sector representing the European Common Market in 1974.
        (ii) How many tonnes of steel did the European Common Market produce in 1974?
(c)   Calculate the percentage increase of the Communist Bloc's proportion of steel production from 1974 to 1985.   (NEAB)

▶ **Question 2**   Mrs McAllister, an agent for a firm, kept a record of the time she spent (including travelling) on each customer she saw. During one particular five-day week, she saw 80 customers and the record of the times spent on them is summarised in Table 11.22.

Table 11.22

Time (t minutes)	$20 < t \leqslant 25$	$25 < t \leqslant 30$	$30 < t \leqslant 35$	$35 < t \leqslant 40$	$40 < t \leqslant 45$	$45 < t \leqslant 50$
Number of customers	8	10	10	30	18	4

(a)   Find the mean number of customers Mrs McAllister saw per day during this week.
(b)   Mrs McAllister's normal working week is 40 hours. Calculate an estimate of the number of hours' overtime she worked during this week.
(c)   Calculate an estimate of the mean length of time Mrs McAllister spent per customer.
(d)   On graph paper, draw a cumulative frequency diagram for this distribution.
(e)   Use your diagram to estimate:
        (i) the interquartile range for this distribution;
        (ii) the number of customers on each of whom Mrs McAllister spent more than the mean length of time found in part (c).   (MEG)

▶ **Question 3** The number of full-time female students in the U.K. in 1991 in various age groups is shown in Table 11.23. (Frequencies are given to the nearest thousand.)

Table 11.23

Age (years)	16–	20–	25–	35–	45–54	Total
No. (thousands)	672	139	34	13	4	862

(a) This information is to be represented in a histogram using a scale of 2 cm to represent 5 years on the age axis and 4 cm² to represent 100 thousand students. Given that the width of the first rectangle is 1.6 cm, calculate its height.
(b) Draw the histogram.
(c) By using mid-interval values, estimate the mean age of female students, giving your answer correct to the nearest tenth of a year.   (NEAB)

▶ **Question 4** A bag contains 5 red discs, 4 white discs and 1 blue disc. Two discs are to be chosen at random, without replacement.

(a) Complete the probability tree diagram in Fig. 11.14.

Fig. 11.14

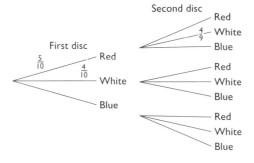

(b) Find the probability that:
    (i) both discs will be red,
    (ii) both discs will be blue,
    (iii) both discs will be the same colour,
    (iv) the two discs will be different colours.   (London)

▶ **Question 5** (Give the answers to this question as fractions in their lowest terms.)
In a game, one red dice and one blue dice are used. Both dice are unbiased, but the faces of the red dice are numbered 1, 1, 2, 3, 4, 5 and the faces of the blue dice are numbered 1, 1, 2, 2, 4, 4.

*'You'll find a diagram ...
not a tree diagram ...
helpful here'*

(a) The two dice are thrown together, find the probability of each of the following events:
    (i) The score on the red dice is an odd number.
    (ii) The score on the blue dice is greater than the score on the red dice.
    (iii) The scores on the two dice are equal.
(b) The two dice are thrown together on two occasions. Find the probability that the score on the blue dice is greater than the score on the red dice on both occasions.   (MEG)

▶ **Question 6** Part of a children's game involves rolling a normal 6-faced dice, then spinning an arrow as shown in Fig. 11.15.
If on the spinner you get:

    a dice – you have another roll of the dice
    a spider – you choose a spider part
    a foot – you move on one space on a board
    a drink – you miss a go

Fig. 11.15

(a)   Find the probability of getting:
   (i)   a spider
   (ii) a foot
   (iii) a drink
(b)   To win a game on his next go, John had to
         either roll a 3 on the dice, then spin a spider
         or roll a 5 on the dice, then spin a foot.
Calculate the probability that John will win on his next go.   (NEAB)

▶ **Question 7**   Mr Meiring travels to work by car on five days each week. He has to cross three busy junctions. He finds that he is delayed three times a week at the first junction, twice a week at the second junction, and once a week at the third junction. A delay at one junction does not affect a delay at any other junction.

(a)   Complete the probability tree diagram in Fig. 11.16, using D for delay, and N for no delay, in the Outcome column.

Fig. 11.16

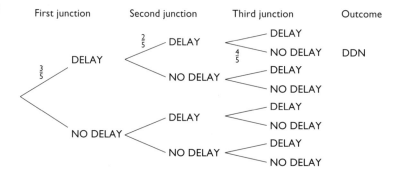

(b)   Find the probability that on any morning he will,
   (i)   arrive at work without being delayed,
   (ii) be delayed at only one of the three junctions.   (London)

▶ **Question 8**   A school entered 50 candidates for GCSE mathematics. There are two papers, each marked out of a maximum of 50. The marks obtained in Paper 1 are shown in Table 11.24 and illustrated by the frequency diagram in Fig. 11.17.

Table 11.24

Mark range	0–4	5–9	10–14	15–19	20–24	25–29	30–34	35–39	40–44	45–49
No. of candidates	0	0	1	1	2	8	19	14	4	1

(a)   Calculate an estimate of the mean mark obtained in Paper 1.

Fig. 11.17

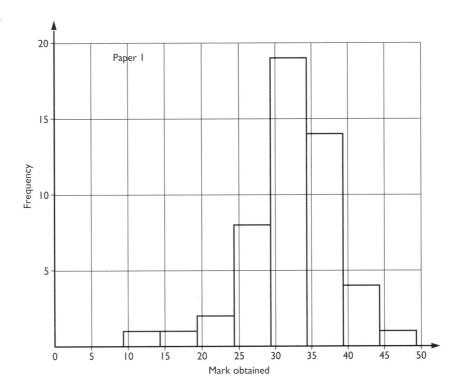

The marks obtained in Paper 2 are shown in Table 11.25.

Table 11.25

27	18	31	12	16	37	24	42	15	23
27	27	42	21	3	12	27	24	34	13
9	29	19	32	24	26	33	15	24	25
24	30	23	13	17	6	39	19	18	38
12	18	18	26	31	24	49	12	23	29

(b) Compile a frequency table for the marks in Paper 2. Use the same classes as Paper 1.

(c) On graph paper, illustrate the data for Paper 2, using the same scales as the frequency diagram for Paper 1.

(d) Comment briefly on the differences between the candidates' performances in the two papers. (You may like to use the fact that the mean mark for Paper 2 is 23.6.)

(MEG)

▶ **Question 9**   When a biased 6-sided dice is thrown, a score of 6 is twice as likely as a score of 5; a score of 5 is twice as likely as a score of 4; and scores of 1, 2, 3, 4 are equally likely. Calculate the probability of:

  (i) a score of 1,
 (ii) a score of 6,
(iii) scoring an even number.

(NEAB)

▶ **Question 10**   In a survey, 100 motorists were asked to record the petrol consumption of their cars in miles per gallon. Each figure was rounded to the nearest mile per gallon and the frequency distribution shown in Table 11.26 was obtained.

Table 11.26

Miles per gallon	26–30	31–35	36–40	41–45	46–50	51–55	56–60
Frequency	4	6	18	34	20	12	6

(a) (i) State the limits of the model class of this distribution.
    (ii) Complete the 'less than' cumulative frequency table in Table 11.27:

Table 11.27

Miles per gallon (less than)	30.5	35.5	40.5	50.5	55.5	65.5
Number of motorists	4	10				

(iii) On graph paper, draw the cumulative frequency curve (ogive) from your completed cumulative frequency table.

(b) Use your cumulative frequency curve to estimate: (i) the median of the distribution; (ii) the interquartile range.

(c) A 'good' petrol consumption is one which lies between 38 and 52 miles per gallon. Estimate the number of motorists whose petrol consumption was 'good'.   (NICCEA)

▶ **Question 11**   Five married couples are at a party.

(a) Two people are chosen at random. Find the probability that:
   (i) they are a married couple;
   (ii) one is a man and one is a woman;
   (iii) at least one man is chosen.

(b) Four people are chosen at random. Find the probability that:
   (i) three women and one man are chosen;
   (ii) no married couple is among the four.   (WJEC)

▶ **Question 12**   The second line of Table 11.28 gives the length of a day in England (in hours and minutes of daylight) at six-weekly intervals from 5 January 1995.

Table 11.28

Date	5 Jan.	16 Feb.	30 Mar.	11 May	22 June	3 Aug.	14 Sept.	26 Oct.	7 Dec.
Daylight (hours–minutes)	8 h 01 m	10 h 03 m	12 h 48 m	15 h 23 m	16 h 40 m	15 h 19 m	12 h 46 m	10 h 03 m	8 h 02 m

(a) Complete Table 11.29:

Table 11.29

Number of weeks after 5 Jan. (x)	0	6							48
Daylight (hours) to 1 decimal place (y)	8.0	10.1						10.1	8

(b) Using scales of 0.2 cm to 1 week and 1 cm to 1 hour along the x and y-axes respectively, draw a graph of y against x, joining your points with a smooth curve.

(c) (i) On the curve, mark the point corresponding to 1 June and label it J.
   (ii) Find the hours of daylight on 1 June.

(d) (i) On your graph, mark the two points at which day is equal to night. Label the left-hand point A and the right-hand point B.
   (ii) For how many weeks of the year is day longer than night?
   (iii) Estimate the data corresponding to point A.   (OCSEB)

▶ **Question 13**   John has a spinner in the shape of a regular pentagon (Fig. 11.18). Scores of 1, 2, 3, 4, 5 are equally likely when the spinner is spun.

Fig. 11.18

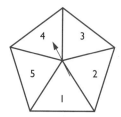

John spins the spinner 200 times and records the scores. Approximately how many times will he score an even number?   (London)

▶ **Question 14**   On any day during the summer of 1986 the probability that it rained was $\frac{1}{6}$. In 1996, because of climatic changes, the probability that it rained on any day during the summer was only $\frac{1}{10}$.

   (a)   Calculate the probability that any 3 days chosen at random during the summer of 1986 were all wet.
   (b)   Calculate the probability that it rained on a particular date during the summer of 1986 and was dry on the same date in 1996.

▶ **Question 15**   Assume that births are equally likely on each of the seven days of the week. Find the probability that, of two randomly selected people:

   (a)   both were born on a Friday;
   (b)   they were both born on the same day of the week;
   (c)   one will have been born on a Wednesday and the other on a Friday.   (NEAB)

▶ **Question 16**   Chess is a game played between two people. Either player can win or the game can end as a draw.
   One person has the white pieces and the other person has the black ones. There is a slight advantage in having white, so a coin is tossed before the game starts. The one who wins the toss plays with the white pieces.

   (a)   Alwyn and Bernard often play one another at chess. When Alwyn has the white pieces the probability that he will beat Bernard is $\frac{3}{5}$, and the probability that Bernard will win is $\frac{1}{4}$.
      (i)   Calculate the probability that Alwyn will win the toss and then win the chess match.
      (ii) Calculate the probability that Alwyn will win the toss but then lose the chess match.
   (b)   When Alwyn has the black pieces the probability that he will beat Bernard is $\frac{2}{5}$, and the probability that Bernard will win is $\frac{1}{2}$.
      (i)   Calculate the probability that Alwyn will lose the toss but then win the chess match.
      (ii) Calculate the probability that Alwyn will lose the toss and then lose the chess match.
   (c)   Use your answers to (a) and (b) to calculate the percentage of chess matches in which:
      (i)   Alwyn will beat Bernard;
      (ii) Bernard beats Alwyn.
   (d)   What percentage of their chess matches are drawn?   (NEAB)

▶ **Question 17**   An experiment involving a chemical reaction was carried out several times. In each experiment, the temperature of the reaction was taken at the end of one minute.

   (a)   Complete the table of results shown in Table 11.30.

Table 11.30

Temperature (°C)	Frequency	Upper limit for temperature (°C)	Cumulative frequency
41.0–41.1	5	41.15	5
41.2–41.3	2	41.35	7
41.4–41.5	7	41.55	14
41.6–41.7	15	41.75	29
41.8–41.9	7		
42.0–42.1	4		

   (b)   How many times was the experiment carried out?
   (c)   On the grid [not provided here], draw a cumulative frequency polygon to show the reaction temperatures.
   (d)   Find the interquartile range of the temperatures.
         (Show all construction lines.)   (NEAB)

▶ **Question 18**   The lengths, in centimetres, of 10 leaves in a sample were:

5.6,   5.8,   4.9,   6.2,   6.8,   4.8,   5.4,   5.9,   5.3,   5.2

(a)   Calculate the standard deviation of these lengths.
(b)   The standard deviation of another sample of 10 leaves was 0.432 cm.
What difference between the two samples is shown by the two standard deviations?

(SEG)

▶ **Question 19**   100 eggs are classified by mass in Table 11.31.

Table 11.31

	Mass (g)	Frequency
Extra small	40–42	1
Small	42–46	3
Medium	46–53	25
Standard	53–62	35
Large	62–75	36

(a)   Draw a histogram to illustrate the data.
(b)   Calculate estimates of the mean and the standard deviation of this sample.
(c)   For a normal distribution it would be expected that more than 95% of the distribution would be contained in the interval mean ± 2 standard deviations. For this sample, using your answers to part (b), calculate the numerical limits of this interval and estimate the percentage of this sample which lies within this interval.

▶ **Question 20**   A gardener tests a fertiliser: he grows some tomatoes with the fertiliser and some without. He records the weights of all the tomatoes grown, see Table 11.32.

Table 11.32

Weight (grams)	Frequency	
	with fertiliser	without fertiliser
$50 < W \leqslant 100$	10	2
$100 < W \leqslant 150$	15	42
$150 < W \leqslant 200$	55	46
$200 < W \leqslant 250$	53	41
$250 < W \leqslant 300$	17	34
$300 < W \leqslant 350$	8	1

(a)   Draw a frequency polygon for each distribution, indicating clearly which is with fertiliser and which is without fertiliser.
(b)   Use the frequency polygons to compare the effects of the fertiliser.   (NEAB)

▶ **Question 21**   For a school project you have been asked to do a presentation of the catering habits of the pupils in your school.
You decide to interview a sample of pupils. How will you choose the pupils you wish to interview if you want your results to be reliable. Give three reasons for your decisions.

(NEAB)

▶ EXAMINATION ANSWERS

A1   (a)   The ones whose angles have got smaller: Japan, European Common Market and USA.
  (b)   (i) Any answer between 79° and 83° would be acceptable.

  (ii) Your part (i) answer $\times \dfrac{704}{360}$ = between 154 and 162 million.

  (c)   Again, the angle measurement can be as much as 2° out, but if you were really accurate, the first angle is 107°, the second 138°, hence the proportional increase is $\dfrac{138 - 107}{107}$. To make this a percentage just multiply this answer by 100 to get 29%.

A2   (a) $(8 + 10 + 10 + 30 + 18 + 4) \div 5 = 16$.
  (b)   Table 11.33 shows how to estimate the total time spent in minutes, which will be 47.7 hours ($2\,860$ min $\div$ 60), so she worked approximately 8 hours overtime.
  (c) $2\,860 \div 80 = 35.75$ minutes   (36 would do)
  (d)   See Fig. 11.19.

Table 11.33

Time	Halfway (m)	f	m × f
20–25	22.5	8	180
25–30	27.5	10	275
30–35	32.5	10	325
35–40	37.5	30	1 125
40–45	42.5	18	765
45–50	47.5	4	190
	Total	80	2 860

Fig. 11.19

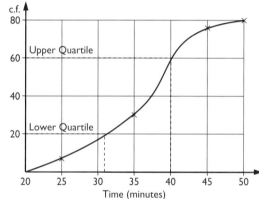

  (e)   (i) Upper quartile $(\frac{3}{4} \times 81)$th = 40.5
        Lower quartile $(\frac{1}{4} \times 81)$th = 31
        Hence interquartile range = 40.5 − 31 = 9.5 minutes
      (ii) Mean length of 35.75 minutes
        Read up to the ogive = 33 people below this mark
        So she would see (80 − 33) = 47 customers for longer than the estimated mean

A3   (a)   To represent 672 (thousands) you need an area of $\dfrac{672}{100} \times 4 = 26.88\,\text{cm}^2$, so if width = 1.6 cm, the height = $\dfrac{26.88}{1.6} = 16.8$ cm.

  (b)   The widths and heights of the other rectangles are given in Table 11.34.

Table 11.34

Age	Width (cm)	f	Height (cm)
16–20	$4 \times \frac{2}{5} = 1.6$	672	$(672 \times 0.04) \div 1.6 = 16.8$
20–25	$5 \times \frac{2}{5} = 2.0$	139	$(139 \times 0.04) \div 2.0 = 2.78$
25–35	$10 \times \frac{2}{5} = 4.0$	34	$(34 \times 0.04) \div 4.0 = 0.34$
35–45	$10 \times \frac{2}{5} = 4.0$	13	$(13 \times 0.04) \div 4.0 = 0.13$
45–54	$9 \times \frac{2}{5} = 3.6$	4	$(4 \times 0.04) \div 3.6 = 0.04$

So your histogram should look like that in Fig. 11.20.

Fig. 11.20

f.d.

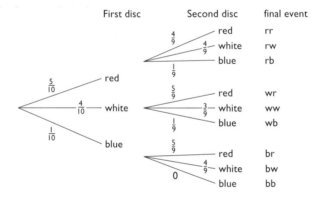

Age (years)

Table 11.35

Age	Midway (m)	f (thousand)	m × f
16–20	18	672	12 096
20–25	22.5	139	3 127.5
25–35	30	34	1 020
35–45	40	13	520
45–54	49.5	4	198
	Total	862	16 961.5

(c) Your table to estimate this should look like Table 11.35.
So your estimated mean will be 16 961.5 ÷ 862 = 19.7 years.

A4 (a) See Fig. 11.21.

Fig. 11.21

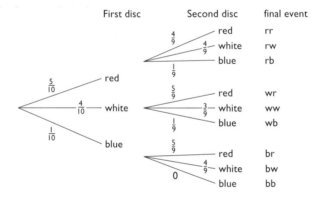

(b) (i) $P(\text{rr}) = \dfrac{5}{10} \times \dfrac{4}{9} = \dfrac{20}{90} = \dfrac{2}{9}$

(ii) $P(\text{bb}) = \dfrac{1}{10} \times 0 = 0$

(iii) $P(\text{same colour}) = P(\text{rr}) + P(\text{ww}) + P(\text{bb}) = \dfrac{2}{9} + \dfrac{4}{10} \times \dfrac{3}{9} + 0 = \dfrac{32}{90}$

(iv) $P(\text{different colours}) = 1 - P(\text{same colour}) = 1 - \dfrac{32}{90} = \dfrac{58}{90}$

A5 (a) (i) $\dfrac{4}{6} = \dfrac{2}{3}$

The best way to indicate all of the equally likely events to help you find the probability of combined events here is to sketch the following diagrams (Figs 11.22 and 11.23).

Fig. 11.22

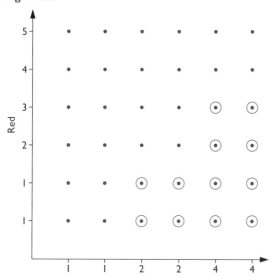

$$\text{Probability} = \frac{12}{36} = \frac{1}{3}$$

(b) $\frac{1}{3} \times \frac{1}{3} = \frac{1}{9}$.

Fig. 11.23

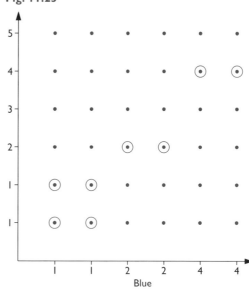

$$\text{Probability} = \frac{8}{36} = \frac{2}{9}$$

A6   (a)   (i) $\frac{5}{12}$ (ii) $\frac{3}{12}$ or $\frac{1}{4}$ (iii) $\frac{2}{12}$ or $\frac{1}{6}$

(b)   A tree diagram may help you to visualise the whole situation, but is not the best method to solve this particular problem.

$$P(\text{roll 3 then spin a spider}) = \frac{1}{6} \times \frac{5}{12} = \frac{5}{72}$$

$$P(\text{roll 5 then spin a foot}) = \frac{1}{6} \times \frac{1}{4} = \frac{1}{24}$$

Add them together to give $\frac{5}{72} + \frac{1}{24} = \frac{8}{72}$

A7   (a)   See Fig. 11.24.

Fig. 11.24

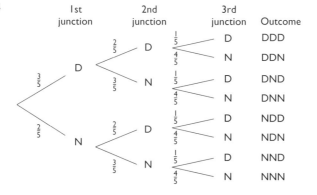

(b)   (i) $P(\text{NNN}) = \frac{2}{5} \times \frac{3}{5} \times \frac{4}{5} = \frac{24}{125}$

(ii) $P(\text{DNN}) + P(\text{NDN}) + P(\text{NND}) = \left(\frac{3}{5} \cdot \frac{3}{5} \cdot \frac{4}{5}\right) + \left(\frac{2}{5} \cdot \frac{2}{5} \cdot \frac{4}{5}\right) + \left(\frac{2}{5} \cdot \frac{3}{5} \cdot \frac{1}{5}\right)$

$$= \frac{36}{125} + \frac{16}{125} + \frac{6}{125} = \frac{58}{125}$$

A8   (a)   Use a table of values as in Table 11.36.

Table 11.36

Mark range	Midway (m)	f	m × f
0–4	2	0	0
5–9	7	0	0
10–14	12	1	12
15–19	17	1	17
20–24	22	2	44
25–29	27	8	216
30–34	32	19	608
35–39	37	14	518
40–44	42	4	168
45–49	47	1	47
	Total	50	1 630

Hence the estimated mean is $1\,630 \div 50 = 32.6$.

(b)   You should have a table of values as in Table 11.37.

Table 11.37

Mark range	0–4	5–9	10–14	15–19	20–24	25–29	30–34	35–39	40–44	45–49
No. of candidates	1	2	6	10	10	9	6	3	2	1

(c)   You should have a diagram as in Fig. 11.25:

Fig. 11.25

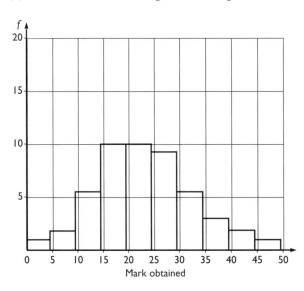

(d)   They performed better on Paper 1 than on Paper 2 as the mean marks of 32.6 on Paper 1 and 23.6 on Paper 2 suggest. However, Paper 2 has a better range and spread of marks than does Paper 1. You could say that Paper 1 was a good GCSE paper as most of the students gained over half marks, where Paper 2 was not, as most of the students scored less than half marks.

A9   Let the probability of scoring a 4 be x, then Table 11.38 illustrates each probability.

Table 11.38

Score	1	2	3	4	5	6
Probability	x	x	x	x	$2x$	$4x$

Hence where the total of the probabilities is 1, then $10x = 1$ and so $x = 0.1$, hence

(i) $P(1) = 0.1$
(ii) $P(6) = 0.4$
(iii) $P(2 \text{ or } 4 \text{ or } 6) = 0.1 + 0.1 + 0.4 = 0.6$

A10 (a) (i) Modal class is 41–50.
(ii) See Table 11.39.

Table 11.39

Miles per gallon (less than)	30.5	35.5	40.5	45.5	50.5	55.5	60.5
Number of motorists	4	10	28	62	82	94	100

(iii) You should have an ogive as in Fig. 11.26.

Fig. 11.26

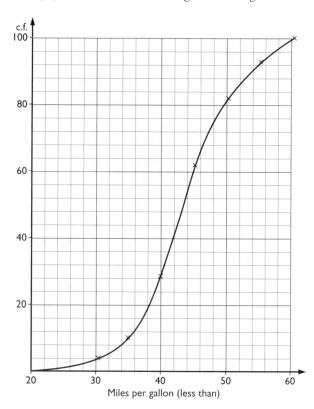

(b) (i) Median – read off the $(101)/2 = 50\frac{1}{2}$th on the c.f. to give 43.8 mpg.
(ii) Upper quartile – read off the $(101) \times \frac{3}{4} = 75.75$th on the c.f. to give 48.5 mpg.
Lower quartile – read off the $(101)/4 = 25.25$th on the c.f. to give 40 mpg.
Hence the interquartile range is $48.5 - 40 = 8.5$ mpg.

(c) Reading up to the ogive and hence the c.f. from 38 and 52 miles you get 17 and 86 respectively. Hence the number of motorists in between this that have 'good' petrol consumption is $86 - 17 = 69$.

A11 (a) (i) The first person can be anybody, so the probability that the next person is married to the first person will be $\frac{1}{9}$.
(ii) Can choose either 'man then woman' *or* 'woman then man', so the probability is
$P(\text{MW}) + P(\text{WM}) = (\frac{5}{10} \times \frac{5}{9}) + (\frac{5}{10} \times \frac{5}{9}) = \frac{50}{90} = \frac{5}{9}$.
(iii) The quickest way is to find $1 - P(\text{no men})$.
$P(\text{no men}) = P(\text{woman then woman}) = \frac{5}{10} \times \frac{4}{9} = \frac{20}{90} = \frac{2}{9}$,
hence $P(\text{at least one man}) = 1 - \frac{20}{90} = \frac{70}{90} = \frac{7}{9}$.
The alternative is to choose either 'man then woman' *or* 'woman then man' *or* 'man then man', so the probability is $\frac{50}{90} + (\frac{5}{10} \times \frac{4}{9}) = \frac{70}{90} = \frac{7}{9}$.

(b) Choose either (WWWM) or (WWMW) or (WMWW) or (MWWW)
(i) which in effect is $4 \times (\frac{5}{10} \times \frac{4}{9} \times \frac{3}{8} \times \frac{5}{7}) = 0.238$
(ii) $P(\text{first person}) = 1$ it can be anybody
$P(\text{next person } not \text{ married to first}) = \frac{8}{9}$
$P(\text{next person } not \text{ married to either of first two}) = \frac{6}{8}$
$P(\text{next person } not \text{ married to either of first three}) = \frac{4}{7}$ hence the probability is
$1 \times \frac{8}{9} \times \frac{6}{8} \times \frac{4}{7} = 0.381$

A12 (a) See Table 11.40.

Table 11.40

Number of weeks after 5 Jan. (x)	0	6	12	18	24	30	36	42	48
Daylight (hours) to 1 decimal place	8.0	10.1	12.8	15.4	16.7	15.3	12.8	10.1	8

(b) See Fig. 11.27.

Fig. 11.27

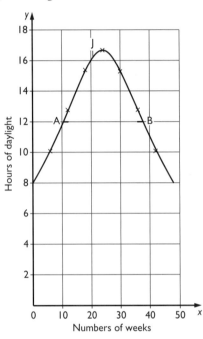

(c) (i) 1 June is 21 weeks after 5 January.
(ii) Hours of daylight on 1 June = 16.3 = 16 hours 18 min.
(d) (i) See Fig. 11.27, points A and B.
(ii) This is the number of weeks between A and B, which is 28 weeks.
(iii) Point A is 10 weeks after 5 January, which is 70 days after 5 January, which corresponds to 16 March.

A13 P(even number) $= \frac{2}{5}$
Estimated number of even numbers $= \frac{2}{5} \times 200 = 80$

A14 (a) $\frac{1}{6} \times \frac{1}{6} \times \frac{1}{6} = \frac{1}{216}$; (b) $\frac{1}{6} \times \frac{9}{10} = \frac{3}{20}$

A15 (a) $\frac{1}{7} \times \frac{1}{7} = \frac{1}{49}$
(b) They could both be born on Sunday *or* Monday *or* etc.
$= (\frac{1}{7} \times \frac{1}{7}) + (\frac{1}{7} \times \frac{1}{7}) + \dots$ etc. $= \frac{1}{49} \times 7 = \frac{1}{7}$
(c) $\frac{1}{7} \times \frac{1}{7} = \frac{1}{49}$

A16 (a) (i) P(win toss) $\times P$(win) $= \frac{1}{2} \times \frac{3}{5} = \frac{3}{10}$
(ii) $\frac{1}{2} \times \frac{1}{4} = \frac{1}{8}$
(b) (i) P(lose) $\times P$(win) $= \frac{1}{2} \times \frac{2}{5} = \frac{1}{5}$
(ii) $\frac{1}{2} \times \frac{1}{2} = \frac{1}{4}$
(c) (i) P(win toss and win) $+ P$(lose toss and win)
$\frac{3}{10} + \frac{1}{5} = \frac{5}{10} = \frac{1}{2}$
(ii) $\frac{1}{8} + \frac{1}{4} = \frac{3}{8}$
(d) Drawn games $= 1 - (\frac{1}{2} + \frac{3}{8}) = \frac{1}{8} \Rightarrow \frac{1}{8} \times 100\% = 12.5\%$

A17   (a)   41.8–41.9   7   41.95   36
41.8–41.9   7   41.95   36
42.0–42.1   4   42.15   40

(b)   40

(d)   Upper quartile = 41.78
Lower quartile = 41.44
Interquartile range = 41.78 − 41.44 = 0.34

A18   (a)   Arithmetic mean = 55.9 ÷ 10 = 5.59
$\Sigma d^2 = (-0.01)^2 + (-0.21)^2 + (0.69)^2 + (-0.61)^2 + (-1.21)^2 + (0.79)^2 + (0.19)^2$
$+ (-0.31)^2 + (0.29)^2 + (0.39)^2 = 3.349$

$\dfrac{\Sigma d^2}{n} = \dfrac{3.349}{10} = 0.3349$

s.d. = $\sqrt{0.3349}$ = 0.58

(b)   This sample has a greater variety of leaf sizes.

A19   (b)

Table 11.41

Mass	m	f	fm	d	d^2	fd^2
40–42	41	1	41	−17.89	320.0	320
42–46	44	3	132	−14.89	221.7	665
46–53	49.5	25	1 237.5	−9.39	88.2	2 205
53–62	57.5	35	2 012.5	−1.39	1.9	66.5
62–75	68.5	36	2 466	9.61	92.4	3 326
		100	5 889			6 582

Estimated mean = 5 889 ÷ 100 = 58.89

$\dfrac{\Sigma fd^2}{n} = \dfrac{6\,582}{100} = 65.82$

s.d. = $\sqrt{65.82}$ = 8.1

(c)   ±2 s.d. = ±16.2 → normal distribution is 42.69 to 75.09
All except the 'extra small' lie in the sample → 99%.

A20   (a)   You should have plotted two polygons using the midway values of each group and their frequencies for the coordinates, not forgetting to bring the polygon down to 0 on the frequency at (25, 0) and (375, 0).

(b)   The weights of plants grown with fertiliser were more consistent than those without. The plants without fertiliser had more plants grown at the lowest and highest weights than with the fertiliser.

A21   You should mention things like:

equal numbers from each school year   randomly select pupils
equal numbers of boys and girls   interview individually
ask all interviewees the same question(s)

Grade checklist	
For grade	**You should be able to do the following:**
B	Construct and interpret cumulative frequency diagrams. Calculate probabilities of combined events.
A	Construct and interpret histograms. Use sampling to investigate a population. Use tree diagrams.
A*	Calculate standard deviation.

SUMMARY

▷ **Average**   There are three different averages:
 Mode   the most frequently occurring item of data
 Median   the middle item of data, once all the data have been put into order
 Mean   the result of adding all the items of data and dividing that total by the total number of items added

▷ **Statistical charts**   Bar charts   Pictograms   Pie charts

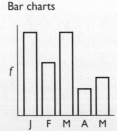
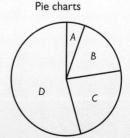

▷ **Histogram**   Similar to a bar chart except that the widths of the bars are often different because it is the *area* of the bar which is equal to the frequency of whatever the bar is representing. The scale of a histogram will usually be continuous.

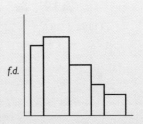

▷ **Cumulative frequency**   Used to find quartiles and the median for large data. If the cumulative frequency diagram is made with straight lines, it is a *cumulative frequency polygon*, otherwise it should be a *cumulative frequency curve*.

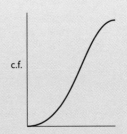

▷ **Scatter diagrams**   Used to plot a lot of points to test for correlation.

If there is a correlation then a *line of best fit* can be drawn in such a way that it represents the best trend of all the data.

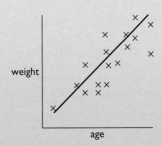

▷ **Probability**   *Equally likely chances* are events that have exactly the same opportunity to happen. The probability of event A happening, P(A), is equal to:

$$\frac{\text{number of ways that event A can happen}}{\text{total number of ways that the equally likely events can happen}}$$

AND   the probability of event A AND event B happening is equal to the product (multiply) of their two probabilities.
OR   the probability of event A OR event B happening is equal to the sum of their two probabilities
Expectation   If in an experiment an event A has a probability P of happening, and the experiment occurs N times, then we would expect event A to happen PN times.

▷ **Standard deviation**   Found by following these steps:

(a)   Find the mean for the given data
(b)   Find the deviations from the mean for each piece of data
(c)   Square each of the deviations
(d)   Find the mean of these squared deviations
(e)   The square root of this mean is the standard deviation (s.d.)

Chapter

12

MA1 work (coursework)

▶ GETTING STARTED

All GCSE mathematics syllabuses include an MA1 component, i.e. a component which seeks to measure your progress in 'using and applying mathematics'. The way this fits into the whole programme of assessment will vary from exam board to exam board and from school to school. Yet there is a common underlying principle behind MA1-based activities, namely to help the student reach a better understanding of mathematics through investigation and problem-solving.

Familiarity with the MA1 activities expected of you will be of help towards the end of year 9 (as you begin to consider seriously your GCSE programme). Still more in years 10 and 11 as you embark on the activities themselves and have to present the outcome of your investigations in written form. This work may be assessed over the two years by many assignments or by one terminal exam.

You will find general aims in your GCSE mathematics syllabus which relate to MA1 work. These will include statements along the following lines. MA1 work will help you, as candidates, to:

- ▶ develop mathematical knowledge in a way which increases your interest and confidence;
- ▶ write and talk about mathematics in a variety of ways;
- ▶ apply mathematics to everyday situations and to begin to understand the part that mathematics plays in the world in which you live;
- ▶ see how a situation can be represented mathematically and then formulate the problem, selecting where necessary a mathematical method to solve it;
- ▶ develop your mathematics by enquiry and experiment by means of practical and investigational work.

▶ **Topic chart** The following topic chart can be completed for each of the topics in 'MA1 work'. Tick the appropriate box when you have first studied that topic. You can also keep a record of when you have revised that topic for the first and second time, etc.

London	MEG	NEAB	NICCEA	SEG	WJEC	IGCSE	TOPIC	STUDY	REVISION 1	REVISION 2
✓	✓	✓	✓	✓	✓	✓	Coursework skills			
✓	✓	✓	✓	✓	✓	✓	Types of coursework			
✓	✓	✓	✓	✓	✓	✓	Investigations and problem-solving			
✓	✓	✓	✓	✓	✓	✓	Extended pieces of work			
✓	✓	✓	✓	✓	✓	✓	Oral and aural			
✓	✓	✓	✓	✓	✓	✓	What the examiner wants			
✓	✓	✓	✓	✓	✓	✓	Pieces of coursework			
✓	✓	✓	✓	✓	✓	✓	Terminal examination of MA1			

WHAT YOU NEED TO KNOW

MA1 work should not be seen as an 'extra' activity which takes place *outside* the classroom. It should rather be understood that MA1 work seeks to encourage and reward good practice in mathematics *wherever* it is performed. Good practical work and pieces of extended work or investigations will be recognised and assessed, and can now form part of the basis for the overall grade.

MA1 work should encourage and support you in developing your knowledge and understanding of mathematics to the best of your ability. You will engage in a variety of 'experiences' of mathematics during your MA1 work programme. These should increase your *awareness* of how mathematics can be used to solve practical problems. It should also, of course, increase your *ability* to put these solutions into practice.

There will be *specific* tasks set and assessed as part of your MA1 work, and you should always be told if a particular piece of work is to be part of coursework assessment or not. So *not all* the work you do during your mathematics course will be coursework; only those specific tasks given and *designated as such* will be called coursework. Although such coursework can be started in year 9 of school, it is usually in years 10 and 11 that coursework is counted towards the GCSE assessment.

Your teachers are responsible for:

▶   telling you which work is part of your coursework, if you are doing this;
▶   telling you what grades or level you have so far reached;
▶   keeping a record of your work and the grades (marks);
▶   telling you if a piece of work is MA1 practice for a terminal examination.

▶ Coursework skills

The actual coursework done and assessed will vary from examination board to examination board and from school to school. It may well vary from class to class, but *all* will be testing the same skills and marking to the same criteria, within three broad areas:

▶   Making decisions on how to solve the problem
▶   Mathematical communication
▶   Reasoning, logic and proof

The vast majority of tasks will be assessed on these three skills. They are the starting points to be used in deciding how the task is to be solved, and they ultimately determine what results you find and the conclusions you draw.

These skills, which are tested through coursework, are listed in rather more detail below (not every task will require you to use every ability on this list).

Making decisions

Ability to:

▶   choose a suitable method to help you solve the problem;
▶   identify necessary information;
▶   check that results are sensible;
▶   break the problem down into manageable stages;
▶   introduce questions of your own to find out more about the problem;
▶   develop the problem further using more complicated mathematics;
▶   consider the effect of different approaches to the problem;
▶   explore an area of mathematics that is unfamiliar to you.

Mathematical communication

Ability to:

▶   explain how you are going to solve the problem;
▶   write out your results clearly;
▶   show results in a table or use diagrams;
▶   use algebra effectively;
▶   link diagram, charts, etc. with clear explanation;
▶   present an accurate and convincing mathematical solution;
▶   use mathematical techniques efficiently to give a full solution.

Reasoning, logic and proof

Ability to:

▶ find easy examples that fit the problem;
▶ look for patterns in your results;
▶ explain the pattern or find a rule from your results;
▶ explain how the pattern works using algebra;
▶ give reasons as to why you've chosen a particular approach to a solution;
▶ give a sound mathematical proof of a complex situation.

We have already listed (in Chapter 3) the particular skills expected at each grade.

▶ Types of coursework

There are two main *types* of coursework that you could be given as assignments:

▶ investigational or problem-solving
▶ extended pieces of work.

In each case you will given the task, told the problem to solve or given the practical work to do. You must have some choice, especially on the extended piece of work, but almost *every* task will be *given* to you.

Investigational or problem-solving

Here you are given a 'question' that needs to be solved by thinking through different strategies, often referred to as a puzzle.

Extended piece of work

Here you are often given a fact then told to find out more about the situation. It is generally a long investigation.

Let us now look at each of these in more detail.

▶ Investigations and problem-solving

In both investigations and problem-solving it is essential to be clear about what it is you have to do, so that you have in mind what the *complete* task is.

(a) read the problem;
(b) do the problem;
(c) write up the problem.

'You must communicate what you have done'

You may also have to *talk* about your solution once you've found it.

All these stages are important and, of course, are linked together since each of the later ones depends on the earlier ones. Remember though, that although you may *solve* the problem in the best of ways, you will get few marks for it if you have not *written it up* properly.

Here we look more closely at these *three stages* and help you work through them with many sample tasks of the type you will meet during years 10 and 11 at school.

Start by reading

Read the question! I know that's obvious, but quite honestly the simplest mistakes are caused by candidates *not* reading the question properly. You need to understand what the *problem* is about, and to know exactly what the problem is telling you and what it is really asking you. You need to read the *question* carefully so that you can sort out a route through the problem to come to a solution. You will need to organise and rewrite the facts (if any are given) into some simple, sensible order. Then think 'what is it I have to find?'.

Task 1 'Square' numbers are the average of the adjacent 'circle' numbers (see Fig. 12.1). What can you find out about the links between 'circle' numbers and the 'square' number for *all* such triangles?

Fig. 12.1

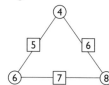

To start:

1. **Read the question. Look at what's given and see what you know:**

    (a) Yes, each square holds the average of the two numbers either side of it.
    (b) 'Circle' numbers add up to give $4 + 6 + 8 = 18$.
    (c) 'Square' numbers add up to give $5 + 7 + 6 = 18$.
    (d) All 'circle numbers are even, 'squares' are not.

    These are the 'simple' things you can notice by looking at the information.

2. **What is it you have to find?**
    You are looking for links between 'square' numbers and 'circle' numbers. For example, we see that *both* 'circle' and 'square' numbers add up to the same. The most important thing is to 'investigate any links you see to find out if these are always true for such triangles, and to see what other possible links you can find'.

Doing the problem

Now we've read the problem we need to sort it out and this will involve the following stages.

▶ Looking for a *route* through our problem (or at least starting out on one).
▶ Getting all the *information organised*.
▶ Looking for *patterns and relationships*.
▶ Finding an *end*.

Looking for a route

Now that you know what you are being asked, you have to sort out a route through your problem (there may well be more than one).
   Here are a few *questions* that you could ask of your given task:

1. Am I looking for *one* answer only?
2. Can I *simplify* the situation in any way?
3. Can I *split the problem* into a few separate parts?
4. Can I *already see a pattern* or not?
5. Do I need to find lots of *similar situations* to investigate?

Then, depending on your answers to all these questions, you can start to organise your route through the problem.
   If we were to answer these questions on Task 1, our *answers* would be:

1. No, there are 'quite a few', so we know we are going to be involved in a number of different routes for different answers.
2. No (this problem is as simple as it could be).
3. Yes, we could split it up into:
    (a) only even circle numbers (or squares);
    (b) only odd circle numbers (or squares).

(We've already seen that *adding* gives a nice link here, so what about subtracting, or multiplying, or even dividing? What about halves, even decimals!)

4. Yes (I can see both types of number add up to the same).

5. Yes (there are thousands you could try, but try to use reasonably small numbers to keep it as simple as possible).

Now we can work out a route to start us off, see Fig. 12.2.

Examiner's note: how you start is important; you should try to start out on an organised route through your problem. Most of the questions raised should be asked 'in your head' and any constructive answers should be written down as *evidence* of your initial thoughts and the way you have gone about breaking the problem down. Starting with the *initial* answers to your questions will set you off on your route.
   Let's look at what 'yes' could mean to your route from the previous question.

Fig. 12.2

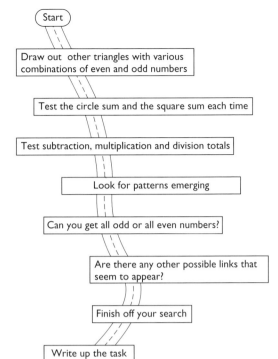

'Simplifying a problem or situation can help'

Question 1: Am I looking for one answer only?
You may answer *yes* to this question for problems like the following.

Task 2   How many different combinations of clothes can I wear if I choose from 4 different pairs of trousers, from 13 different shirts and from 7 different pairs of socks?

If, as here, you know that there is only *one* answer, your route will be entirely devoted to getting to that one answer. Therefore in this task we should avoid getting caught up in exploring interesting patterns that do *not* help us arrive at our single answer. (Keep that approach for another opportunity when you may need to extend a problem of your own.)

However, if your answer here was *no*, as it would be in Task 1, then you *are* in a situation where you need to be exploring the various patterns that you think of.

Question 2: Can I simplify the situation in any way?
Often if the problem is given in a 'real world' situation then the answer will be *yes*, as in the next task.

Task 3   A new town was being built with all the roads straight. The council, for safety reasons, needs to put an extra large lamppost at each crossroads. Find out the greatest number of extra large lampposts needed by the council for the new town for the various number of roads that could be built.

This problem simplifies to one of drawing straight lines to cross each other rather than counting how many crossroads you have created (Fig. 12.3).

Fig. 12.3   ● Lamppost

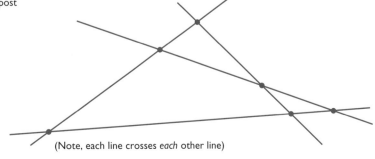

(Note, each line crosses *each* other line)

Question 3: Can I split the problem up into a few separate parts?
Your task could give rise to a number of situations in which you would be advised to break the task down into separate parts.

Fig. 12.4

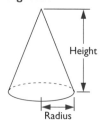

Height

Radius

Task 4   Find a way of making a cone to a specified height and radius (Fig. 12.4).

The task looks short and simple, but will involve your sorting out quite a few problems:

(a)   How do you make a cone? (Answer: from a sector).
(b)   From the given dimensions of this sector what will be the height and radius of the cone?
(c)   From the previous question can you now 'turn the tables' so that you can predict what sector is needed for a given cone?
(d)   Prove that it works by making the cone.

These are four separate but linked problems, each of which needs sorting out.

Question 4: Can I already see a pattern or not?
Here you will either see one (as in Task 1) or not. If *yes*, then you have your starting point and can explore that. If *no*, then you need to look for a pattern to *check* whether or not one can be identified at this stage.

Question 5: Do I need to find lots of similar situations?
If yes, then you will need to think carefully about what similar situations you could investigate. Try to create some pattern or order in the situations you choose.
    For example, in Task 2 you could investigate what happens with 1 shirt, 1 pair of trousers and 1 pair of socks, then 1 shirt, 1 pair of trousers and 2 pairs of socks up to 2 shirts, 3 pairs of trousers and 4 pairs of socks, and look for any *patterns* to help you *predict* the final answer you are seeking.

Getting your information organised

'Organise your information using tables, if appropriate'

Once you have set off on your route you will be finding data or information, usually as a result of experiment or from an organised trial of different situations.
    The way that you *record* your information is very important. It will gain or lose you marks, and good recording will help you to see patterns that arise from the situations.
    Look at the problem below and see what links you can find.

Task 5   James, Philip, Jarrad, Ben, Michael, Alison and Suzy were the members of a Subbuteo league, and had to play each other twice only and not on the same date. Each game lasted for an hour and no-one could play more than 2 games per day. James cannot play on a Monday, Wednesday or Friday. Philip can only play on Tuesday, Wednesday and Thursday. Jarrad can play on Monday, Tuesday and Friday. Ben can play on Wednesday and Friday only. Michael cannot play on Wednesday, Thursday or Friday. Alison is free to play any day except Sunday. In fact none of them can play on Sunday, but they can all play on Saturday. Suzy cannot play on Tuesday or Thursday. Arrange a fixture list that will enable all the members of the league to play each other twice (not on the same day). Try to arrange it to last as few days as possible.

Solution   After reading through the question carefully, and maybe twice, you can produce a grid, as in Table 12.1, to illustrate the information you have been given.

Table 12.1

	Mon	Tues	Wed	Thurs	Fri	Sat	Sun
James	✗	✓	✗	✓	✗	✓	✗
Philip	✗	✓	✓	✓	✗	✓	✗
Jarrad	✓	✓	✗	✗	✓	✓	✗
Ben	✗	✗	✓	✗	✓	✓	✗
Michael	✓	✓	✗	✗	✗	✓	✗
Alison	✓	✓	✓	✓	✓	✓	✗
Suzy	✓	✗	✓	✗	✓	✓	✗

Then, from the information in Table 12.1, you can start to complete the problem.

Fig. 12.5

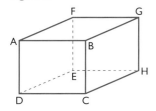

'Use a systematic
approach to solving the
problem'

Task 6   How many different routes are there from A to G in Fig. 12.5, using the edges only?
Each route must not use the same edge more than once.

Solution   It is not a good idea just to write down routes as you see them. Try to be organised;
start with the routes using 1 edge only.

1 edge:	You cannot do this route with only one edge (notice that AG is *not* an edge)
2 edges:	A → B → G and
	A → F → G are the only two routes to find. Put them in a list as:
	ABG
	AFG
3 edges:	You cannot do this with three edges
4 edges:	ABCHG
	ADCBG
	ADCHG
	ADEFG
	ADEHG
	AFEHG

Notice how you should be systematically looking from point A. Here it has been done
alphabetically, AB ..., then AD ..., then AF ..., and so on.

Then we would look for the 5-edge routes (but you wouldn't find any), then look for the
6-edge routes, etc. So, to look for information efficiently you need to be organised in your
search and your recording.

Looking for patterns
Very often, the quicker you can find a pattern from your data, then the sooner you can stop
experimenting and move on to the next stage of 'finding an end'.

Turn again to Task 3, the new town problem. Simplify the situation, record any findings,
and then look for patterns. For example (see also Fig. 12.6):

2 roads	need	1	lamp
3 roads	need	3	lamps
4 roads	need	6	lamps
5 roads	need	10	lamps

Fig. 12.6

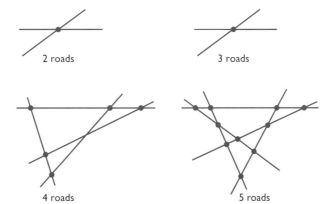

You need to be careful here that you try to draw each new road in such a way as to give the
most crossroads needing *extra large* lampposts.

Now look at Table 12.2 for any patterns

Table 12.2

Roads	2	3	4	5
Lampposts	1	3	6	10

If you look at the *differences* in the bottom row of the table you will see that there is a pattern
(Fig. (12.7).

Fig. 12.7

1 →	3 →	6 →	10 →	?
	+2	+3	+4	?

Hence the next number is $10 + 5 = 15$, so for 6 roads we will need 15 lampposts.

You then need to see if you can find the link between the *number of roads* and the *number of lampposts*, so that you could work out easily how many lampposts you would need for, say, 150 roads. So, let's look at Table 12.3 for our new extended table of results.

Table 12.3

Roads	2	3	4	5	6	7	8	____ n
Lampposts	1	3	6	10	15	21	28	?

You are looking for the *relationship* that exists between roads and lampposts.

(a) Try simple *addition* or *subtraction* – nothing!
(b) Try simple *multiplication* or *division* – nothing!
(c) Look at the *factors* of each lamppost number, see Table 12.4.

Table 12.4

Roads	2	3	4	5	6	7	8
Lampposts	1	3	6	10	15	21	28
	(1×1)	(1×3)	(2×3)	(2×5)	(3×5)	(3×7)	(4×7)

On first inspection you may see nothing, but then if you *double* the smallest number in each product you get the results set out in Table 12.5.

Table 12.5

Roads	2	3	4	5	6	7	8
$2 \times$ Lampposts	(1×2)	(2×3)	(3×4)	(4×5)	(5×6)	(6×7)	(7×8)

Now we can see the pattern that gives

roads n
$2 \times$ lampposts $(n - 1) \times n$

'Here is a pattern we have found'

Hence from n roads we get:

$\frac{1}{2} \times (n - 1) \times n$ **lampposts**

You can easily check this formula with any of the results we have already found, e.g. 7 roads $= \frac{1}{2} \times 6 \times 7 = 21$ lampposts. Look for patterns, and then use these patterns either to find a relationship or to predict a certain result.

Have you now got an answer to your problem? If not then you probably need to look at the problem in a *different way*. It can often happen that you seem to get nowhere, and when you *are* in this situation you need to look again and maybe turn the problem round.

Task 7 A mathematical milkman had to leave 18 pints of milk at a school each day. He always left the bottles in a 4 by 6 crate, see Fig. 12.8.

Fig. 12.8

Fig. 12.9

Fig. 12.10

O	X	O	X	O	O
O	O	O	X	X	O
O	X	O	O	X	O
O	O	O	O	O	O

O = milk bottles
X = space

Fig. 12.11

X	X				
X		X			
	X	X			

Now, *every* row and *every* column had in it an even number of bottles. How could he do this and can you find a number of different ways? Draw your answer on the grid in Fig. 12.9.

Solution   The problem is best thought about by using counters or even pieces of paper to represent the bottles. Then by trial and error you can find one solution, then other solutions.

For example, there is an even number of bottles in each row and in each column of the crate shown in Fig. 12.10.

Yet, the problem is easier if it is looked at from the other end. That is, instead of the bottles, look for the spaces (there are only 6 of these).

Now the problem is much easier – do one row at a time. One of many solutions is shown in Fig. 12.11.

So look out for the situations that can be looked at in quite a different way and so become much simpler.

Finding an end

You will get to a stage where you have got the answer to the task, or, if there are a number of possibilities, then you have arrived at a number of solutions.

If the problem was an open-ended investigation, like Task 1, then you must decide when enough is enough, i.e. when you have found *sufficient* relationships to end the task. Unfortunately there is no simple rule like 'three relationships will do' or 'four sides of paper is sufficient'. There will be times when one or two relationships will be sufficient while at other times perhaps four or five can usually be found.

Look through the model coursework solutions later in the chapter. These will give you an idea of how much material might be sufficient. Remember though – it will be the quality of your material and not the quantity that really matters.

Writing up

This is where you really do need to be very careful. You need to write up all the relevant things you did. You need three parts:

(a) *Introduction:* state the problem and what it was that you planned to do.
(b) *The route:* clearly show *all* the trials that you have done, with clear diagrams and tables illustrating the results. State the relationships found and their relevance. Do not just show results here – say what you did to find them.
(c) *Conclusion:* you need here to say how you proved your results. Did you test out your findings? You need to give a clearly reasoned answer to the problem, or to summarise the relationships found.

'Important stages in writing-up your investigation'

All the writing up must be of your *own* work. You may have been part of a group, but if you write up a result you must be able to understand where it came from and how it was found. This is important, for not only will you have to sign a declaration at the end of the course to say that it is your own work, but you may also be required to *talk* about your conclusions. This *oral work* can be part of the coursework and as such can be included in your coursework assessment. Hence:

read well → plan well → be thorough in your route → find conclusions then write them up

The route is summarised in Fig. 12.12.

Fig. 12.12

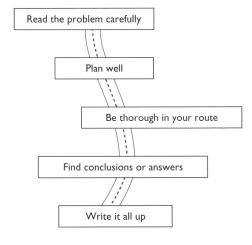

It is usually a very good technique to keep *rough notes* of your work at each stage – the reading, the planning, the patterns found and the conclusion, and *then* to write it all up neatly at the end.

Access to a word processor can be very useful in recording and writing up your work. Remember to leave spaces for inserting your diagrams. Check with your teacher that you can use a word processor when writing up your material.

▶ Extended pieces of work

This will be a piece of work for which there is usually no one correct answer, but a *variety of different possibilities* depending on the situation.

The treatment of an extended piece of work will be similar to that for an investigation or problem-solving. Of course, the activity of 'investigation' may be at the very heart of the extended piece of work. What is vital is that you select a piece of work that you can work on yourself and can make as long or as short, as complicated or as simple as you wish. Of course, the more comprehensive the investigation is, the better the mark it can achieve.

Researching

One example of an extended piece of work could be the following:

Fig. 12.13

'There are many stages involved in an extended piece of work'

Task 8   Choose a busy roundabout or road junction near to you and find how much traffic uses this junction and what the likely effect of traffic lights could be (you decide on the timing of the lights).

Solution   Clearly you need a junction with a lot of traffic, and you need to:

(a)   find out how much traffic uses it from each direction;
(b)   find the average waiting time to get into the main flow;
(c)   try to simulate lights.

Quite a problem, but a real one as many town planners will tell you.

You need to select your junction. Make it one that you have easy access to, since you may be there quite often over a short space of time.

Then do a survey on *how much* traffic uses the junction from each direction. You can probably only sensibly count one road flow at a time.

12.14

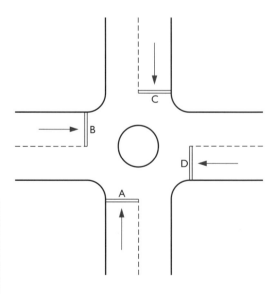

Fig. 12.15

Monday	4.00 → 4.30 count at A
	4.30 → 5.00 count at B
Tuesday	4.00 → 4.30 count at C
	4.30 → 5.00 count at D
Wednesday	4.00 → 4.30 count at B
	4.30 → 5.00 count at A
Thursday	4.00 → 4.30 count at D
	4.30 → 5.00 count at C

So, as in Fig. 12.14, you need to count at A, B, C and D, on different days. To make allowances for different days you would be advised to use a timetable similar to Fig. 12.15.

Fig. 12.16

This is already four hours of just counting but do use a tally chart, as in Fig. 12.16.

Of course you could get help in the survey. Friends, brother or sisters will probably enjoy helping you.

Next you need to calculate *how long* each car has to wait at a junction. Here you probably will need a friend to help you since you need a stopwatch to count the seconds that each car has to wait once it has got to the junction. Again, as before, you need to spread the count over a few days and do different junctions at different times.

Then you can work out on *average* how long each car waits, and you know how many cars use each junction.

Next, you *simulate* a set of traffic lights. Let's suppose that we had the following figures from a survey, see Table 12.6.

Table 12.6

Junction	Number of cars per minute	Number of seconds wait per car
A	15	5
B	6	8
C	11	4.3
D	8	7.6

We can see that the flow from A and C is the largest, hence they should be given a longer time at green. A starting point could be (for safety, don't forget to allow for amber as well as green):

AC   green for 30 seconds
         amber for 5 seconds
BD   green for 15 seconds
         amber for 5 seconds, etc.

Now consider the AC flow. Use the largest traffic flow of 15 per minute, hence 8 every 30 seconds with no waiting.

After the next 25 seconds (5 + 15 + 5), 7 cars are waiting. It now becomes clear that we need to know how long it takes traffic to go through the lights when green to avoid a stoppage at a junction. So go to a junction where there *are* traffic lights to see how many cars usually go through at green and in what time.

Clearly this is becoming a large project – an *extended piece of work*, and a lot of time will be spent in research, looking at figures, simulating situations, trial and error for different times, until at last you reach a firm conclusion that:

either – lights would be a good idea and suggest the timing of them
or   – lights would not help the flow at all.

Presentation

A lot of work will have gone into this project, so give it full value. Say what you have done, giving a good explanation of the nature of the problem and of the tasks you set yourself, and remember to give all your results. Show clearly the *use* you have made of the results and suggest any extra work you might now need to do.

▶ Whatever you did in this project, put it down with clear explanations as to *why* you did it.
▶ Then give your conclusions, with good clear reasons why you have come to the decision you have.
▶ Present your work neatly and clearly. Again a word processor could clearly be an advantage to you here, but don't forget to insert your diagrams to help illustrate the points that you are making.

Conclusion

In every type of coursework these three main principles will always apply:

▶ Plan the work before you start.
▶ Do the work thoroughly and thoughtfully, writing notes on what you have done.
▶ Communicate all your work, in either oral or written form, depending on what you have been requested to do.

You can be given guidance by your teacher and help by parents or friends, but at the end of the day it is up to *you* to demonstrate what *you* can do.

▶ Oral and aural

Part of your coursework assessment could be on how well you can speak mathematics and on how well you can listen and think out mathematics. It is done in two quite different ways: *oral* and *aural*.

The differences between oral and aural always seem to confuse teachers, as well as students.

Oral

An *oral* task might be you talking to someone about what you have done in a problem, or you giving a spoken answer to some questions.

For example, you could have been given the task 'how much does a piece of paper weigh?' You might then be given the question 'explain why you did it that way'. How you answer is important:

▶ Do you *know* why you did it that way?
▶ Can you *explain clearly* why you did it?

These are the main ideas that the assessor (who may well be your teacher) is looking for. In other words, can you *communicate* your mathematical ideas verbally?

'Practice makes perfect' is an old saying, but one which contains a lot of truth. Do ask yourself (or perhaps each other) these types of question and get used to expressing yourself in response to such questions.

'The oral is about your ability to talk mathematics'

Try to *say* what you have done confidently. It may have been wrong, but the oral assessment is not about the right answer, it is about 'how well you can talk mathematics'.

Practise with your parents or friends. Get them to ask some of the following questions and then to comment on your answers. (Of course, you could try some of them!)

Situation 1

1 What is a polygon?
2 What is the 'interior angle' and the 'exterior angle' of a polygon?
3 Describe a regular octagon.
4 Explain how you could find the size of the interior angle of a pentagon.

Situation 2

Write down any two odd numbers. Add them up and also find their difference.

'Practice talking about mathematical situations'

1 What do you notice?
2 Do you think this will always happen?
3 How will you check out the last answer?
4 What do you think you will get with two even numbers?

Situation 3

Find the exact weight of one pint of milk, not including the bottle.

1 How did you do it?
2 Why did you do it like that?
3 Comment on your accuracy.
4 How could you have been more accurate?

Well, how did you, or your parents, get on? These are some of the types of question you can expect from the oral part of your assessment. Please, just try to *say* what you did, being as confident as you can. Don't make up the explanation because that is always noticed and will lose you marks.

After each piece of coursework has been done (or even during it), get someone to ask you some of the following questions. Practise *speaking* your answers to such questions.

1   What was the easiest part of the problem?
2   What was the hardest part of the problem?
3   How on earth did you start it?
4   What things did you assume?
5   What help did you need in solving the problem?
6   Can you explain exactly what it was that you had to find out?
7   What have you found out from this problem?
8   What possible extension of this problem could you suggest to try out?
9   What part of the task did you enjoy?
10 How did you record all the data found out?
11 How did you check your results?
12 What can you say about the accuracy of your figures?
13 Have you learnt anything special from this piece of work?

Aural

'An aural test will involve you in writing down your responses'

An *aural* test is the name given to the situation where you listen to a question or a problem and *then write down* your response or answer.

I suppose these are what used to called 'mental tests'. You could be given some reference sheets, such as timetables or charts, to use. The question will usually be the type that you could well be expected to do in your own head at the shops, on a journey or at work.

These aural tests will usually be assessed at your *particular tier*, i.e. Higher. Try the following. (The Intermediate tier test is included for practice.) Get someone to read the following aural tests to you and see how you get on. Each question should be read twice; then time should be allowed for you to *write down* your answer before giving you the next question. The answers are at the end of this section.

Intermediate tier aural test

1   A car park has 15 rows of cars with 30 cars in each row. How many cars are there in the car park altogether?
2   My cat eats $\frac{3}{4}$ of a tin of cat food each day. How much does she eat in four days?
3   A road has marked out on it seven car-parking spaces, each 3 metres long, and a space at each end of $2\frac{1}{2}$ metres. How long is the road?
4   It takes Janet 20 minutes to walk to school. She walks back home at twice the speed. How long does it take her to walk home?
5   When hot, a metal bar will expand by 5%. What is the expansion of an 80 centimetre-long metal bar when hot?
6   The source of the Nile was discovered by Captain J. H. Speke in 1862. How long ago was that?
7   Write down an approximate answer to 789 divided by 42.
8   Valerie turned up for a date with Richard 12 minutes late. Richard had arrived three minutes early. How long did Richard have to wait for Valerie to turn up?
9   Victor bought a cassette player marked at £20 plus VAT at a rate of 15%. How much VAT did Victor pay?
10 The temperature at midnight was $-6\,°C$. At midday today the temperature was $7\,°C$. By how much did the temperature rise between midnight and midday?

Higher tier aural test

1   Archimedes discovered his theorem in the year 287 BC. How long ago was that?
2   What is the length of a side of a square of area 64 square centimetres?

3   Write down the next square number after 169.
4   Karen has to post 243 leaflets. They come in packs of 25. How many packs will Karen need?
5   John, who earns £810 a month, is given a 7% wage increase. What is John's increase in wages?
6   How many hours is 1000 minutes?
7   What is the approximate length of a diagonal of a square of side 8 centimetres.
8   Katie drove 150 miles in $2\frac{1}{2}$ hours. What speed was she doing?
9   Write down the next prime number after 37.
10   What is the cost of 21 booklets at 99p each?

Answers to Intermediate tier aural test

'Check your answers'

1	450	1 mark	
2	3 tins	1 mark	
3	26 metres	1 mark	
4	10 metres	1 mark	
5	4 cm	1 mark	
6	134 years	1 mark	(add on a year for each year after 1996)
7	20	2 marks	(18, 19 or 21 ... give 1 mark)
8	15 minutes	1 mark	
9	£3	1 mark	
10	13 degrees	1 mark	

(Add on 1 mark if no more than 1 unit not given)

Having marked yourself, now grade yourself below:

Grade B	11 or 12 marks
Grade C	9 or 10 marks
Grade D	7 or 8 marks
Grade E	5 or 6 marks

Answers to Higher tier aural test

1	2283 years	1 mark	(add on a year for each year after 1996)
2	8 cm	1 mark	
3	196	1 mark	
4	10	1 mark	
5	£56.70	1 mark	
6	16 (and 40 minutes) or $16\frac{2}{3}$	1 mark	
7	11 cm	2 marks	(1 mark for answer between 11 and 11.5)
8	60 mph	1 mark	
9	41	1 mark	
10	£20.79	1 mark	

(Add on 1 mark if all units are given)

Having marked yourself, now grade yourself below:

Grade A*	13 marks or over
Grade A	11 or 12 marks
Grade B	9 or 10 marks
Grade C	6, 7 or 8 marks

▶ **What the examiner wants**   You will usually present your coursework throughout the two-year course (or the one year of a one-year course) at times given to you by your teacher. Most pieces of coursework will only take you a few hours to complete. Of course, some of the coursework is supposed to be extended work, and this will last considerably longer than two or three hours.

Do present your coursework on time. It will help if you keep to a schedule. You might set yourself *target* dates for doing the research, writing up some rough notes, writing a final version and so on. This will help you to avoid having a lot of coursework to complete as the deadlines approach.

Your work should be presented as clearly as possible. As I have suggested before, a word processor could help your presentation, for your work does need to be as clear as you can make it. Use carefully drawn, well labelled diagrams wherever possible and try to explain what you *wanted* to do, what you *did* do and what you *found out*.

In most cases the first person to mark your coursework is your teacher, but it could also be looked at by an external examiner to see that all is well with the school's assessment.

Throughout your course, you will be presenting pieces of coursework that illustrate the different abilities being assessed. Any one task may contribute to one, some or all of these abilities (see below). Your teacher should be able to convey to you how well you did and what your strengths and weaknesses were even if he/she cannot give you the mark itself.

Abilities to be tested

The abilities being tested include the following.

Understanding the problem

1   How well have you shown your *understanding* of the problem? Have you understood it all; have you misunderstood it altogether, or have you only understood a part of the problem? The extent of your understanding will be clear through your initial explanation of the problem in your introduction and in your final conclusions.

2   Did you manage to look at the initial problem and then to identify *exactly what it was* you needed to find out? Or did you just get on with it by trial and error? In other words, were you able to identify any mathematical principles that were relevant to the problem set?

3   Have you found the best *way* to tackle the problem, or, rather, a suitable way, for in many cases there is *no best* way? Have you gone a long way round the problem instead of finding a shorter route that was readily available? Sometimes you may have no choice of method, as only one will get you the answer, but usually there are a number of ways – some being better than others.

4   Have you been able to break the task down into smaller tasks or have you tried to solve it all at once? You should always be looking to see if you can simplify your problem by making it into a number of smaller problems.

All these different aspects will indicate how well you were able to understand the given problem and what your response has been to that understanding.

'An outline of the abilities tested during coursework activities'

Working on the problem

1   Did you collect enough *information* for your enquiry? Were you able either to create your own data by suitable experiments or to find the data from reliable and suitable places?

2   How well did you then *process* this information? Were you able to use your collected data in a sensible and useful way?

3   Did you *carry out your calculations* sensibly? For instance, did you *round off*, where necessary, to an appropriate degree of accuracy? In fact, were you able to make sensible approximations beforehand so that you could tell if your results were *realistic* when you found them? This estimation could well be assessed orally, as it is not always easily written into your account. Did you also *check* your results and calculations?

4   How well did you *overcome difficulties?* Did you in fact state your difficulties and then explain how you got round them? You would not always have difficulties (I hope), but on many assignments they will be there (and will often be anticipated by your teacher). How well you recognised them and sought to overcome them will be an important part of the assessment.

5   How *organised* have you been during the assignment? Have you clearly organised your *task* beforehand and gone through it in a logical way? Have you organised your *data* in such a way as to help you identify patterns or to pick out relationships? The more organised you were, the easier it should have been to complete the task and the more marks you are likely to earn.

6   Have you made efficient use of *mathematical language and shorthand* (symbols)? Or have you written everything out longhand? Where it can be used, you should use the symbolism of mathematics (simple algebra for relationships, set notation, $+, -, \times, \div,$

etc.). This will all help to make the presentation less like an essay and more like a piece of mathematics coursework.

How you work out the problem is up to you, and you must therefore clearly state how you did it and why. Try not to leave out things that you did; even including those thoughts that did not seem to work will make a valuable contribution to your coursework.

Making conclusions

1   Could you *identify all the patterns* within the situation and how far could you *generalise* from the patterns identified? That is, could you write down some formula or relationship you have found out from the problem? For example, in the series of numbers 2, 6, 10, 14, 18, 22, ..., the pattern is 'going up in fours from the number 2' and the nth term can be expressed as $2 + 4(n - 1)$. For instance, the 5th term is $2 + 4(5 - 1) = 18$. In fact, have you been able to generalise in mathematical language or did you have to use words?

2   How well could you make logical deductions from your sorted data? For example, you may have done some work on triangles, all with the same height and base length. Could you deduce that *all* the triangles with the same base and height have the same area?

3   When you state your conclusions, how have you *proved* them? Have you just stated what you noticed from your initial data, or have you then gone out to prove, or at least to check with other examples, that what you have found out is generally true?

4   How far have you been able to suggest any *possible extensions* to the task at hand? For instance if your work has all been on triangles, you could suggest what links this could have with quadrilaterals or parallelograms. You might be able to suggest further work which might be undertaken in this respect.

The whole object of problem-solving is to come up with an answer of sorts. It is how you *arrive at* this answer, and how well you *set out your reasons* for your conclusions that will determine the final assessment of your coursework. It is *not* just a simple case of finding the answer. It is much more about your ability to reason out your conclusions mathematically and clearly.

All the examination boards will assess the coursework along similar lines. Here we look at a few actual coursework tasks and how they might be approached.

▶ **Sample pieces of coursework**

What might your coursework look like? Let us look at a few tasks and see what the coursework could look like at the end.

Task 1

A square grows in the following way, see Fig. 12.17.

Fig. 12.17

'Approach to finding a route'

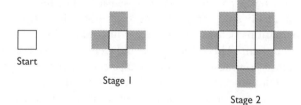

Start

Stage 1

Stage 2

1   Show how this growth continues.
2   What relationships can you find between the stage, the area and the perimeter of the shapes?

Before starting
Consider the problem and read it through. We can see that a possible route through the problem is to:

1   draw the next few stages;
2   make out a table of stage, area and perimeter (we could think about 'new areas of growth', i.e. the shaded squares, and about the total area of the shape);

3   look for patterns within the table;
4   write up the solution, stating what was found out.

One solution to this is provided below, but try the problem yourself first. Only then see if what you have done is along the lines of my proposed solution.

Possible solution
The pattern of new growth can be seen to take the following form, see Fig. 12.18.

Fig. 12.18

'Identifying a pattern'

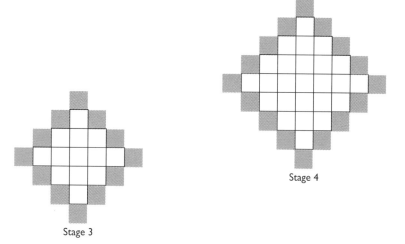

Stage 4

Stage 3

A table of each stage with new growth area, total area and perimeter was constructed, see Table 12.7.

Table 12.7

Stage	New growth area	Perimeter (edges)	Total area
1	4	12	5
2	8	20	13
3	12	28	25
4	16	36	41

1 Consider the relationship between 'stages' and 'new growth area' (Table 12.8) It looked to me as if each new growth had another four squares added on each time. This would then make stage 5 have 16 + 4 which is 20 new squares. I tested this out and, as you see in Fig. 12.19, stage 5 *does* have 20 new squares.

Table 12.8

Stages	1	2	3	4
New growth	4	8	12	16

Fig. 12.19

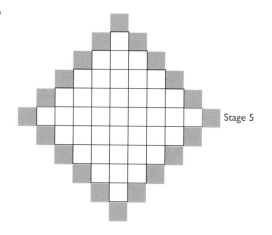

Stage 5

Writing the table out (Table 12.9) led me to say that stage n would have $4 \times n$ new growth squares.

Table 12.9

Stage	1	2	3	4	5
New growth	(1×4)	(2×4)	(3×4)	(4×4)	(5×4)

So the relationship between stages and new growth is:

▶   new growth = 4 times the stage number or
▶   new growth stage $n = 4n$ squares

2 Consider the relationship between 'stages' and 'perimeter' (Table 12.10)   It looks as if each stage has another 8 edges added onto the perimeter. This would suggest that stage 5 has a perimeter of $36 + 8$ which is 44 edges. Checking this in stage 5 (Fig. 15.19) I found it to be true.

Table 12.10

Stage	1	2	3	4
Perimeter (edges)	12	20	28	36

Rewriting the table out (Table 12.11) led me to say that stage n will have a perimeter of $(8 \times n) + 4$ edges. So the relationship between stages and perimeter is:

▶   Perimeter = eight times stage number, add on four, or
▶   perimeter of stage $n = 8n + 4$.

Table 12.11

Stage	1	2	3	4	5
Perimeter (edges)	12	20	28	36	44
	$(8 \times 1) + 4$	$(8 \times 2) + 4$	$(8 \times 3) + 4$	$(8 \times 4) + 4$	$(8 \times 5) + 4$

3 Consider the relationship between 'stages' and 'total area' (Table 12.12)   Looking at the differences in the total area row (Fig. 12.20), the next difference looks like being $16 + 4$ which is 20 squares. This gives the total area in stage 5 as $41 + 20$, which is 61 squares. By counting the squares in stage 5 (Fig. 12.19) this was found to be true.

Fig. 12.20

5   13   25   41
  8   12   16

Table 12.12

Stage	1	2	3	4
Total area	5	13	25	41

Writing the table out (Table 12.13),

Table 12.13

Stage	1	2	3	4	5
Total area	5	13	25	41	61
I noticed	$4 + 1$	$12 + 1$	$24 + 1$	$40 + 1$	$60 + 1$
and then	$(2 \times 2) + 1$	$(2 \times 6) + 1$	$(2 \times 12) + 1$	$(2 \times 20) + 1$	$(2 \times 30) + 1$

I now tried to get the pattern of what multiplies to the 2, i.e.

$$2 \qquad 6 \qquad 12 \qquad 20 \qquad 30$$
$$\text{or} \quad 1 \times 2 \quad 2 \times 3 \quad 3 \times 4 \quad 4 \times 5 \quad 5 \times 6$$

This is quite a nice pattern. Hence I can rewrite the earlier table as Table 12.14.

Table 12.14

Stages	1	2	3	4	5
Total area	5	13	25	41	61
	$2(1 \times 2) + 1$	$2(2 \times 3) + 1$	$2(3 \times 4) + 1$	$2(4 \times 5) + 1$	$2(5 \times 6) + 1$

This led me to say that stage *n* would have a total area of

▶ $2 \times n \times (n + 1) + 1$ squares, or
▶ $2n(n + 1) + 1$ squares

So the relationship between stages and total area is:

▶   total area = 2 times stage times stage add 1, then add another 1.

This is written much better in algebra as:

▶   total area of stage $n = 2n(n + 1) + 1$ squares

Summary of conclusions
For any stage *n*:

▶   new growth area $= 4n$ squares
▶   perimeter (edges) $= 8n + 4$
▶   total area $= 2n(n + 1) + 1$ squares

Hence, taking as an example stage 10, this would have:

▶   new growth of 40 squares
▶   a perimeter of 84 (edges)
▶   a total area of $(20 \times 11) + 1 = 221$ squares

Fig. 12.21

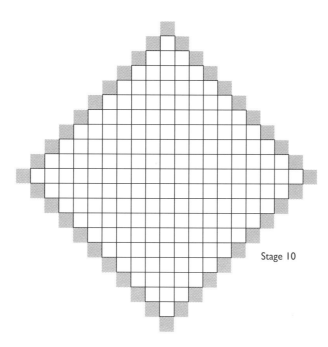

Stage 10

Figure 12.21 is stage 10, and it does have these properties. This is evidence that the relationship is indeed correct.

The *level* or *tier* of your entry for mathematics GCSE will determine how much of that piece of coursework you would be expected to do. For example, only the *Higher tier* students would be expected to find out the relationship between stage and total area! Only the *Higher and the Intermediate* tier students would be expected to find the algebraic relationship for the first two investigations.

   Notice how I did not write an essay, but instead used tables or figures wherever possible. Also notice that, as far as possible, each suggested relationship was tested and the results shown.

Task 2

Choose a book that does not have too many pictures in it, and estimate how many words it contains.

Before starting

You need to choose a book that at least interests you. I chose *Hallowe'en Party* by Agatha Christie. I then sorted out my route to an answer:

1   Estimate how many words to a line.
2   Estimate how many lines per page.
3   Calculate final answer.

Solution

My task was to find out how many words the book *Hallowe'en Party* had in it. I could have counted them all, but decided that that would take too long and would be boring and a waste of my time.

So I decided to estimate the number of words in the following way:

1   Estimate how many words per page.
2   Multiply the number of pages by the estimated number of words per page to give the final answer.

Estimating how many words per page   I chose a few pages at random and counted the number of words in a number of lines:

    page 67   114 words in 14 lines
    page 123   106 words in 12 lines
    page 179   121 words in 13 lines

giving a total sample of 341 words in 39 lines, i.e.

$\dfrac{341}{39}$ which is 8.74 words per line

Now I had to estimate how many lines per page. Again I took a sample and found that:

    page 27 had 37 lines
    page 93 had 42 lines
    page 141 had 37 lines
    page 189 had 42 lines

giving an average of $(37 + 42 + 37 + 42) \div 4 = 158 \div 4 = 39.5$ lines per page.
    Hence I can estimate that each page will have:

    $8.74 \times 39.5 = 345.23$ words on it.

The book consists of 192 pages, one of which is almost blank, giving a figure of 191 pages. So I estimate that each of the 191 pages has 345.23 words, giving a total of:

    $191 \times 345.23 = 65\,938.93$.

This rounds off to 66 000 words.
    My conclusion then is that the book *Hallowe'en Party* was written using 66 000 words.

There is no other way to check this other than to count them all, but it possibly could be made more accurate by taking a *larger sample* of lines and pages if this degree of accuracy were not thought appropriate.
    This task could be given to any level of ability, and the grade you will receive for the work will depend on how you took your sample and how well you have described it.

Task 3

Fig. 12.22

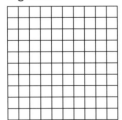

Using the 10 cm × 10 cm pieces of cm² paper as shown in Fig. 12.22, make at least four boxes with different volumes.
    What will be the largest possible volume and what size will the box be?
    Make this box with the greatest volume.

Before starting

We can see that to make boxes from these pieces of paper we need to cut out squares from the corners, then fold up and sellotape them together. I need to do this for different sized squares on the corner, then I need to see which has the biggest volume. After that I try to see if I can make the volume bigger.

Solution
To make boxes from a 10 cm by 10 cm piece of paper, I need to cut out squares and tape them up. The *nets* of the first four boxes that I made are shown in Fig. 12.23.

Fig. 12.23

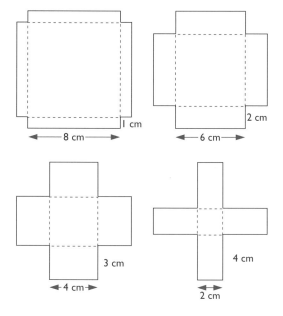

The volumes are calculated by length × width × height. The results are given in Table 12.15.

Table 12.15

Side of square cut out (cm)	Volume of box (cm³)
1	8 × 8 × 1 = 64
2	6 × 6 × 2 = 72
3	4 × 4 × 3 = 48
4	2 × 2 × 4 = 16

Clearly the largest volume here is 72 cm³, but I suspect that this is not the largest possible since I have so far only used whole numbers (integers) for the sizes of squares to cut out.

To help us find what the largest volume might be, I drew a graph of volume against length of square cut out, see Fig. 12.24.

Fig. 12.24

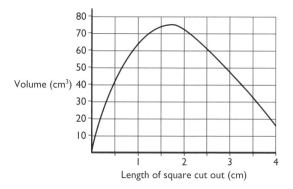

The graph indicated that the volume gradually increased with larger squares cut out until just before 2 cm, when the volume then started to decrease.

From the graph I could see that this largest volume was going to be when the square cut out had length between 1 cm and 2 cm. I now calculated the volume from various squares being cut out from 1.1 cm to 1.9 cm with the rule:

volume = length × breadth × height

Where x is the length cut out:

$$volume = (10 - 2x) \times (10 - 2x) \times x$$
$$= x(10 - 2x)^2$$

(See Fig. 12.25.)

Fig. 12.25

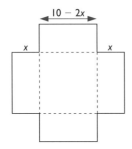

My results are shown in Table 12.16.

Table 12.16

Length of square (cm)	Volume (cm³)
1.1	66.924
1.2	69.312
1.3	71.188
1.4	72.576
1.5	73.5
1.6	73.984
1.7	74.052
1.8	73.728
1.9	

I did not need to work out the volume with $x = 1.9$ since I can already see that the largest volume is between 1.6 and 1.8 cm. I then just tried squares of side 1.65 cm and 1.75 cm to be as close as I could (Table 12.17).

Table 12.17

Length of square (cm)	Volume (cm³)
1.65	74.0685
1.75	73.9375

We now suspect that the largest volume lies between 1.6 and 1.7.

By now I could see that I was getting close. I wanted to be as close possible, so I wrote the following computer program to calculate the volumes between 1.6 cm and 1.7 cm:

```
10 REM    VOLUME
20 FOR    X = 1.6 TO 1.7 STEP 0.01
30 LET    V = X*(10−(2*X)↑2)
40 PRINT  X, V
50 NEXT   X
```

This gave me the following results:

```
1.6      73.9840001
1.61     74.0091241
1.62     74.0301121
1.63     74.0469881
1.64     74.0597761
1.65     74.0685001
```

1.66	74.0731841
1.67	74.0738521
1.68	74.0705281
1.69	74.0632361
1.7	74.0520001

This showed the greatest volume was 74.0738521 cm^3 when the square cut out is of side length 1.67 cm.

Conclusion
Greatest volume 74 cm^3 with a box of dimensions $8.33 \times 8.33 \times 1.67$. The net for this box is given in Fig. 12.26 (at a reduced scale).

Fig. 12.26

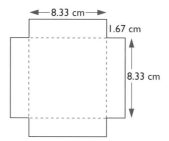

This task could be given to any level of ability. It is the *extent* to which you have gone in trying to find the maximum volume and your ability in *explaining* what you have done that will determine your grade on this assessment. Also taken into account will be how well you constructed all the boxes, and how accurate you were, especially with the last one.

Of course, the use of a computer to do a lot of the calculations might be considered over the top, but if you *do* have the ability and the right equipment, then there is every reason to use it – as long as you have shown how and why and not just said 'the computer gave me the answer'.

These suggested 'model pieces of coursework' are, in each case, only one suggested way of arriving at your solution. It is quite acceptable to end up with similar results obtained by using different methods, so long as you are clear about what you did and have explained all you did.

Summary

To sum up then, in your coursework you must always:

▶   read and think about the problem;
▶   plan a route through it;
▶   think about what equipment you might need for the problem;
▶   do the problem;
▶   check your results;
▶   generalise where possible to the best of your ability;
▶   write up exactly *what* you did, stating *why* you did what you did;
▶   read through the write-up to see if you have missed anything.

Try to avoid rushing the work. Give it the time to develop properly; otherwise you will be underselling yourself. Remember, the coursework marks are worth 20% of your total marks.

▶ Terminal examination of MA1

Each examination board has a syllabus that will assess the same skills as outlined in this chapter through a terminal examination. You will be given approximately $1\frac{1}{2}$ hours to answer two problems, allowing you to demonstrate the qualities discussed earlier in this chapter (p.226).

You will receive a mark for each of the three parts:

▶   making decisions
▶   communicating
▶   reasoning, logic and proof

The *best* mark of the two questions for *each part* will be the one which is counted. These three (best) marks will be added together to give you your final mark for MA1 assessment.

You have two possible strategies:

▶ Spend an equal amount of time on both problems, doing each of them to the best of your ability.
▶ Choose the one problem that you can see a clear route through; do that one well, and then spend some time on the other problem just in case (for one part) you can improve your first mark.

There is no general rule about which strategy is the best, but for each individual there will be a decision to be made about how you will tackle the paper. My advice is to choose the second option. In other words, select first the problem that you can see your way through clearly and to which you think you will be able to produce a very good solution. Do not only answer one problem though, since you are clearly then putting 'all your eggs in one basket'.

If you decide that no particular question seems straightforward to you, then choose the first option, spend an equal amount of time on each problem, but do get yourself to a solution in both cases.

You may find that after practising these types of examination question, one strategy suits you more than the other, in which case you will have a good idea of what you will do in the examination. Indeed, practice of the questions is the best way to revise and prepare for this examination paper.

Below is a selection of MA1-type examination questions and pointers to their solutions.

▶ MA1 EXAMINATION QUESTIONS

▶ **Question 1**
Strange Pythagoras

When Jan and Paul were reading a book about the Pythagoras theorem they noticed the following statement:

All triangles with respective sides of length $m^2 + n^2$, $m^2 - n^2$, and $2mn$, are right angled.

Here m and n are called generating numbers, see Fig. 12.27.

Fig. 12.27

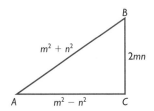

(a) Prove that the statement in the book is true for all values of m and n.
(b) Investigate for consecutive numbers m and n.
(c) Investigate for values of m and n that are triangle numbers.   (NEAB)

▶ **Question 2**
Calendar patterns

Fig. 12.28

M	A	Y			19	94
Sun	Mon	Tue	Wed	Thu	Fri	Sat
1	2	3	4	5	6	7
8	9	10	11	12	13	14
15	16	17	18	19	20	21
22	23	24	25	26	27	28
29	30	31				

After Bill had investigated number patterns in the calendar shown in Fig. 12.28, he wrote a summary of his findings (Fig. 12.29).

Fig. 12.29

If you take any block of four numbers, like:

4	5
11	12

or

16	17
23	24

I think the following rules work.

Rule 1
If you add the pairs of numbers in the opposite corners of a block you get the same answer:

$$4 + 12 = 16 \quad \text{and} \quad 16 + 24 = 40$$
$$5 + 11 = 16 \qquad\qquad 17 + 23 = 40$$

Rule 2
If you add all four numbers, the answer is always in the 8 times table:

$$4 + 5 + 11 + 12 = 32 \qquad \text{and} \qquad 16 + 17 + 23 + 24 = 80$$
$$32 = 4 \times 8 \qquad\qquad\qquad 80 = 10 \times 8$$

Rule 3
if you multiply the pairs of numbers in the opposite corners of a block, the two answers always differ by 7:

$$4 \times 12 = 48 \qquad \text{and} \qquad 16 \times 24 = 384$$
$$5 \times 11 = 55 \qquad\qquad 17 \times 23 = 391$$
$$55 \text{ is 7 more than 48} \qquad 391 \text{ is 7 more than 384}$$

(a) Are Bill's three rules always true?

(b) For each rule, explain how you would convince someone that your reasoning is correct.

(c) Write down some rules of your own based on this calendar.
    Check whether your rules are always true. (NEAB)

▶ **Question 3
Security alarms**

Security alarms are to be installed in the Gold and Diamond Warehouse. Inside the large rooms of the warehouse, stock is arranged in square blocks, each of the same size. Passageways run alongside these square blocks. Each security alarm can scan down the length of one block in all directions, as shown in Fig. 12.30.

Fig. 12.30

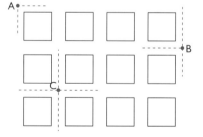

An alarm at A can cover 2 blocks
An alarm at B can cover 3 blocks
An alarm at C can cover 4 blocks

Mary and Tom are planning where the alarms should be placed so that they use the minimum number, but every passageway must be covered.

In one storage room, four blocks are arranged in a square (Fig. 12.31).

Fig. 12.31

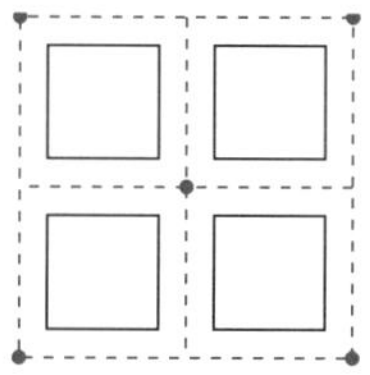

Tom thinks they need five alarms. Mary says they only need 4.

Can you find a connection between the size of the warehouse and the minimum number of alarms needed? Investigate the situation. (NEAB)

▶ **Question 4**
Border tiles

Fred decides to cover the kitchen floor with tiles of different colours. He starts with a row of 4 tiles the same colour (Fig. 12.32).

Fig. 12.32

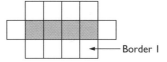

He surrounds these 4 tiles with a border of tiles of a different colour (Fig. 12.33).

Fig. 12.33

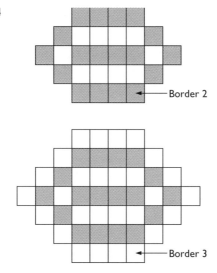

Border 1

The design continues as shown in Fig. 12.34.

Fig. 12.34

Border 2

Border 3

Fred writes $t = 4b + 6$, where t is the number of tiles and b is the border number.

(a)   Check whether Fred's formula is correct.
(b)   Emma wants to start with 5 tiles in a row.

Fig. 12.35

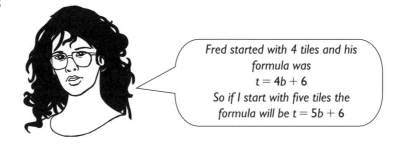

Fred started with 4 tiles and his
formula was
$t = 4b + 6$
So if I start with five tiles the
formula will be $t = 5b + 6$

Check Emma's statement in Fig. 12.35 and show that it is not correct.
(c)   Investigate a generalisation which will help you to find the number of tiles in each border, starting with any number of tiles.   (NEAB)

▶ **Question 5**
Joining dots

These rules are for a game for two people.

Rule 1   Draw 4 dots on a piece of paper.
Rule 2   Take it in turn to join two dots with a line.
Rule 3   No more than 3 lines can join a dot.
Rule 4   No line must cross a line already drawn.
Rule 5   The person who goes last wins.

A completed game is shown in Fig. 12.36.

Fig. 12.36

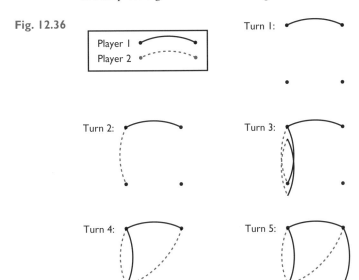

Play the game a few times.
Find the maximum number of lines you need to draw, to win the game.
What happens if you change Rule 1?
What happens if you change the other rules?   (SEG)

▶ **Question 6
Hand luggage**

Air passengers are allowed to take one item of hand luggage on the flight. Airlines 1 and 2 have different rules about the size of the hand luggage, see Figs 12.37 and 12.38.

Fig. 12.37

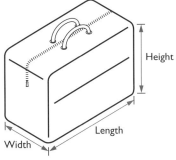

Airline 1
Length + width + height of
hand luggage must not
be more than 150 cm

Fig. 12.38

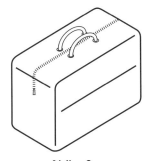

Airline 2
The volume of hand luggage
must not be more than 60 000 cm^3

Investigate, for each airline, suitable designs of hand luggage which will satisfy the rule and be as large as possible, but made from the smallest amount of material (see Fig. 12.39 for example).   (SEG)

Fig. 12.39

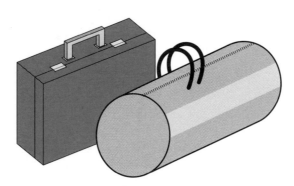

▶ **Question 7**
Polygon puzzles

In any polygon puzzle, the number in a triangle is equal to the sum of the numbers either side of it, see Figs 12.40 and 12.41.

Fig. 12.40

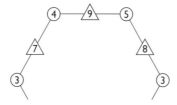

Fig. 12.41

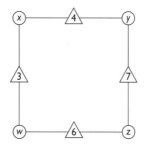

For this square puzzle

$$x + y = 4$$
$$y + z = 7$$
$$w + z = 6$$
$$x + w = 3$$

one possible set of solutions is $x = 1$, $y = 3$, $z = 4$, $w = 2$.

Investigate the solutions for other polygon puzzles.   (SEG)

▶ **Question 8**
Hugh's problem

Hugh makes the following statement: For any value of n (where n is a whole number) the expression $4n + 1$ can be written as the sum of two square numbers, allowing zero as one of the numbers if necessary.
For example:

when $n = 0$, $4n + 1 = 1 = 0^2 + 1^2$

Therefore this statement is true when $n = 0$.

when $n = 1$, $4n + 1 = 5 = 1^2 + 2^2$

Therefore this statement is true when $n = 1$.
Show that, in general, the statement made by Hugh is not true.   (WJEC)

EXAMINATION ANSWERS

A1
Strange Pythagoras

▶ *Making decisions*   You should decide to see if the sets of consecutives and the triangular numbers create a particular set of values for the side of the triangle *ABC*.
▶ *Communicating*   You should make tables of your results, in particular tables showing the values of the sides of the triangle *ABC*. You should have been confident in your use of algebra to prove the first rule, and made a good attempt to prove, through algebra, any rules you find in the next two parts.
▶ *Reasoning and proof*   You should use words and symbols, writing rules as for consecutive *m* and *n*, that $AB = BC + 1$, and that, for the triangular numbers, where $m = t(t + 1)$, $n = t(t - 1)$. Maybe you also found out that *AC* is always a perfect cube.

A2
Calendar patterns

▶ *Making decisions*   You should select another block of four numbers different in some way from the first, look for patterns and then look for ways in which you could write the numbers in each block in terms of algebra. You could state some rules to be investigated, and look for patterns in the numbers in each block of 9 numbers.
▶ *Communicating*   You should have used patterns found or written the numbers in each block as algebra, and used this to show whether Bill's rules are true or not. You should produce a clear and logical account of your work.
▶ *Reasoning and proof*   You should search for patterns and make clear statements about which rules work based on the evidence produced. You should give some mathematical justification for your generalisations, giving comments on the reasons.

A3
Security alarms

▶ *Making decisions*   You should decide to investigate say $1 \times n$ grids; check your results and see if they are sensible. Then you should investigate $2 \times n$ grids, then go on to $m \times n$ (rows × columns) grids, using patterns already found. You should have seen the need to investigate the pattern when the number of rows and columns are both even.
▶ *Communicating*   You should draw diagrams showing alarms in different positions. You should record the results for the minimum number of alarms and put these into some form of table. You could use the symmetry of the situation to predict the numbers for diagrams too big to be drawn.
▶ *Reasoning and proof*   You should make some general statements based on the table referring to odd and even. You should have made the generalisation that the number of alarms needed is $\frac{1}{2}(m + 1)(n + 1)$, except when both *m* and *n* are even, when it then becomes $\frac{1}{2}(m + 1)(n + 1) - \frac{1}{2}$.

A4
Border tiles

▶ *Making decisions*   You should start your investigation with 5 tiles and draw some clear diagrams, then attempt to find a formula for 5 starting tiles. This should then be developed to investigate say 6 starting tiles.
▶ *Communicating*   You should count the number of tiles for at least three borders, completing the table. You should use the formula $t = 5b + 6$, collating results and finding the formula wrong, then searching for the correct formula. You should make good, clear use of algebra throughout your work.
▶ *Reasoning and proof*   You should show that Fred's formula works and then find that Emma's formula does not work, finding the correct formula to be $t = 4b + 8$. You may also find that $t = 4b + 2(n - 1)$.

A5
Joining dots

▶ *Making decisions*   You should play the game in a systematic way for different numbers of dots. You should pose your own questions about the rule changes and analyse your results.
▶ *Communicating*   You should present your results in diagrams and tables, maybe even graphing your results. You should use algebra as soon as possible in the explanations.

▶ *Reasoning and proof*   You should make some observations from your results such that when the number of dots (D) is even then the maximum number of lines (N) is a multiple of three. You should be able to see the patterns and generalise to:

$$N = \tfrac{3}{2}D \text{ (when } D \text{ is even)} \quad \text{and} \quad N = \frac{3D-1}{2} \text{ (when D is odd)}$$

▶ A6
Hand luggage

▶ *Making decisions*   You should try out a few numerical examples which satisfy the given conditions from the airline. You could then consider some different shapes and alternative strategies, maybe even considering nets of the luggage.

▶ *Communicating*   You should use tables, diagrams and graphs clearly expressing what you have found.

▶ *Reasoning and proof*   You could test various thoughts such as, 'maximum volume occurs when surface area is at a minimum'. You ought to include some of the rules:

Airline 1: $150 = W + L + H$,   volume WLH,   surface area $= 2(WL + WH + LH)$
Airline 2: $60\,000 = LWH$

where $W = $ width, $L = $ length, $H = $ height, but then also include other factors for different shaped bags.

▶ A7
Polygon puzzles

▶ *Making decisions*   You should work systematically to produce a solution through trial and improvement or try an algebraic approach.

▶ *Communicating*   You should make drawings, tables of results and explain the significance of the results.

▶ *Reasoning and proof*   You could make generalisations and test them, such as 'when opposite sides add up to 10 there is always a solution', giving reasons to justify your statements.

You should find that either there are an infinite number of solutions or there is none. If the opposite pairs of numbers add up to the same number, there will be a family of answers, otherwise there are no solutions.

▶ A8
Hugh's problems

▶ *Making decisions*   You should start at $n = 0$ and go on in a systematic way until you find a situation that does not work. Then you should decide to extend the problem by allowing any number of square numbers to be used, and try using a different formula.

▶ *Communicating*   You should put the results down in a logical order so that we can see how many and which square numbers are being used. You should explain why you are extending the problem.

▶ *Reasoning and proof*   You should show why Hugh's solution is wrong and be able to argue the case for any number of square numbers, accepting that you cannot prove this. After using different formulae you could decide to include all integers and the use of differences of square numbers.

INDEX

Longman - for all your study guide needs

Addison Wesley Longman publishes a wide range of curriculum-related books to help you with your studies. If you have enjoyed using this book and have found it useful, you can now order others directly from us - simply follow the ordering instructions below.

Don't forget to tell your fellow students about *Longman Study Guides* - they might find them useful too!

HOW TO ORDER

A full list of titles is given overleaf. Decide which title(s) you require and then order in one of the following ways:

by post
Fill in the quantity alongside the title(s) you require, select your method of payment, complete your name and address details and return your completed order form and payment to:
Addison Wesley Longman Ltd
PO BOX 88
Harlow
Essex CM19 5SR

by phone
Call our Customer Information Centre on 01279 623923 to place your order, quoting mail number: HESG1

by fax
complete the order form overleaf and fill in your name and address details and method of payment, and fax it to us on 01279 414130.

by e-mail
E-mail your order to us on awlhe.orders@awl.co.uk listing title(s) and quantity required and providing full name and address details as requested here. Please quote mail number: HESG1. Please do not send credit card details by e-mail.

Mail no: **HESG1**

Your Name _____

Your Address _____

_____

Postcode _____ Telephone _____

Method of payment

☐ I enclose a cheque or a P/O for £ _____ made payable to Addison Wesley Longman Ltd
☐ Please charge my Visa/Access/AMEX/Diners Club card

Number _____ Expiry Date _____

Signature _____ Date _____

(please ensure that the address given above is the same as for your credit card)

Prices and other details are correct at time of going to press but may change without notice. All orders are subject to status.

☐ *Please tick this box if you would like a complete listing of York Notes Literature Guides (suitable for GCSE and A-level English students)*

LONGMAN   Addison Wesley Longman

LONGMAN HOMEWORK HANDBOOKS (KEY STAGE 3)
£7.99 each unless otherwise stated

QTY *(0582)*

1	_____ 29330 8	English (KS3)
2	_____ 29331 6	French (KS3)
3	_____ 30423 7	French pack*(KS3) (£12.99)
4	_____ 30425 3	French cassette (KS3) (£6.00)
5	_____ 29329 4	German (KS3)
6	_____ 30427 X	German pack*(KS3) (£12.99)
7	_____ 30428 8	German cassette (KS3) (£6.00)
8	_____ 29328 6	Mathematics (KS3)
9	_____ 29327 8	Science (KS3)

LONGMAN GCSE STUDY GUIDES
£9.99 each unless otherwise stated

10	_____ 30481 4	Biology
11	_____ 31538 7	Business Studies
12	_____ 30482 2	Chemistry
13	_____ 31539 5	Economics
14	_____ 30484 9	English
15	_____ 30483 0	English Literature
16	_____ 30485 7	French
17	_____ 03839 1	French pack* (£14.99)
18	_____ 03836 7	French cassette (£6.00)
19	_____ 30486 5	Geography
20	_____ 30487 3	German
21	_____ 03837 5	German pack* (£14.99)
22	_____ 03838 3	German cassette (£6.00)
23	_____ 30495 4	Higher Level Mathematics
24	_____ 30494 6	Information Technology (£10.99)
25	_____ 30496 2	Mathematics
26	_____ 30497 0	Music
27	_____ 31540 9	Physics
28	_____ 28700 6	Psychology
29	_____ 31542 5	Religious Studies
30	_____ 30498 9	Science (£10.99)
31	_____ 22651 1	Sociology
32	_____ 22652 X	Spanish
33	_____ 24509 5	Spanish pack* (£14.99)
34	_____ 24511 7	Spanish cassette (£6.00)
35	_____ 23771 8	Technology
36	_____ 30545 4	World History

LONGMAN GCSE EXAM PRACTICE KITS

37	_____ 30381 8	Biology £4.99)
38	_____ 30383 4	Business Studies (£4.99)
39	_____ 31191 8	English (£4.99)
40	_____ 30384 2	Geography (£4.99)
41	_____ 30385 0	Mathematics (£4.99)
42	_____ 30379 6	Physics (£4.99)
43	_____ 30380 X	Science (£5.99)

LONGMAN GCSE REFERENCE GUIDES *£6.99 each*

44	_____ 05788 4	Biology
45	_____ 05790 6	Chemistry
46	_____ 05072 3	English
47	_____ 05077 4	French
48	_____ 05074 X	Mathematics
49	_____ 05794 9	Physics
50	_____ 05076 6	Science

GCSE SURVIVAL GUIDE *£2.95*

51	_____ 05078 2

_____**YORK NOTES LITERATURE GUIDES** *(see overleaf)*

LONGMAN A-LEVEL STUDY GUIDES
£9.99 each unless otherwise stated

52	_____ 22569 8	Accounting (£10.99)
53	_____ 31545 X	Biology
54	_____ 31652 9	Business Studies
55	_____ 31546 8	Chemistry
56	_____ 05782 5	Computer Science
57	_____ 27688 8	Economics (£10.99)
58	_____ 31656 1	English
59	_____ 05784 1	French
60	_____ 24495 1	French pack* (£14.99)
61	_____ 24497 8	French cassette (£6.00)
62	_____ 05173 8	Geography
63	_____ 31654 5	German
64	_____ 24498 6	German pack* (£14.99)
65	_____ 24508 7	German cassette (£6.00)
66	_____ 28702 2	Government and Politics (£10.99)
67	_____ 31549 2	Law (£10.99)
68	_____ 31550 6	Mathematics (£10.99)
69	_____ 31551 4	Modern History
70	_____ 27690 X	Physics
71	_____ 31655 3	Psychology
72	_____ 27691 8	Sociology

LONGMAN A-LEVEL EXAM PRACTICE KITS *£6.99 each*

73	_____ 30386 9	Biology
74	_____ 30387 7	Business Studies
75	_____ 30388 5	Chemistry
76	_____ 30389 3	Mathematics
77	_____ 30390 7	Psychology
78	_____ 30382 6	Sociology

LONGMAN A-LEVEL REFERENCE GUIDES *£6.99 each*

79	_____ 06394 9	Biology
80	_____ 06390 6	Chemistry
81	_____ 06396 5	English
82	_____ 06398 1	Mathematics
83	_____ 06392 2	Physics (£7.99)

LONGMAN HANDBOOKS *£7.99 each*

84	_____ 09965 X	Botany
85	_____ 08810 0	Chemistry

LONGMAN PARENT'S AND STUDENTS' GUIDES
£2.99 each

86	_____ 29971 3	Longman Parent's Guide to Pre-school Choices and Nursery Education
87	_____ 29975 6	Longman Parent's Guide to Key Stage 1 of the National Curriculum
88	_____ 29974 8	Longman Parent's Guide to Key Stage 2 of the National Curriculum
89	_____ 29973 X	Longman Parent's Guide to Key Stage 3 of the National Curriculum
90	_____ 29972 1	Longman Parent's Guide to GCSE and Key Stage 4 of the National Curriculum
91	_____ 29978 0	Longman A-level Survival Guide
92	_____ 29969 1	Longman Students' Guide to Vocational Education
93 to	_____ 29970 5	Longman Students' Guide to Returning Learning
94	_____ 29976 4	Longman Students' Guide to Higher Education

* pack = book and cassette